ADVANCED TOPICS
IN SCIENCE AND TECHNOLOGY IN CHINA

Zhejiang University is one of the leading universities in China. In Advanced Topics in Science and Technology in China, Zhejiang University Press and Springer jointly publish monographs by Chinese scholars and professors, as well as invited authors and editors from abroad who are outstanding experts and scholars in their fields. This series will be of interest to researchers, lecturers, and graduate students alike.

Advanced Topics in Science and Technology in China aims to present the latest and most cutting-edge theories, techniques, and methodologies in various research areas in China. It covers all disciplines in the fields of natural science and technology, including but not limited to, computer science, materials science, life sciences, engineering, environmental sciences, mathematics, and physics.

Songhua Xu
Francis C.M. Lau
Yunhe Pan

A Computational Approach to Digital Chinese Painting and Calligraphy

With 122 figures

AUTHORS:

Dr. Songhua Xu
Computer Science Department
Yale University
New Haven, CT 06511, USA
E-mail: songhua@aya.yale.edu

Prof. Yunhe Pan
College of Computer Science,
Zhejiang University,
Hangzhou 310027, China
Email: pan@zju.edu.cn

Prof. Francis C.M. Lau
Department of Computer Science,
University of Hong Kong
Pokfulam Road, Hong Kong
E-mail: fcmlau@cs.hku.hk

ISBN 978-7-308-05728-8 **Zhejiang University Press, Hangzhou**
ISBN 978-3-540-88147-6 **Springer Berlin Heidelberg New York**
e-ISBN 978-3-540-88148-3 **Springer Berlin Heidelberg New York**

Series ISSN 1995-6819 Advanced topics in science and technology in China
Series e-ISSN 1995-6827 Advanced topics in science and technology in China

Library of Congress Control Number: 2008936090

**Co-published by Zhejiang University Press, Hangzhou and Springer-
Verlag GmbH Berlin Heidelberg**

Springer is a part of Springer Science+Business Media
springer.com

Cover design: Frido Steinen-Broo, EStudio Calamar, Spain
Printed on acid-free paper

For my parents and grandmother.   —S.H. Xu

For Jimmy.   —F. Lau

Preface

We are in the age of pervasive computing with computing permeating every facet of our living. In many cases we have access to a plenitude of excessive computing power which we do not know what to do with; the situation was exactly the opposite decades ago when computers were in their infancy. Since we are no longer constrained by computing resources, it is high time that computer science research should attempt to set foot in domains that are hitherto not so much charted. Art or certain forms of art are one such domain.

There is a long trace of efforts by talented artists to try unremittingly to transform the computer into a novel art creation tool, even at times when computers were outrageously expensive, clumsy and had very limited power. This is probably part of the "artist's nature"—to take advantage of anything on earth *for art's sake*. But until recently the limited amount of computing power available to any ordinary person had meant more hindrances than opportunities to the innovative artists who fancied using the computer to do art.

Seeing all the recent technical possibilities and the bilateral (that is, the technologists' and the artists') very strong desire to let the computer have a serious role in art, we feel that computer art will certainly be among the few topics being intensively pursued by many in the very near future as well as for many years to come. This book represents a possible contribution to these efforts.

We cannot wait to say that by committing to this book project we were not setting out, not at all, to try to replace the practice, method, habit and process of traditional art creation. Not at all, as that is already part of human nature, so to speak. Our ambition in our journey to explore digital art is to look for or perhaps fabricate computer-assisted means that can extend the bounds and enrich the experience of art creation, and we hope by so doing we may open up new exciting venues and genres for the aspiring artists, which were not feasible with the traditional approach. This book presents some of the preliminary and original work done by us during the past six years, which was sparked off by this vision.

The first piece of work reported in this book is the design and construction of an electronic hairy brush (e-brush for short) and its associated digital painting system. As computing is so pervasive, we believe an e-brush could make painting and calligraphy more accessible to more people for more applications. We apply and develop computer science methods and algorithms, especially those falling in the categories of computer graphics and interactive techniques, for the basic e-brush as well as extended features for trying out new artistic effects by the painter that are not possible with a traditional brush. The basic e-brush targets a faithful emulation of the real brush, thus providing artists with a digital replica of their original creative environment, but with lots of added convenience. The success of the e-brush, or any e-brush for that matter, will represent an example of the positive impact technology can have on the practice of art creation. We hope to see more examples in the future of the computer and art being united in yet another innovative way to do art.

Other than serving for a human artist (who is in command) in interactive mode, the computer can produce meaningful artwork all by itself. We demonstrate that possibility by a prototype system for the automatic creation of beautiful calligraphy, and a system to turn Chinese paintings into animation. Taking advantage of some state-of-the-art algorithms and techniques in the field of artificial intelligence, the calligraphy system is bestowed with the ability to computationally appreciate and evaluate the quality of a piece of Chinese calligraphy; the ability also enables the system to produce facsimiles of artistic Chinese calligraphic art, or to synthesize new original ones automatically. The animation system can generate Chinese painting-styled animation of very high visual quality with a minimal amount of user involvement. These systems and their generated samples demonstrate how machine intelligence can be converted into "machine artistry", the manifestation of which may or may not need the participation of the human artist.

The more we engage ourselves in these projects, the more we realize that there in fact exist unlimited opportunities for the computer to influence art (and vice versa too). Unfortunately, relatively very little has been done so far. We hope this little book can bring out the awareness and help set off some keener interest among computer science researchers as well as art folks on the topic of "computational art".

Our work as you can see has a clear bent towards Chinese art forms. In fact the very long Chinese history has nurtured an extremely rich culture and system of Chinese traditional fine arts, which are increasingly becoming more mainstream, or on a par with Western arts, around the globe. We believe getting involved in the creation of Chinese fine arts with a computational approach presents many unique challenges. Just like the interest Chinese cuisine has enjoyed, we hope even more interest and effort will be accorded to the furtherance of Chinese arts, including possibly new ones in digital form. With the excitements of the 2008 Beijing Olympic Games still lingering on, we wish not just the spirit of sports but also that of arts will prevail.

We welcome your suggestions, comments and criticisms from any angle, and let's together make this interdisciplinary area of research as popular as the Louvre!

Target Audiences

This is a technical book on an interesting area in computer science—computer graphics and its application in fine arts. The book focuses on Oriental digital arts, in particular Chinese calligraphy and painting. It offers a multi-disciplinary treatment, in particular from the angles of computer graphics, interactive techniques and artificial intelligence. It discusses the unique difficulties and challenges of using the computer to produce Oriental fine arts of paintings and calligraphy. It then presents some successful research results by the authors and the lessons and engineering experiences behind these efforts. The book serves as a good reference for computer science and information engineering researchers interested in this topic. For practicing artists the book offers a fresh view on the emerging medium of e-art. It can also be used as a reference text or supplementary reading material for a graduate course on digital arts and design or related disciplines.

A Quick Tour of the Contents

Part I discusses the general relationship between computer science and fine arts. It dwells on a few fundamental questions like whether the digital computer is indeed a tool well suited for art creation purposes. It then makes a brief survey of the popular forms of digital arts, and discusses why it is technically challenging to pursue digital arts.

We probe into the state-of-the-art research in digital painting and drawing in Part II. We delve into these existent research works and published works because they form the larger context enfolding our computational approach to Chinese painting and calligraphy. Since there is very limited research on digital painting or calligraphy studies, we dedicate the whole part to surveying digital painting work; we concentrate on those automatic approaches that rely heavily on machine intelligence and interactive techniques which are also our main tools in our expedition to explore computational Chinese painting and calligraphy.

In the next three parts (Parts III, IV, V) we expound our first-hand research and development in digital Chinese paintings and calligraphy. They form the main technical bulk of this book. Their contents bear on two broad areas in computer science respectively: computer graphics and interactive techniques being one and artificial intelligence being the other. The organization of the three parts are as follows, from the viewpoint of the "techniques" used:

(1) Part III discusses how to apply *computer graphics and interactive techniques* to implement a software system to support interactive digital painting and calligraphy;
(2) Part IV discusses how to deploy *artificial intelligence* algorithms and methods to automatically generate artistic Chinese calligraphy;

(3) Part V discusses how to use the *combination of computer graphics and interactive techniques and artificial intelligence* to create animations of Chinese paintings.

The three parts can also be considered from the angle of the digital art form(s) being treated:

(1) Part III discusses how to interactively create *Chinese paintings and calligraphy*;
(2) Part IV focuses on the problem of the intelligent generation of *Chinese calligraphy*;
(3) Part V is devoted to the intelligent animation of *Chinese paintings*.

The book concludes with a series of thoughts and perspectives on future work. The book should not really just end there as the list can go on and on. But space is at a premium.

Permissions

We thank the following publishers and organizations for their kindness in granting us the permissions to use or reprint in this book the materials we published with them in the past.

(1) With permission from ACM, Chapter 11 contains materials from the paper: S.H. Xu, Y. Xu, S.B. Kang, D.H. Salesin, Y.H. Pan, and H.Y. Shum. Animating Chinese Paintings through Stroke-based Decomposition. *ACM Transactions on Graphics*, 25(2): 239–267,Los Angeles, CA, USA: ACM Press, April 2006. http://doi.acm.org/ 10.1145/1138450.1138454 © Copyright by ACM, Inc. 2006.
(2) With permission from IEEE, Chapter 8 and Chapter 9 contain materials from the paper: S.H. Xu, F.C.M. Lau, K.W. Cheung, and Y.H. Pan. Automatic Generation of Artistic Chinese Calligraphy. *IEEE Intelligent Systems*, 20(3): 32–39, May/June 2005, IEEE CS Press. http://doi.ieee-computersociety.org/ 10.1109/MIS.2005.41 © Copyright by IEEE 2005.
(3) With permission from Eurographics, Chapter 3 and Chapter 4 contain materials from the paper: S.H. Xu, M. Tang, F.C.M. Lau, and Y.H. Pan. A Solid Model Based Virtual Hairy Brush, in the *Proceedings of the 23rd Annual Conference of the European Association for Computer Graphics* (Eurographics '02), Saarbrucken, Germany, September 2002, The Eurographics Association. Also in *Computer Graphics Forum*, 21(3): 299-308, editors: G. Drettakis and H.P. Seidel, Oxford, Blackwell Publishers. © Copyright by Eurographics Association 2002.
(4) With permission from Eurographics, Chapter 5 contains materials from the paper: S.H. Xu, F.C.M. Lau, F. Tang, and Y.H. Pan. Advanced Design for a Realistic Virtual Brush, in the *Proceedings of the 24th Annual Conference of the European Association for Computer Graphics* (Eurographics '03), Granada, Spain, September 2003, The Eurographics Association. Also in *Computer Graphics Forum*, 22(3): 533-542, editors: P. Brunet and

Acknowledgements

For our work in Chapter 4, we thank www.chinapage.com for supplying us with real artwork by famous Chinese calligraphers. We are grateful to Victor Ostromoukhov whose comments helped improve our presentation.

For our work in Chapter 11, we would like to especially thank Yuanyuan Su, who produced the animations using our program needed for the chapter. Ce Liu and Yanyun Chen contributed some of the paintings appearing in that chapter and they helped us better understand the nature of Chinese painting. Dongyu Chao assisted us with the illustrations in the chapter. We are grateful to all of them.

We thank the following organizations for granting us permission to reproduce the materials we published with them in the past this book.

The authors for Chapter 11 are Songhua Xu, Yingqing Xu, Singbing Kang, David Salesin, Yunhe Pan, and Heungyeung Shum. We appreciate very much the fruitful cooperation with our colleagues over the past six years, especially William Cheung, Feng Tang, Congfu Xu and Min Tang. We thank all our graduate students for their participation in our research, in particular Hao Jiang, Wenxia Yang (Michelle), Haisheng Tan, Xiantao Jiao. Hao Jiang participated in the writing of Chapter 10.

We thank some of the fellows of the Chinese Academy of Sciences and the Chinese Academy of Engineering and experts in the field for giving us very valuable advice on this research, particularly Fuqing Yang, Guojie Li, Xiaofei Xu, Jian Lv, Miaoliang Zhu, L.M. Patnaik, and Roni Rosenfeld.

We thank the following professors and officers for their administrative support and services during all those years while we were doing the research reported in this book: Yueting Zhuang, Yimin Wang, Chun Chen, Qiang Fu, Weidong Chen, Jianping Duan, Li Chen, Weidong Geng, Fei Wu, Qunsheng Peng, Huixiang Gong, Deren Chen, Yonggang Yu, Jingxiang Dong, Dexiong Song, Xiuzi Ye, Jiaoying Shi, Tingzhan Jin, Zhenlian Chen, and Shumin Gao.

We acknowledge the kind support in terms of resources that have come from the College of Computer Science & Technology, Graduate School and President's Office of Zhejiang University as well as the Department of Computer Science at the University of Hong Kong.

We thank the following institutes and organizations for providing funding or other forms of support for this research: the Hong Kong Research Grant Council (grant number: HKU7145/05E), Xiaoping Deng Memorial Foundation, Central Committee of Chinese Youth League, Chinese Association of Scientists, Chinese Ministry of Education, Chinese Association of Students, Elite Youth Foundation of Zhejiang Province, International Educational Institute, Association for Advancement of Artificial Intelligence, Kechen Chu Memorial Foundation, China Scholarship Council, GE Fund, GE China, HP China, IBM China, Rockwell China, Nokia China, SigmaTel Corporation and Microsoft Research Asia.

We thank Chen Zhang and Jianzhong You of Zhejiang University Press and the editors of Springer for their support and assistance during the writing as well as during the publication process.

The first author would like to express his appreciation to Walter Bodine, Betty Bodine, Andrew Cunningham, Hugh Hedges and Jane Hedges for their warm encouragement and continuous care during the book writing process.

P.R. China
October 2008

Songhua Xu
Francis C.M. Lau
Yunhe Pan

Contents

Part IV Automatic Generation of Artistic Chinese Calligraphy

8 Principles of Automatic Generation of Artistic Chinese Calligraphy

---

Part V Animating Chinese Paintings

Part VI Perspectives

Part I

Introduction

1

Computer Science and Fine Arts

1.1 Why Use Computers for Arts?

"Why use computers for arts?" "What are the advantages of digital arts?" These questions seem to assume computers are already applicable to arts. But is the computer by its very nature a kind of art creation tool? Only if this answer is affirmative can we go on to discuss what sorts of artistic results would the computer be able to generate and the advantages. It turns out that for many practicing artists, a large part of their artistic talent or training is about how to make use of literally anything on earth that happens to fall into their grip to do art creation. Of course, the computer is included. But an artistic genius could still produce wonderful artwork even when the tool is inferior. So the real question is whether the computer is really a good or suitable tool for art creation for all.

1.1.1 Computer as an Art Tool

Whether the computer can be labeled as belonging to a certain class requires a definition of the class. For our inquiry here, the class is the class of artistic tools. We have a very challenging problem here since even the definition of what is art and what is not has never been widely agreed upon and is likely to remain so into the future. In the absence of a given definition, we venture to suggest some criteria for what might be considered a suitable tool for art creation.

An art tool is some kind of a metaphor which

(1) has certain material shape and is specially designed to serve a purpose;
(2) lends convenience to the creation of novel artwork;
(3) supports certain generality in its functionality so that when suitably applied, it could produce a range of different results reflecting the different traits of the individual users.

By the first criterion, an art creation tool is either from nature or artificially designed and manufactured and it must be easy to hold on to physically.

It must have a shape, volume and mass. This excludes anything that is not at all tangible, which exists perhaps only in spiritual or psychological realms. The second criterion postulates that an art creation tool is not just any tool but one that can promote, encourage and facilitate the process of art creation, as well as the exploration of new interesting artistic effects. So an art tool has a very clear functionality and it must be artistically useful. The third criterion says an art creation tool must have a reasonably wide applicability. It must be able to produce a multitude of results, including some new, previously unseen ones. Therefore a pre-programmed electronic device or digital recorder which can only play recorded music cannot be called an art creation tool since it does not permit variation of its end effects. But an electronic piano is an art tool since it allows users to generate different music under their control. Given these criteria, we can now try to answer the question of whether the computer as a tool qualifies for art creation or not.

First and foremost, a computer is purposely designed and manufactured to achieve certain human intellectual goals. It has its own unique form of existence and way of functioning. Its outputs, though in digital formats, always have a certain clearly-defined representation and can be universally accessed through that representation, without regard to the machine and people operating it.

Second, modern computers have enabled many new ways of creating old and new types of information which are artistically interesting, some of which would be difficult to achieve otherwise. For instance, some sound effects generated by an electronic piano can never be produced by any acoustic instrument. In movie production, computer-generated effects such as the massive repetition of some patterns commonly found in recently-made hi-tech films by Pixar and the like would be prohibitively expensive and labor intensive to achieve, if at all feasible. At this juncture we feel we should touch on one important feature of computers which has effectively facilitated the art creation process and yet is not as widely recognized and appreciated as it should be—machine intelligence. Not many would oppose the point that even the most creative people are under the influence of history, society, education background, family, and so on, and no one can be completely original in the absolute sense. In comparison, although a machine's intelligence is also affected by its input knowledge, simulated intelligence in a computer is very different in nature from human intelligence. We do not imply that machines are more intelligent than human beings, which as a matter of fact is far from being possibly true in the foreseeable future. What we really want to say is that because of the different ways of thinking leading to the two types of intelligence, we should let them be mutually promoting and stimulating. This is especially important for art creation activities where the artists are constantly, sometimes desparately, in search of original ideas which really would require intelligence in multiple dimensions. In this regard perhaps it might be more beneficial to train a computer to be an imagining artist than a disciplined and self-motivating engineer. And instead of the self-aggrandising goal of attaining a powerful level of machine intelligence to completely replace human intelligence in art creation, it makes more sense to gear computing intelligence to cooperate with biological intelligence. Like man-made organs being transplanted onto human bodies in order to save or improve lives, the human faculty of creativity may function to its fullest extent when complemented by machine intelligence.

Lastly, for the third criterion, computers would never lack variational possibilities. In fact the computer has too much variational space in which to exercise its power. That can be easily seen for instance in the field of computation complexities which deal with the extreme technical difficulties caused by too large a problem space. There one important task is to try to reduce substantially the variational possibilities in the problem space. Now in the realm of computational art, as opposed to preferring a reduced space, the huge space (of possible ideas satisfying an artistic requirement or ambition) is wonderful news to the artists.

By the above analysis we can now safely conclude that the computer should be an ideal and suitable tool to be used in art creation, despite the fact that it was originally designed for scientific computing and information management tasks.

1.1.2 Computer as an Exceptional Art Tool

Additionally, one may want to include a "skill" dimension in the set of criteria. That is, *the tool's performance should reflect proportionately the skill level of the user, and produce a result that is commensurate with the skill of the user.* But on the other hand, unlike other tools we all have seen and used so far, the computer can sometimes produce a professional result for a novice user. This is where machine intelligence comes in, and with machine intelligence the computer is fundamentally different from all other (art) tools. It can be intelligent and completely autonomous where the word "autonomous" means that the computer can perform certain acts that may not be requested by the user or attainable within the user's skill set. Going for the extreme, we can even have a computer generating a piece of art completely without a user. Several chapters in this book actually discuss work done under this category, in particular the chapters in Part IV.

In summary, the computer not only can qualify itself as a standard art tool in the conventional sense, but also distinguish itself as an exceptional art tool which can help people to accomplish art creation tasks not originally reachable by their own skills as well as perform art creation autonomously with or without guidance from a user.

1.1.3 Computers as Mind-talkers

We feel that in digital arts computers can play a special role between a human artist and a tool—in "talking" with the human artist in the digital art creation process. In this sense computers are like a mind talker accompanying the artist throughout his journey of idea seeking, exploration, refinement and development.

Such a role for the computer has recently gained some noticeable recognition in some fields of computer science, in particular computer-aided design and human computer interaction. Some interesting discussion has taken place over the term CAD. Historically, it stands for *computer-aided design*. However, people now realize that in the past CAD [Sum74, TLM83] actually was all about computer-aided documentation and expression [Dur02]. Upon such a reflection, more people become motivated to study what they call the real computer aided design systems, in which the systems are not to create designs automatically or semi-automatically, but more to inspire the designers to innovate. But when these intelligent suggestions or inspirations become more substantial, human intelligence and machine intelligence crash into one another, giving rise to a design which may be beyond the reach of either type of intelligence.

For painting, sculpture, graphical design and some other forms of digital arts, there are situations where the features or structure of the artwork may not have been completely conceived before the artist sets out to create them. Admittedly there could be many factors affecting how the artwork eventually emerges, which include the tool factor. The artwork may be a cross product of the artists' skill set, creation motivation and the peculiar functioning of the tool, where the versatility and variability of the tool may have a very strong bearing on the art creation.

It is feasible to carefully design a computer system so that it can suggest different "voices" based on machine intelligence when collaborating with human artists in their search for innovative art creation ideas. In these scenarios, the computers may appear to have its own mind, which actually descends from the mind and talent of some human beings. This brings out the issue of consciousness and unconsciousness and the display of human talents in both states.

Traditionally computers as art tools are considered a means to deliver artistic designs or concepts conceived by human artists, the entire process of which is conducted strictly subject to the conscious mind of the artists. Now people are increasingly interested in using the computer to push for more exposure of the unconscious part of human intelligence. Though often unrealized, this part is still a part of human intelligence, which is hard to trigger, and is not possible to measure qualitatively. If the computer can indeed stimulate the unconscious thinking of a highly trained brain, it can facilitate and encourage the displaying of the brain's hidden design and creative talents. Such stimulated intelligence or skills are only invocable when both computers and human artists are working together. It is similar to the real-world phenomenon that when one intelligent mind talks with another, they would see a third one appearing in the midst of them.

There is nothing fundamentally new about computers as tools assisting in art creation or for other similar purposes. It has been a common practice for centuries for architects to use a pencil to stimulate their creative thinking during their design work, especially at the early stages of the design. Indeed we are not talking about the chances for some novice to create a world masterpiece, but rather a seasoned professional to get imbued with ideas which he normally would not think of. Thanks to the voices from the computer, the artist now has a much wider scope in which to search for new ideas and design motivations. Therefore computers as tools are no longer only for delivering and presenting those ideas that are fed to them; they become collaborator of the artist, and the situation becomes the conscious part of the artist's mental faculty talking with the unconscious part. The intelligence and artistry achieved jointly by an artist and a computer can be greater than the sum of the two, if operating separately.

In summary, there are two different design goals in making the computers an art tool: one is to design a computer with the best artistic intelligence and the other is to design a computer with the best capability to stimulate the invisible skills and talents of the human artist. And the two, can happen at the same time. In the ideal situation, a great piece of *human* artwork which is computer-assisted can also be a great piece of *computer* artwork.

1.2 Digital Arts

1.2.1 What Are Digital Arts?

Literally, the term *digital art* could refer to any form of arts which has a certain deployment of digital means during the art creation process. However, simply digitizing, storing, transmitting, or retrieving digitally a piece of art does not count, which may be referred to, as just technology support for arts. We should point out the boundary between digital art and digital support for art is not always that clear-cut. For digital arts there can be two broad categories: either it is a form of traditional art, but has been migrated onto some digital medium; or it is a previously non-existent form of art now made possible with the support of digital technologies. At present, digital arts predominantly belong to the first category while truly novel art forms which only exist in the digital domain but do not have a real-world counterpart are relatively still very rare.

1.2.2 Manual or Automatic Art Creation

There exist many dimensions by which different forms of digital arts can be classified, e.g., the dimension of the input method, the kind of sensations the art piece induces, the way to present or perform the piece, etc. Here we concentrate on a particular dimension which can be seen as a key parameter for organizing our research work presented in the book: the dimension of how much work is done by the user (manually) versus that done by the computer (automatically). Along this dimension, the art creation process can range from completely manual to completely automatic, and hence correspondingly, the contribution by the computer through machine intelligence to the artistry of the result ranges from 0 to 100%, so to speak. We can say that if the computer's contribution is larger than a certain threshold, the result is *computer art* or *intelligent computer art*. The 100% manual option requires a tool, electronic or not, which satisfies the "skill" criterion as mentioned in Sect. 1.1.2. 100% automatic or something in that neighborhood requires a tool that is intelligent (hence possibly violating the skill criterion). Results from the lower part of the range may be called *human art* or more explicitly, *human art assisted by the computer*. Fig. 1.1 summarizes the different possibilities.

Referring again to the scale just presented and Fig. 1.1, towards the upper end of the spectrum, the computer can make up for what the user lacks in skill. A trivial example is that an unskilled user who cannot draw a straight line or a smooth curve can rely on the computer to (intelligently) complete the straight line or curve for him. Generalizing, the computer will be more than able to draw a beautiful looking stroke with rich texture for the user; this is exactly the problem we study in Chapter 11 of this book.

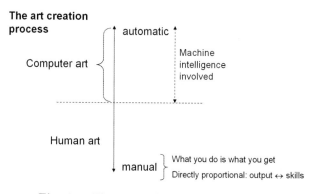

Fig. 1.1. The range of art creation processes

1.2.3 Three Elements of Digital Arts

We propose three key elements or concepts involved in the process of art creation: (1) the tool, (2) the materials, and (3) the created art and its presentation. As an example, Table 1.1 shows the instances of these key elements in digital painting and computer music, respectively. Fig. 1.2 fits the elements into a conceptual pipeline. If one so wishes, and if one or more of (1) to (3) are in digital form, the result may be called digital or electronic art.

Table 1.1. Three key elements in digital painting and computer music

Elements	In digital painting	In computer music
Tool	Paintbrush	Music keyboard
Materials	Paints or ink	Different kinds of sounds or notes
Art creation and its presentation	Whole painting	A music performance

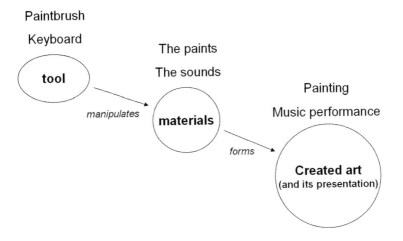

Fig. 1.2. The art creation "pipeline."

1.2.4 Classification of the Book Chapters

By adopting the simple taxonomy proposed in Sect. 1.2.3 and considering the spectrum discussed in Sect. 1.2.2, the contents of the technical core of this book can be labelled as shown in Table 1.2.

Table 1.2. A view of the contents of the book. For Chapter 11, the stroke-based Chinese painting animation system we developed is the tool; the key-frames and the animated strokes are the materials, and the generated painting animation is the art creation

Chapters	Elements	Mode
4	Tool, Material	Manual
5	Tool	Manual
6	Material	Manual
7	Tool	Manual
8–10	Art creation	Automatic
11	Tool, material and art creation	Semi-automatic, semi-manual

1.3 Examples of Digital Arts

Different kinds of digital arts span a wide spectrum, including digital music, digital painting, digital sculpturing, digital dance, and digital movies, just to name a few. We give a brief overview of some of the most popular ones in this section.

1.3.1 Digital Film

Digital film or cinema has become one of the most common experiences in our everyday life in the 21st century, sometimes without us knowing it. Their coming about and sophisticated demands have helped shift computer graphics and virtual reality research into high gears. Today a significant portion of US films have been produced with intensive employment of digital technologies to achieve stunning visual impression but at much reduced cost. Filmmakers like digital effects in fact, because they are absolutely safe on the set. Examples of successful digital films include: *Forrest Gump, Titanic, Toy Story, Harry Potter, The Lord of the Rings* and *Spider-Man*. Digital films and their special effects are a popular topic for any popular magazine or TV/film guide today. We suggest interested readers try a search for the keywords "digital film" or "digital cinema" in Amazon (www.amazon.com). As of August 2007, a search for the first keyword in Amazon returns over nine hundred book records and a search for the latter keyword returns over three hundred book records.

1.3.2 Digital Painting

Talking about painting using the computer, Photoshop would probably be the first one to spring to mind. Sue Chastain listed the top ten other art-oriented software programs in November 2006 (http://graphicssoft.about.com), which are: Corel Painter, ArtRage, Microsoft Expression Graphics Designer, Sketch-Book Pro, Project Dogwaffle, Deleter CGillust, Pixarra TwistedBrush, PhotoArtMaster, Studio Artist.

Because this is exactly the topic of this book and there exist abundant work in the area of digital painting, we dedicate an entire chapter (Chapter 2) to survey the work of computer science research on painterly rendering.

1.3.3 Computer Music

Digital music, also known as computer music, is probably the field that has attracted the most attention from computer scientists and engineers, and is the most established form of digital arts. There is a dedicated organization known as *International Computer Music Association* (http://www.computermusic.org) promoting computer music research. There is also a dedicated quarterly journal on the topic: *Computer Music Journal*. Another periodical which targets the non-academic readers is the UK-based monthly magazine *Computer Music*. Academic conferences relating to computer music include the *International Computer Music Conference* (ICMC), *Computer Music Modeling and Retrieval* (CMMR) and the *International Conference on New Interfaces for Musical Expression* (NIME). There are some computer science conferences in other fields which have special tracks on computer music, e.g. the *International Joint Conferences on Artificial Intelligence* (IJCAI) and the *National Conference on Artificial Intelligence* (AAAI). The whole scope of computer music is very broad, which can only be sufficiently covered by many books, e.g. [Roa92, Man94, Roa96, DJ97, Cop01, Nel05].

The study of computer music covers but is not limited to the following areas:

Algorithmic composition: It focuses on proposing algorithms to compose new music pieces.

Computer-assisted composition: It aims at providing assistance in a composition process by a human composer, rather than replacing completely the human composer.

Computer music programming languages: This is to design new special purpose languages for computer music applications, including low-level sound synthesis, high-level music production, etc. Some famous ones include ABC, ChucK, CMix, CMusic, Common Lisp Music, CSound, Haskore, HMSL, jMax, jMusic, Max/MSP, Music I, Music-N, Nsound, Nyquist, OpenMusic, Q-Audio, Real-time CMix, SuperCollider SynthEdit, etc.

Digital audio workstation: This is a hardware/software system providing various functions in music promotion: recording, editing, music playback, etc.

Digital signal processing and synthesizer: This approaches music processing and production from a signal processing-point of view.

Human-computer interaction: This aims at new designs of human-computer interaction via hardware or software to make computer music applications work in better ways.

Physical modeling: This is about using physically-based modeling and simulation to synthesize new sound effects, usually through equations or algorithms.

Music information retrieval: An important area as the amount of music data increases at a phenomenal rate; many issues relating to intellectual property, music representation and analysis, special purpose database support, etc. need to be considered.

More information can be found in Wikipedia's computer music webpage (http://en.wikipedia.org/wiki/Computer_music).

1.3.4 Digital Sculpture

Research on digital sculpture can be roughly classified into the category of software solutions and the category of hardware solutions.

For the first category, algorithmic attempts have made dealing with large scale sophisticated geometry models more efficient in terms of the rendering and transmission, more user-friendly in terms of the digital sculpture metaphors and model acquisition, and more flexible and accurate in terms of the model representation. These studies are known to the general graphics community as *3D graphics*, and are covered in major graphics conferences like ACM Siggraph (www.siggraph.org) and Eurographics (www.eg.org). Two biennial specialized conferences are entirely dedicated to these studies—the *International Conference on 3D Digital Imaging and*

Modeling (www.3dimconference.org) and the *International Symposium on 3D Data Processing, Visualization and Transmission.*

As to the latter category people are fascinated by new hardware and what they can do. Collins [Col97] mentioned a comprehensive set of equipment essential for digital sculpture practices, which are organized into three groups: 1) Those for the purpose of data acquisition, including scanning probe microscopes, confocal microscopes, 3D laster scanners, scanning electron microscopes, MRI machines, CT scanners and 3D Ultrasound machines. 2) Those for the purpose of data visualization, including Cave Automatic Virtual Environment (CAVE), LCD stereo shutter glasses, Virtual Reality (VR) headsets. 3) Those for the purpose of form realization, including 3D printers, rapid prototyping systems such as computer-aided cutter/plotter devices, laser sintering/fusing machines, thermoplastic extrusion systems, stereolithographic systems, computer-controlled plasma and laser cutters, Electro-Discharge Machining (EDM) systems, automated hi-pressure waterjet cutters, sand and glass bead blasting equipment, stereolithographic systems and ballistic particle machines. Many of these hardware pieces were originally invented for other applications in such areas as Computer-Aided Design (CAD), visualization, virtual reality, Computer-Aided Manufacturing (CAM) and Computer-Aided Geometry Design (CAGD). They now serve for digital sculpture research and practice, by making the human-computer interaction component of digital sculpture more friendly, natural, familiar and efficient.

1.3.5 Computer Dance

The team led by Paradiso in MIT Media Lab invented an expressive footwear [PH97, PHB00]. They embedded in a pair of shoes a sensory system capable of acquiring 16 degrees of freedoms concerning the tactile, inertial and positional conditions of the shoes. The sensors there communicate with a controlling microprocessor wirelessly. The entire system achieves a greater 50 Hz response rate. Because of the large amount of sensory information being sampled in real time, they can measure the very detailed, versatile and multimodal gestures of human feet. This system represents a significant step forward from traditional foot motion sensory systems which could only capture tapping of toes and heels, or translational positions. The sampled minute foot gestural information is then mapped to certain music patterns so that the dancer can control the progression of the music through dancing. This is the so called *computer-augmented dance performance*, which is the major target application of their system. A wide range of users including gymnasts, jugglers and dancers have tried their system, and improvising choreographers seem to have found the system most useful.

Biehl et al. devised an arm wearable device called the *mobile dynamic music device* based on a biaxial accelerometer to measure the absolute acceleration force of an exerciser's right biceps movement in real time for estimating the pace of the exercising person when he is running or walking. Their system then relies on a derived model based on the exerciser's pace to dynamically adjust the music to be played to the exerciser [BAB06].

Ip et al. [IHT02] proposed a novel digital performing art form based on traditional dancing. In the interactive environment they constructed human body motions are captured in real-time using motion capture devices. The acquired motion data are then transformed into interesting 3D visual forms and displayed on a large screen. From an angle, the human motions can be viewed as a special kind of brush, a "body brush" manoeuvered by dancing to paint visual patterns on a large canvas.

1.3.6 Computer Puppetry

The study of computer puppetry is interesting because it is concerned with the motion transferring problem from a human performer to a virtual character. One of the earliest pioneers in this field is Lee Harrison III, who won the 1972 National Academy of Television and Sciences Award for his early work on acquiring a human performer's body motion for controlling the movement of a cartoon character, and for the resultant commercial system called Scanimate which was very popular for TV logo production in the 1960's. The review paper by Sturman on computer puppetry [Stu98] covers this early, seminal system together with several commercially successful computer puppetry companies and systems such as DreamWorks Animation SKG, Inc. (www.dreamworksanimation.com), Simgraphics (www.simg.com), Protozoa (www.protozoa.com), Windlight (www.windwardmark.net), DreamTeam, Digits 'n Art (http://www.dnasoft.com/). Sturman then draws upon experiences in MIT Media Lab's computer puppetry research and discusses three key technical and performance challenges for making successful computer puppetry systems, including body performance, facial animation and lip synchronization.

Concentrating on natural and expressive body performance of computer puppetry, Shin et al. [SLSG01] studied the problem of how to map the motion of a human artist to an animated character whose size and proportion may be very different from the actual performing artist's. The key technical problem their work had to deal with is how to dynamically and efficiently choose the important aspects of the motion features to preserve, during motion mapping in an on-line scenario. This decision on what to respect and what to tailor is necessary because it is not possible to reproduce all aspects of the original motion for a target object having different sizes and proportions. This problem is generally and technically known as *motion retargetting* in computer graphics [RGBC96, Gle97, Gle98, LS99, BLCD02, PSS02, TK05, CBK+06, PL06]. Shin et al. argued that only through a dynamic online decision process could what is important be suitably determined according to the context of the motion. Achieving this goal constitutes the most part of their work. In addition, robustness is another goal in their pursuit since typical captured motion data are very noisy due to the functioning mechanism of the motion capturing devices. And coping with this noisy input in real time for computer puppetry is a challenging algorithm design task. Their system was successfully used to produce daily children's TV programs and for news broadcasting on the election of the Korea National Assembly on Korean national television.

1.3.7 Computer Calligraphy

Artistic characters and font sets have been widely used in postcards, the publishing industry, advertisements on posters as well as video production, etc. If we consider them a type of digital arts, it is probably the most widely deployed digital art form. Calligraphy is like computer fonts "on the loose" because the same character of a calligraphic style may put on a different look in different places, which makes calligraphy a much greater challenge for the computer. In our work we confine the scope of computer calligraphy to be the generation of aesthetic characters automatically. Since the character sets for most of the Western languages, e.g. English, Latin, Cyrillic, and Greek, all have a very small size, typically below 100, manual production of a character set in any customized style is not so big a deal. This is probably one of the reasons why current research efforts on computer calligraphy are almost exclusively on Oriental languages, such as Chinese, Japanese and Korean. The character sets of these languages have thousands or tens of thousands of characters.

Computer calligraphy research on the above three languages tend to be very similar in terms of techniques and algorithms since these character sets share many common features. Dongjun's book [Don07] gives a good introduction to computer calligraphy studies, with a focus on Chinese calligraphy research in particular. In the book they also presented their work on generating new styles of Chinese strokes based on some statistical models. Yamasaki and Hattori [YH96] studied the problem of having a computer to form brushwritten Kanji characters based on some calligraphic knowledge. Wang and Lee [WL01] appealed to anisotropic diffusion techniques to turn calligraphic documents into binary forms. Despite the heavy noises usually present in ancient calligraphy writing tablets, they have achieved very satisfactory experimental results. Wong et al. [WLI05] analyzed Chinese calligraphy images to inversely determine the parameters of the paintbrushes used to create a calligraphy writing. Okabe et al. [OSN05] proposed a new rendering method for generating line renditions in paintbrush styles using the Hidden Markov Models (HMMs). Yu and Peng have synthesized very realistically looking Cao Shu styled Chinese calligraphy through texture mapping a parameterized stroke contour [YP05]. Lo et al. [LKWY06] proposed and constructed a robot for creating Chinese calligraphy and paintings. All in all this is still a relatively new area having received far less attention than most other digital art forms. Most of the existent work is still concentrating on the represention issue of aesthetic Oriental characters and the provision of efficient and compact font system support. Part IV of this book looks at some of our work on the automatic generation of artistic Chinese calligraphy.

We have mentioned the font a few times. In fact, there is an intimate relationship between computer calligraphy research and the development of font systems. For the latter the most classical and influential work is Tex and Metafont by Knuth in the seventies [Knu79]. Knuth's work directly or indirectly set off in the following decades a long series of efforts dedicated to research and development of font systems, e.g. [Gli84, FK85, How87,

HB91, YH96, BNFR98, ZWS00, TK01, Pac01, BLM01, BOB05, TSW06, LS06, Lar06]. Also related is the study on automatic recognition of characters, more popularly known as Optical Character Recognition (OCR). There is a large body of papers published in such journals as *Pattern Recognition Letters* and *IEEE Transactions on Pattern Analysis and Machine Intelligence* on OCR studies.

1.4 Why Digital Arts Are Computationally Challenging?

In this section we examine a few major hurdles to digital art research. These hurdles collectively make digital art a very challenging area for research.

1.4.1 Lack of Semantic Understanding

Traditionally it is the artist himself who has the deepest understanding of the art pieces he created. What about when the artist is the computer? It is well known that automatic semantics understanding is computationally very difficult to achieve, and is recognized as one of the big road blocks in artificial intelligence research. Little progress has been made over the past several decades. So we have the awkward situation where the machine that has generated a piece of digital artwork does not actually understand its artistic value. That means even when the machine has succeeded in generating an acceptable piece artwork, it does not necessarily know that it has succeeded. This is so because the machine has only blindly followed some preprogrammed routine, or it has generated the result by some random choice. The situation is analogous to that of a student, who never attends a class and knows literally nothing about a course, successfully passing an exam through blind guesses or reciting what is in an answer sheet. It is therefore unlikely that the computer will be able to repeat its success in its future creations systematically.

1.4.2 The Versatile Nature of Art

Having some uniqueness and being able to maintain it is a key to success in artwork creation. Unlike in many industry applications where massive copying happens a lot, copying is fatal in original artwork creation. Therefore to achieve uniqueness or distinctiveness must be included as one of the goals in art creation. To be able to meet such a goal by the computer, a large search space of possible solutions is highly desirable, which could mean some changes to the problem solving structure. But most computer programs are built with fixed routines to address a fixed class of problems sharing a common representation and formulation. Thus the ability to automatically vary the problem solving structure to stretch to the utmost in search of a solution is not always supported. In fact, during design time, the human architect may not even be fully aware of the full spectrum of needs when the program is put to use to create novel artworks.

1.4.3 Aesthetic Evaluation and Feedback

In designing our systems we are constantly aware of the incompatibility, sometimes conflict, between exact and soft reasoning. Computers are designed to operate on binary values and be precise in representation, reasoning and evaluation. In contrast, these functions in our brains do not seem to follow any clear and strict mathematic principle. We commented in the previous section on the hindrance to success caused by the computer's blindfolding in evaluating a piece of artwork. To get around the problem, the presence of a feedback loop might offer some help. This same idea is also commonly entertained in many branches of computer sciences, e.g. the backward propagation mechanism in training a neural network. Because the computer cannot quite tell what is aesthetically pleasing, without the availability of such any feedback signal, performance optimization through any automatic means is hard to realize. The feedback loop helps make iterative improvement possible, which in fact is a strategy used in many other kinds of algorithms. But overcoming this hindrance requires not only ideas from computer science. After all, the whole cognitive mechanism behind aesthetics evaluation in the human brain is still a mystery and likely to remain so a long while. Before the working principles governing the biological process of aesthetics evaluation can be clearly revealed, expecting a functionally comparable or equivalent computational simulation device is fantasy.

1.4.4 Inhomogeneity between the Two Types of Intelligence

As discussed in Sect. 1.1, human intelligence and machine intelligence come from very different roots and are fundamentally very different. This is both good and bad news. Good news because human beings and machines can compensate for each other's shortcomings; bad news because this implies that knowledge is represented and processed differently in each model, making it a barrier to the exchange of knowledge between the two. People and machine perceive things differently, think differently, and consequently also tend to create things differently. To fruitfully combine human intelligence and machine intelligence by grafting one onto the other, we need to find a "cut" by which the two forms of intelligence could be seamlessly integrated. This cut is difficult to find, if one exists, and how the two forms of intelligence may be brought together to meet and communicate is non-trivial.

Recently, a flurry of research efforts has taken place which tries to create a kind of intelligent graphical user interface to put human intelligence into collaboration with machine intelligence. The challenge behind this is how to design the most natural way to carry out human computer interaction. Ill-conceived interaction patterns could easily destroy the creative mood and enthusiasm of the user.

References

[BAB06] Jacob T. Biehl, Piotr D. Adamczyk, and Brian P. Bailey. Djogger: a mobile dynamic music device. In *CHI '06: Extended Abstracts on Human Factors in Computing Systems*, Quebec, Canada: ACM Press, pages 556–561, 2006.

[BLCD02] Christoph Bregler, Lorie Loeb, Erika Chuang, and Hrishi Deshpande. Turning to the masters: motion capturing cartoons. In *SIGGRAPH '02: Proceedings of the 29th Annual Conference on Computer Graphics and Interactive Techniques*, San Antonio, TX, USA: ACM Press, pages 399–407, 2002.

[BLM01] Michael Bernard, Chia Hui Liao, and Melissa Mills. The effects of font type and size on the legibility and reading time of online text by older adults. In *CHI '01: CHI '01 Extended Abstracts on Human Factors in Computing Systems*, Seattle, WA, USA: ACM Press, pages 175–176, 2001.

[BNFR98] Dan Boyarski, Christine Neuwirth, Jodi Forlizzi, and Susan H. Regli. A study of fonts designed for screen display. In *CHI '98: Proceedings of the SIGCHI Conference on Human Factors in Computing Systems*, Los Angeles, CA, USA: ACM Press/Addison-Wesley Publishing Co., pages 87–94, 1998.

[BOB05] Jared Benson, Ken Olewiler, and Nancy Broden. Typography for mobile phone devices: the design of the qualcomm sans font family. In *DUX '05: Proceedings of the 2005 Conference on Designing for User Experience*, San Francisco, CA, USA: American Institute of Graphic Arts, page 58, 2005.

[CBK+06] Cristobal Curio, Martin Breidt, Mario Kleiner, Quoc C. Vuong, Martin A. Giese, and Heinrich H. Bülthoff. Semantic 3D motion retargeting for facial animation. In *APGV '06: Proceedings of the 3rd Symposium on Applied Perception in Graphics and Visualization*, Boston, MA, USA: ACM Press, pages 77–84, 2006.

[Col97] Dan Collins. The challenge of digital sculpture: or how to become better tool users. In*Proceedings of the 6th Biennial Symposium on Art and Technology*, Connecticut College. Available as http://www.asu.edu/cfa/art/people/faculty/collins/digital_sculpt. html, 1997.

[Cop01] David H. Cope. *Virtual Music: Computer Synthesis of Musical Style*. The MIT Press, 2001.

[DJ97] Charles Dodge and Thomas A. Jerse. *Computer Music: Synthesis, Composition, and Performance*. Schirmer, 2nd, 1997.

[Don07] Jun Dong. *Introduction to Computer Calligraphy (In Chinese)*. Beijing, China: Science Press, 2007.

[Dur02] Fredo Durand. An invitation to discuss computer depiction. In *NPAR '02: Proceedings of the 2nd International Symposium on Non-photorealistic Animation and Rendering*, Annecy, France: ACM Press, pages 111–124, 2002.

[FK85]   David R. Fuchs and Donald E. Knuth. Optimal prepaging and font caching. *ACM Transactions on Programming Languages and Systems*, 7(1):62–79, 1985.

[Gle97]   Michael Gleicher. Motion editing with spacetime constraints. In *SI3D '97: Proceedings of the 1997 Symposium on Interactive 3D Graphics*, Providence, RI, USA: ACM Press, pages 139–148, 1997.

[Gle98]   Michael Gleicher. Retargetting motion to new characters. In *SIGGRAPH '98: Proceedings of the 25th Annual Conference on Computer Graphics and Interactive Techniques*, Orlando, FL, USA: ACM Press, pages 33–42, 1998.

[Gli84]   Ephraim P. Glinert. A large font virtual terminal interface: a software prosthesis for the visually impaired. *Commun. ACM*, 27(6):567–572, 1984.

[HB91]   Roger D. Hersch and Claude Betrisey. Model-based matching and hinting of fonts. In *SIGGRAPH '91: Proceedings of the 18th Annual Conference on Computer Graphics and Interactive Techniques*, Los Angeles, CA, USA: ACM Press, pages 71–80, 1991.

[How87]   John E. Howland. A system for compiling fonts. In *APL '87: Proceedings of the International Conference on APL*, Dallas, TX, USA: ACM Press, pages 349–355, 1987.

[IHT02]   Horace H. S. Ip, Young Hay, and Alex C. C. Tang. Body-brush: a body-driven interface for visual aesthetics. In *MULTIMEDIA '02: Proceedings of the 10th ACM International Conference on Multimedia*, Juan-les-pins, France: ACM Press, pages 664–665, 2002.

[Knu79]   Donald E. Knuth. *Tex and Metafont: New Directions in Typesetting*. American Mathematical Society; Bedford, MA, USA: Digital Press; Providence, RI, USA: ACM Press, 1979.

[Lar06]   Joshua Larrabee. Dear notebook: font memoirs. *Interactions*, 13(4):10–13, 2006.

[LKWY06] Ka-Wah Lo, Ka-Wai Kwok, Sheung-Man Wong, and Yeung Yam. Brush footprint acquisition and preliminary analysis for Chinese calligraphy using a robot drawing platform. In *IEEE/RSJ International Conference on Intelligent Robots and Systems*, Beijing, China: IEEE Computer Society, pages 5183–5188, 2006.

[LS99]   Jehee Lee and Sung Yong Shin. A hierarchical approach to interactive motion editing for human-like figures. In *SIGGRAPH '99: Proceedings of the 26th Annual Conference on Computer Graphics and Interactive Techniques*, Los Angeles, CA, USA: ACM Press/Addison-Wesley Publishing Co., pages 39–48, 1999.

[LS06]   Jonathan Ling and Paul Van Schaik. The influence of font type and line length on visual search and information retrieval in web pages. *International Journal of Human Computer Studies*, 64(5):395–404, 2006.

[Man94]   Peter Manning. *Electronic and Computer Music*. Oxford, UK: Clarendon Press, 1994.

[Nel05]   Mark Nelson. *Getting Started in Computer Music.* Thomson Course Technology, 2005.

[OSN05]   Yuta Okabe, Suguru Saito, and Masayuki Nakajima. Paintbrush rendering of lines using hms. In *GRAPHITE '05: Proceedings of the 3rd International Conference on Computer Graphics and Interactive Techniques in Australasia and South East Asia,* Dunedin, New Zealand: ACM Press, pages 91–98, 2005.

[Pac01]   Keith Packard. The xft font library: architecture and users guide. In *ALS '01: Proceedings of the 5th Annual Conference on Linux Showcase and Conference,* Berkeley, CA, USA: USENIX Association, pages 22–22, 2001.

[PH97]   Joseph A. Paradiso and Eric Hu. Expressive footwear for computer-augmented dance performance. In *ISWC '97: Proceedings of the 1st IEEE International Symposium on Wearable Computers,* Cambridge, MA, USA: IEEE Computer Society, page 165, 1997.

[PHB00]   Joseph A. Paradiso, Kai Yuh Hsiao, and Ari Benbasat. Interfacing to the foot: apparatus and applications. In *CHI '00: Extended Abstracts on Human Factors in Computing Systems,* The Hague, Netherlands: ACM Press, pages 175–176, 2000.

[PL06]   Frederic Pighin and J. P. Lewis. Facial motion retargeting. In *SIGGRAPH '06: ACM SIGGRAPH 2006 Courses,* Boston, MA, USA: ACM Press, page 2, 2006.

[PSS02]   Sang Il Park, Hyun Joon Shin, and Sung Yong Shin. On-line locomotion generation based on motion blending. In *SCA '02: Proceedings of the 2002 ACM SIGGRAPH/Eurographics Symposium on Computer Animation,* San Antonio, TX, USA: ACM Press, pages 105–111, 2002.

[RGBC96] Charles Rose, Brian Guenter, Bobby Bodenheimer, and Michael F. Cohen. Efficient generation of motion transitions using spacetime constraints. In *SIGGRAPH '96: Proceedings of the 23rd Annual Conference on Computer Graphics and Interactive Techniques,* New Orleans, LA, USA: ACM Press, pages 147–154, 1996.

[Roa92]   Curtis Roads. *The Music Machine: Selected Readings from Computer Music Journal.* Cambridge, MA, USA: The MIT Press, 1992.

[Roa96]   Curtis Roads. *The Computer Music Tutorial.* Cambridge, MA, USA: The MIT Press, 1996.

[SLSG01] Hyun-Joon Shin, Jehee Lee, Sung-Yong Shin, and Michael Gleicher. Computer puppetry: an importance-based approach. *ACM Transactions on Graphics,* 20(2):67–94, 2001.

[Stu98]   David J. Sturman. Computer puppetry. *IEEE Computer Graphics and Applications,* 18(1):38–45, 1998.

[Sum74]   R. J. Summers. A computer-aided system (CAS) for the design, manufacture, test, and documentation of digital printed circuit boards. In *DAC '74: Proceedings of the 11th Workshop on De-*

sign Automation, Piscataway, NJ, USA: IEEE Computer Society, pages 273–278, 1974.

[TK01] Sivan Toledo and Lars Knoll. Font subsetting and downloading in the postscript printer driver of qt/x11. In *ALS '01: Proceedings of the 5th Annual Conference on Linux Showcase and Conference*, Berkeley, CA, USA: USENIX Association, pages 23–23, 2001.

[TK05] Seyoon Tak and Hyeong-Seok Ko. A physically-based motion retargeting filter. *ACM Transactions on Graphics*, 24(1):98–117, 2005.

[TLM83] Mikko Tervonen, Hannu Lehikoinen, and Timo Mukari. Integrated computer-aided design, documentation and manufacturing system for PCD electronics. In *DAC '83: Proceedings of the 20th Conference on Design Automation*, Piscataway, NJ, USA: IEEE Computer Society, pages 436–443, 1983.

[TSW06] Stefan Thiemert, Martin Steinebach, and Patrick Wolf. A digital watermark for vector-based fonts. In MM&Sec '06: *Proceeding of the 8th Workshop on Multimedia and Security*, Geneva, Switzerland: ACM Press, pages 120–123, 2006.

[WL01] Shenzheng Wang, Hsijian Lee. Dual-binarization and anisotropic diffusion of Chinese characters in calligraphy documents. In *ICDAR '01: Proceedings of the Sixth International Conference on Document Analysis and Recognition*, Washington, D.C., USA: IEEE Computer Society, pages 271–275, 2001.

[WLI05] Sam T.S. Wong, Howard Leung, and Horace H.S. Ip. Model-based analysis of Chinese calligraphy images. In *Proceedings of the Ninth International Conference on Information Visualisation*, London, UK: IEEE Computer Society, pages 221–226, 2005.

[YH96] Toshinori Yamasaki and Tetsuo Hattori. Computer calligraphy–brush written kanji formation based on the brush-touch movement. In *IEEE International Conference on Systems, Man, and Cybernetics*, Vancouver, Canada: IEEE Computer Society, pages 1736–1741, 1996.

[YP05] Jinhui Yu and Qunsheng Peng. Realistic synthesis of Cao Shu of Chinese calligraphy. *Computers and Graphics*, 29(1):145–153, 2005.

[ZWS00] Douglas E. Zongker, Geraldine Wade, and David H. Salesin. Example-based hinting of true type fonts. In *SIGGRAPH '00: Proceedings of the 27th Annual Conference on Computer Graphics and Interactive Techniques*, New Orleans, LA, USA: ACM Press/Addison-Wesley Publishing Co., pages 411–416, 2000.

Part II

Computer Science in Painting: A Brief Survey

2

Computer Science in Paintings or Drawings

2.1 Introduction

What is digital painting? Wikipedia offers an easy definition [Wik07]: "Digital painting is an emerging art form in which traditional painting techniques such as watercolor, oils, impasto, etc. are applied using digital tools by means of a computer, a digitizing tablet and stylus, and software."

The studies of the generation or augmentation of digital paintings and drawings are at the core of Non-Photorealistic Rendering (NPR) research. In fact the early NPR endeavors were exclusively dedicated to this topic. The skill set needed by digital painting research overlaps considerably with that of NPR studies. Thus a tour of the general NPR field can also serve as a good introduction to the field of digital painting research. There are two dedicated books on the broad field of non-photorealistic rendering [GG01, SS02]. We by no means want to repeat what is already in that literature, but rather to aim at giving readers a more focused view of the possible algorithmic means and the state-of-the-art achievements from these techniques. We avoid the gory details in this chapter, but refer interested readers to the relevant papers.

Lansdown and Schofield gave a survey on early representative NPR algorithms [LS95]. More recently, an in-depth survey was contributed by Hertzmann [Her03] on the so-called Stroke-Based Rendering (SBR) techniques; he defined SBR to be "approaches to creating non-photorealistic imagery by placing discrete elements such as paint strokes or stipples."

2.2 Automatic Generation of Paintings and Drawings from Photographs

This is a frequently visited, fruitful but classical problem in the field of NPR.

2.2.1 Early Pioneering Work

Saito and Takahashi engaged in the earliest pioneering work in generating non-photorealistic rendering images for enhancing visual communication, which is not always possible to achieve through photorealistic renditions [ST90]. Probably they are the first ones in computer graphics research to demonstrate how NPR-styled rendition could effectively enhance the visual appreciation of complex 3D shapes, which promises rich application values across a multitude of fields, including line drawing illustration, topographical maps, bird's eye maps, sumi-e paintings, medical imaging and surface analysis. In their seminal paper, it is argued that a faithful rendering of scenes does not necessarily translate into a visual presentation that communicates most effectively to the viewer, nor offers a visual content that is the easiest to perceive and grasp. Even though this may sound like common sense to many, their voice opened up the field of NPR at a time when the whole field of computer graphics research was geared towards achieving a photorealistic replication of real world sceneries. In the same paper they also showed how non-photorealistic rendering and photorealistic rendering styles could be simultaneously adopted for even greater visual effects. The case example they suggested was about edge enhancement, by which a line art drawing emphasizing object silhouettes is superimposed on top of a photorealistic rendering of the scene.

To realize the expressive rendering effects they desired, which have often been used as classical NPR examples in books, course materials and survey articles, they proposed the concept of G-buffers to be used to store geometric properties generated in the middle of the traditional photorealistic rendering process. Each G-buffer is dedicated to storing one kind of geometric information, e.g. the depth field or the normal vector field. It has been 17 years since the publication of their original paper, and much of the algorithmic details on how to operate G-buffers for achieving expressive rendering effects, e.g. the methods for generating discontinuity lines, edge lines, contour lines, and curved hatching, no longer represent the start-of-the-art methods for generating stylistic rendering. Nonetheless, the very idea of utilizing, manipulating, combining intermediate rendering results, generated in the photorealistic process to achieve non-photorealistic effects, still stands as an inspiration for current day research on automatic generation of painterly renditions.

Furthermore, the above paper also introduced the practice of caching intermediate results from a photorealistic rendering process. Users can benefit from this when experimenting with different stylistic rendering effects—by playing with these cached results that give instant visual feedback and without having to recompute all the rendering steps. This is another motivation to introduce G-buffers—to accelerate the rendering. Even though these days computers are running at a speed that is orders of magnitude faster than the computers at that time, some painterly rendering algorithms compute very slowly due to the sophisticated calculations the algorithms have to go through. So the idea of caching partial results is still very popular in the design of contemporary painterly rendering algorithms, e.g. [Her01], as well as in the design of advanced rendering algorithms, e.g. [XLJP06].

Haeberli [Hae90] pioneered the generation of painterly rendering images through computing an ordered collection of brush strokes . He proposed "By controlling the color, shape, size, and orientation of individual brush strokes, impressionistic paintings of computer generated or photographic images can easily be created", which later becomes almost a stereotype for painterly rendering generation from photographs. His foundational insight came from an observation of the working style of impressionists—"Impressionist painters use brush strokes to control light to simulate objects without modelling object detail explicitly. Only a few brush strokes are needed to represent a standing figure, a person's face at a distance, or a tree. By carefully selecting tile location, color, size and direction of brush strokes, they control visual information to communicate abstract images to the viewer." His proposed algorithmic technique approximating the impressionistic painting tradition is to sample the input photograph at some chosen brush stroke locations and then create the strokes with certain colors. The interactive painting program he developed works in a remarkably simple fashion, which nevertheless can achieve amazing quality of results. More concretely, his program allows the end users to pick certain locations on the canvas for brush stroke placement. For every one of these stroke locations, the color of the stroke is simply assigned as the color of that location in the reference input photograph. A slightly refined version is to pick a brush stroke location as a randomly picked position in the surrounding area of where the user clicks his mouse. Besides the stroke position and color, the user can also interactively control the stroke size, direction and shape; the brush stroke size could be either determined according to the speed at which the user moves his mouse or through key pressing; the brush stroke orientation could be determined according to the direction of the mouse moving trajectory or based on the user mouse click patterns; the brush shapes are either picked from an offered set of predetermined geometry shapes or drawn by the user. As a result, visually very differently styled painterly renderings could be produced from the same input photograph.

Haeberli proposed another important idea in the same paper which is also intensively referred to by later NPR researchers, i.e. to paint by relaxation. The idea is to start with a painterly rendering approximation to the original photograph, which is in the form of a collection of brush strokes. Then an iterative optimization process is executed to minimize a certain objective function measuring the difference in terms of the visual appearance between the input photograph and the painterly rendering result. The optimization method Haeberli adopted is through stochastically perturbing the brush stroke attributes. He shows two abstract paintings successfully created through this method, one using 100 rectangular brush strokes and the other 100 Dirichlet domains; both are artistically very impressive and with a quality easily exceeding what is attainable by most amateurs.

2.2.2 Representative Recent Work

More recently, Hertzmann [Her98] introduced a method to render a photograph in a painterly rendering style by progressively matching the original source photograph with painterly styled strokes; the procedure yields a visual approximation to the photograph, which may appear artistically more attractive or visually more pleasing than the original photorealistic version. Brush strokes are created in such a way as to ensure that their orientations align well with the gradient directions in the original photograph. The stroke placement also follows an order in which larger strokes are picked and placed first and then the smaller strokes. Variations of painting style are possible by tuning the parameters controlling the selection and placement of the brush strokes, such as brush sizes, appearance approximation accuracy to the original photograph, stroke blurring effect, stroke curvature, minimum and maximum stroke lengths, opacity of strokes and color jitteriness. All these have an effect on the overall visual impression of the resultant painterly rendering. Specifically, the algorithm achieves satisfactory visual results for the styles of impressionists, expressionists, colorist wash and pointillists.

Hertzmann also introduced a lightweight algorithm for producing painterly rendering results with a viscous oil painting look and a 3D feel [Her02]. The key to generating the 3D styled effect is that, in addition to carrying a texture map, as is traditionally handled in digital painting, each stroke is also associated with a height map and an opacity map. This way, the entire painting is assigned with a height field and an opacity field. Through rendering the whole painting via bump-mapping using the Phong shading model, 3D appearance of strokes under lighting can be successfully achieved. During the computation of the lighting effect, the normal of each pixel on a stroke is calculated according to the derivatives of the local stroke height field. This leads to the result that boundaries between adjacent strokes appear like edges after applying lighting, yielding a compelling 3D feel in the final rendition. The height map and opacity map are acquired beforehand and assigned to strokes randomly on the fly. Because of the simplicity of the data structure and the algorithm scheme, his algorithm is amenable to efficient implementation. Hardware-based MIP-mapping strategy can be further employed to achieve acceleration, which would automatically scale the textures of brush strokes to fit the strokes' sizes. His algorithm could very effectively generate painterly rendering in embossed style under plausible lighting effect from an input photograph.

A relaxation-based framework to automatically produce painterly rendering according to an input photograph is later proposed by Hertzmann [Her01]. The major advantage of this new framework for generating automatic painting is that the user does not need to specify how brush strokes are to be painted; rather, they only need to give an energy function describing the visual preferences expected of the painting to be generated. This mode of operation echos the ideal situation expected of computer artwork generation people only need to tell the computer what they want, but not how to achieve that. Given such an energy function, the search-based energy minimization process literally plays the process of composing the painting result with a set of ordered brush strokes. The search is essentially executed by a relaxation algorithm, with the assistance of various search heuristics. Hence the name *paint by relaxation*. Another merit of this energy function-guided framework for automatic painting generation is that it is capable of producing a family of painterly rendering styles. This feature is realized through allowing the overall energy function to be defined as a summation of several energy terms, each specifying a desired sub-goal with respect to the resultant painting. Some example energy terms include the visual approximation to the input photograph, and the economy of paint usage and strokes and the stroke covering area in the painting. The beauty of such a compositional structure is that users can now express their different preferences by adjusting the parameters associated with the energy terms. These two features together represent an important advancement in the study of automatic painting generation as it was novel then to provide a uniform framework and a high-level user interface for creating a variety of painting styles using the same piece of code. The software system built according to the algorithm also would not let the energy minimization framework dominate the painting process and leave little room for the end users to participate. As such, the interface also provides for interactive changing of painting style, specifying a particular style over a region of the painting, and adding or deleting strokes.

But no tools are without flaws. The above algorithm has two major problems stemming from its very structure of automatic painting and the process of minimizing a uniformed energy function. The first problem is that it is very hard to control or design by pure intuition an energy function to achieve a certain painting style. The other problem is that the optimization of the overall energy function is a non-trivial process, requiring a number of advanced computational steps and a long time to compute, making it an obstacle for interactive painting.

The above method also touches upon the problem of generating painterly rendering for videos by preferring a painting style that uses strokes in an economic way. In [Lit97], an algorithm for automatic generation of impressionistic effects is introduced with a focus on video applications. To generate a single frame of image in the impressionistic style, brush strokes are initially generated with their positions, lengths, radii and orientations determined either uniformly or according to some simple standard image processing algorithm. For example, brush strokes can be initially placed uniformly with user specifiable spacing. The brush stroke orientation can be chosen to be a constant direction, or follow the direction where the colors in the input original image are constant or nearly constant. The latter brush stroke orientation has the benefit of the resultant strokes always following the objects in a scene, as if the strokes have been glued to the object in an animation sequence. All these four parameters of a stroke element, i.e. position, length, radius and orientation, will then undergo a random perturbation process to give a richer visual appeal as if it is hand drawn. This algorithm also introduced a stroke clipping step to trim those parts of the strokes going past the edges in the reference image. This makes the resultant painting in observance of the silhouette structure in the reference image. The brush strokes are then rendered with textures having R, G, B values and an opacity channel.

Apart from the above algorithmic processing procedures to generate a painterly rendered result in the impressionistic style from an input photograph, temporal coherence is additionally enforced since the automatically-generated images are to be compiled into a jiggle-free animation. The key to realizing this is to rely on automatically detected optical flow fields from an input video sequence to define the motion for the generated brush strokes. Special care is needed to avoid brush strokes being distributed too densely or sparsely after stroke movement by adding or deleting strokes on the fly during stroke movements. When introducing new strokes for this reason, a Delaunay triangulation based method is used. The idea is very simple: a Delaunay triangulation is first applied based on the brush stroke centers, which results in a mesh having the property that no triangle inside would have too large an area. Then for each of those sparse areas which do not contain any brush stroke centers, a new stroke center and consequently a brush stroke will be introduced. Experiment results prove that satisfactory temporal coherence can be successfully achieved when compiling an animation sequence based on the individual frames in the impressionistic style produced by the algorithm.

Freeman et al. [FTP03] introduced a simple yet very effective algorithm for translating styles of line art drawings. Although the paper is mostly concerned with style translation, we feel it is closely related to the problem of automatic generation of painterly rendering effects as the line art drawing in the source style can be easily obtained through tracing a photograph, as demonstrated by the authors themselves in the paper. Their algorithm consists of two phases. In the first phase, the style of the line art drawing is captured by a fitting process in which a subset of line samples are fitted into the line art drawing in the source style using a least squares method. After the fitting, the drawing in the source style is represented as a linear combination of the line samples. The computed weighted coefficients associated with these line samples become the encoding for the drawing. Given this encoding, in the second phase, to generate a different style for the same line art drawing, the algorithm applies the weights to another set of line samples which are drawn by artists in the target style. The set of line samples is essentially an ordered set of primitive lines for the artists to use during their drawing. To preserve the original content of the drawing, when picking the line samples, particular care is taken to guarantee that the same line sample drawn in different styles occurs always in the same position in the sample sets. That is, if in a line sample set for a jaggy style, the 5th sample is a long, loopy line, then for all other line sample sets the 5th sample must also be the same long, loopy line, but in a different style. By this design, the styles of lines can be separated from the line contents. Such a separation is the key to successful style translation, which also explains why an encoding of weighted parameters can carry the content of a line art drawing.

The paper also brings out the conflict between the goal of faithfully fitting the drawing in the source style and the goal of successfully translating the style of the drawing into a new one. The conflict can be understood as the issue of overfitting from a machine learning's perspective. To resolve this the author introduced a K-nearest neighbour method in the fitting stage. Instead of using all the lines in the sample set to fit the input source drawing, only K most similar lines (in shape) to the lines in the source drawing are selected and actually used. Empirical results show that when K equals six, the best balance between the quality of the fitting and style translation can be reached. The reason behind the performance boost due to adopting this restricted set of sample lines can be understood from the locally weighted regression method [AMS97] in machine learning theory. With the deployment of the K-nearest neighbour method in the fitting phase followed by a squares approximation, a good-quality, content preserving style translation for line art drawings can be realized with the assistance of carefully chosen line sample sets in multiple styles.

The success of the learning-based drawing style translation algorithm comes from its example-based design which overcomes many difficult problems that will otherwise be encountered in the conventional parametric approach; these problems include how to parameterize the shapes in the drawing, and how to subsequently process the derived signals taking care of both the frequency and phase components of the signals.

2.2.3 Generating Paintings via Human-computer Interaction

So far all the painterly rendition generation methods we have looked at are based on algorithmic processing. Recently there is a trend to employ Human Computer Interaction (HCI) approaches for extracting an abstract representation of the painting. Most of us would agree that information delivery could be made more emphatic by the selective abstraction of certain visual information. The abstraction could be a painting or a drawing. With the new HCI technologies, we now have a better means to understand how the human visual system works, which can help us to decide A computer system could carry out image content abstraction in a guided manner and in a close resemblance to the functioning of the human brain, instead of the traditional approaches based on numeric algorithms. The idea explored by DeCarlo and Santella in their paper [DS02] is one example of this category.

The key innovative idea behind the construction of their new photograph stylization and abstraction system is the use of an eye-tracker, which can passively measure the eye movement of a viewer. The captured information is a sequence of triplets where the first two entries in a triplet are the XY coordinates of the fixation point of the eye ball and the third entry records the period of time the viewer fixes his eye in the position. These fixation points are very revealing about a user's attention when he is watching a displayed image on the computer screen. The algorithmic part of their work lies in establishing a hierarchical representation of the image and the subsequent abstraction of the image based on the acquired user attention data. To execute these tasks, first the target image is segmented into multiple regions, from which a pyramid representation of the image is later constructed based on the hierarchical structure suggested by the containment relationships of regions. Such a containment relationship is justified by the scale-space theory [Lin94] and computed through performing image segmentation on various scales. Once the pyramid structure of the image is established, the algorithm then tries to assign an eccentricity value to each region in the image hierarchy based on the sampled user eye fixation data. These eccentricity values are key to the image content abstraction which is carried out in a later stage of the algorithm. Before the determination of the eccentricity values, a collection of fixation circles are first derived according to the sampled triplet sequence of user attention data from the eye-tracker. These circles are centered at the fixation points and have the size of the viewer's fovea. Given the fixation circles, eccentricity is assigned for each region according to their respective overlapping with the fixation circles and the angular distance between the closet point in the region and the fixation point. These derived eccentricity values are then used to collapse regions which are estimated to receive very low user attention. This leads to a pruning of the image representation pyramid. During pruning, the size of the region, the length of the eye fixation period, and color contrast between the region and those of its neighbouring regions are all taken into account. After the pruning is finished, the algorithm assigns a constant color to the remaining image regions, thus realizing the image content abstraction. Finally, bold edge lines are drawn if they are judged to be important according to a model of visual acuity, which works by considering the eccentricity value, line length and length of the eye fixation period for the borders across the regions. After all the processing, the input image is converted into a stylized and abstract painting featuring regions of constant color and bold edge lines according to the user attention distribution captured by the eye-tracker device.

2.3 Automatic Generation of Painterly Rendering Animation from Videos

Hertzmann and Perlin [HP00] introduced a painterly rendering algorithm specifically designed for producing flicker-free videos in painting styles. The algorithm suggested in [Her98] is employed to generate a painterly rendering image for the first frame of a video segment. Then, to ensure the whole video will be free of flickering, two methods are applied: 1) subsequent frames are generated through something *painting over*; 2) optical flow of the input reference video is computed and used to warp the frames to realize flow-based painting. The first method, painting over, helps realize an iterative updating mechanism for generating non-heading frames in a video sequence. The motivation behind this is that if each frame is generated individually, the lack of temporal coherence would cause a serious problem in the result animation. The idea to avoid that is to start with the painterly rendering result of a previous frame when a new frame is to be generated, i.e. painterly rendition generation through "painting over" the previous frame. This way the frame-to-frame coherence can be much improved. To make the painting over process robust against video noise which can cause flickering, a technique called "difference masking" is further employed. The use of a difference mask will make the algorithm update the painterly rendition in only those regions with significant motions. Cumulative difference masking is traced to deal with motions that happen gradually, such as the fade-in or fade-out effects.

The second method of utilizing optical flow is to use the detected flow to warp both the image frame in the input reference video and the corresponding brush strokes. Doing this makes the strokes follow the motions of their corresponding objects, to yield a resultant animation that is more natural and vivid, and also to further reduce flickering. With this method the brush strokes do not have to be repainted constantly and mechanically which could result in those so-called paint-on-glass artifacts.

The above algorithm for generating painterly animation has an interesting, interactive painting application, which the authors refer to as "living painting". This application uses an ordinary video camera to acquire a live video of an exhibition area. The taken video is then processed into painterly styled animation using their algorithm. The resultant animation is projected onto a large projection screen inside the hall somewhere. Visitors can perform in front of the video camera and watch and play with the automatically generated painterly animation on the screen. Another application of this algorithm, which the authors also demonstrated, is to convert a footage of a recorded jazz performance into some painterly rendering animation; the converted result was actually made into a music video later on.

2.4 Interactive Generation of Painterly Rendering Images

In addition to fully automatic conversion from photographs to rendered paintings, there are interactive systems which make reference to input photographs during an interactive stroke painting process in order to reduce the amount of tedious individual stroke drawing work. Unlike those automatic painterly rendering generation algorithms and systems, artists have to really work with these systems interactively to develop a painterly rendering result. But in return, the artists now have more space to display their artistic talents and to pursue their artwork creation interests.

The interactive pen-and-ink illustration system described in [SABS94] is one such system. An input photograph to that system serves as a reference for controlling various visual factors in producing a pen-and-ink illustration. The photograph can serve as a tonal guidance for controlling the darkness of the stroke texture; it can serve as a source image from which edges can be detected to use as outlines or for stroke clipping; it can serve as a map for the stroke drawing area according to the intensity values of the pixels in the photograph; it can also be used to suggest the orientation of strokes and the texture for best illustrating the shapes of curved surfaces. During interactive painting, users are mostly concerned with the the choices of textures and tones; according to these inputs, the system would automatically complete the individual strokes. That is, users concentrate on working with high-level painting metaphors and leave the low-level stroke related work to the computer. This liberates the illustrators from the otherwise labor intensive drawing work of providing massive sketch strokes to achieve the desired tone and texture. To supplement the high-level automation the system provides in introducing and placing individual strokes, the user can also draw single strokes to suggest certain particular shapes or to highlight specific regions. Hence, the user has both the convenience of an intelligent stroke drawing function and the freedom and flexibility to work as much as desired on important selected areas. Some high-level stroke editing options are also provides. It was shown that using the system, very nice pen-and-ink illustrations can be interactively produced in minutes or at most a few hours by untrained users.

Salisbury et al. [SWHS97] extended the above system by taking into account the orientation of strokes when producing illustrations in pen-and-ink style. Similar to the system introduced in [SABS94], this new system needs a greyscale image as initial input to specify the tone of the expected pen-and-ink illustration. The new features of the system include: 1) users can provide a direction field to indicate the direction of strokes during the stroke placement process; 2) users can provide a stroke example set for the algorithm to pick from on the fly as the template for the strokes when generating the illustration. These extra considerations relative to the algorithm introduced in [SABS94] significantly enhanced the expressiveness of the computer-generated pen-and-ink illustrations. This new system also incorporated an interesting matching algorithm to measure at each execution of the algorithm the difference between the produced pen-and-ink illustration and the original input greyscale image. The matching algorithm computes the difference between the greyscale reference image with the (blurred) version of the currently generated pen-and-ink illustration wherein the blurring filters have variable sizes in proportion to the lightness in the input reference image. This measurement of the degree of approximation to the given reference image is needed to guide the introduction of new strokes and for the termination condition of the whole algorithm. In a low level view of the algorithm, during its execution, careful processing is carried out to orient, bend and clip each new stroke upon its introduction.

2.5 Automatic Generation of Painterly Rendering from 3D Models

Many consider paintings and drawings to be a reflection of the 3D reality in the artists' mind. Computer scientists, in particular computer graphics researchers, are therefore interested in trying to reproduce or mimic such a subjective reflection using the computer. Especially during the past twenty years, many research efforts have been dedicated to the problem of generating painterly rendering drawings or paintings from 3D geometry models. Here we briefly look at some of the representative works.

2.5.1 Automatic Generation of Illustrations and Line Drawings from 3D Models

Dooley and Cohen started one of the earliest studies on automatic generation of illustrations for 3D geometric models in an attempt to create informative illustrations but without dragging in a lot of confusing details [DC90a, DC90b]. In [DC90a], several categories of lines intended for conveying different geometric meanings are first studied, which include boundary lines, silhouette lines, discontinuity lines and contour or isoparametric lines. And then a set of illustration rules are set up to be used for determining line drawing parameters based on user input and an inference function derived from illustration principles that artists often employ. The inference algorithm carefully suggests the line end conditions, line width and space for dash lines. A example case is given which demonstrates how effectively structures and details of nontrivial geometry models can better be illustrated by computer generated line based drawings than a photorealistic rendering of the model. Especially in regions where there exists intensive occlusion in the model itself, structures and geometry details of the model can be clearly seen in the illustrations which are not possible with photorealistic rendering from any viewing direction. Their second paper [DC90b] focuses on the same problem, except that the emphasis is put on how to augment surface rendering rather than line rendering.

Winkenbach and Salesin in [WS94] summarize the principles adhered to by professionals in practice on how to make communicative pen-and-ink illustrations. They point out the dual function of strokes in pen-and-ink illustrations which is that strokes serve to deliver both the texture and tone in drawings; and subsequently propose the concept of *stroke texture*, which refers to a number of strokes being used collectively in computer-generated pen-and-ink illustrations for achieving both the desired texture and tone. They also propose a resolution-dependent stroke rendering strategy which suggests that the stroke introduction process should take into account the resolution of the output media. Probably the most outstanding contribution of the paper is that they successfully demonstrated, via the examples of quite a few complex architecture models, how a number of the above well-established principles for making pen-and-ink illustrations could be effectively supported and realized in an automatic fashion based on information available inside the traditional computer graphics pipeline.

One of the major limitations in the above system is that the algorithm could only work with polyhedral models with flat-shaded surfaces. The same authors fixed this limitation in a follow-up paper [WS96] so that models described by parametric curved surfaces, such as B-splines, NURBS or revolutionary surfaces, could all be automatically painterly rendered. This improved algorithm relies on the surface parameterization to produce directions for making hatches, which unfortunately do not always exist; or even when they do exist, they may not be descriptive enough for the underlying shapes. Hertzmann and Zorin propose yet another algorithm [HZ00] capable of producing line-art illustrations for smooth surfaces. The new algorithm could deal with models with piecewise-smooth free-form surfaces. One clever strategy this paper employs is for the algorithm to take as input polygonal mesh models and then to infer the smooth surface model from the meshes. This way, the algorithm need not assume that the model for processing has to have an explicit parameterization. The algorithm first detects object silhouettes according to geometric duality. Once detected, the silhouette curves are segmented into smooth parts with constant visibility. To introduce hatches, the algorithm relies on direction fields which could be defined either in the image space or in the object space and then projected onto the image space. The produced direction fields are ensured to be smooth ones, which guide the hatching introduction process.

Gooch et al. [GGSC98] treated the problem of generating illustrations under the same framework for creating traditional photorealistic renditions. With this perspective they contributed a non-photorealistic lighting model which is capable of producing technical illustrations using a standard graphics pipeline. The design of such a lighting model is based on the observations of characteristic conventions in technical illustrations in practice, including: 1) dark curves are always used for depicting edges; 2) matte objects are shaded in a color with certain warmth or coolness to suggest surface normal, rather than in black or white; 3) no shadowing effects are presented; 4) metal objects are always rendered as if being anisotropic. According to these four observations, the traditional photorealistic Phong lighting model is tailored to automatically achieve a non-photorealistic lighting effect meeting the expectations of the above. More concretely, points 1 and 3 above are easy to satisfy. The key lighting model design work is thus given the task of satisfying points 2 and 4. To achieve the effect expected in point 2, a tone-based shading mechanism is introduced which changes the traditional diffuse shading model to include two terms, one for the lighting contribution from a cool color and the other for the lighting contribution from a warm color. The weighting parameters balancing these two terms are determined according to the cosine of the angle between light direction and surface normal. The authors also made a design decision to always use blue and yellow tones to "insure a cool to warm color transition regardless of the diffuse color of the object." With such a preset choice, the cool color is computed from a linear combination of blue and black while the warm color is computed from yellow and the object's color. Such a linear blending essentially achieves a so-called undertone effect which is often used by artists empirically to reach the goal stated in point 2 above. Finally, to produce an anisotropic look for metallic objects, twenty stripes in randomly set intensities are mapped onto the object surface following the object's parametric axis that demonstrates the maximum curvature. Experiment results confirm this simple treatment could very effectively communicate whether an object is made of metal or not, and thus helps satisfy the requirement in point 4 above. We feel that the elegance of this new method of automatically generating technical illustrations lies in its seamless integration into the existing photorealistic rendering pipeline by only customizing the lighting model while leaving the rest of the graphics pipeline intact. This makes the implemented framework have a close resemblance to the standard graphics pipeline. Also, because technical illustration generation in this algorithm is solely dependent upon the given geometry model, temporal coherence naturally results, which makes the method perfect for animation or video production.

There has been much interest in generating line art drawings according to a given geometry model. The many proposals include contours, silhouettes [NM00, IHS02], discontinuities in the depth buffer [ST90], creases [WS94, MKG+97], ridges and valleys [IFP95, IZ95, Ste99], crest lines [LFM96], coherent stylized silhouettes [KDMF03], suggestive contours [DFRS03], temporally coherent suggestive contours [DFR04], formulated silhouettes [WV03], and apparent ridges [JDA07]. In the proposal for using suggestive contours to convey shapes [DFRS03], DeCarlo et al. defined suggestive contours as the locations where the dot product of the surface normal and the viewing vector reaches positive local minimum rather than being zero as in the definition for traditional contours. A more intuitive definition for suggestive contours is also offered which refers to those points that are contours in nearby viewpoints but yet do not have corresponding contours in any closer views, where the distance metric uses the radial distance. The suggestive contours always appear in the visible parts of a surface. The suggestive contours either anticipate or extend traditional contours and can merge smoothly with traditional contours if the latter appears. To compute suggestive contours, an object-space algorithm and an image-space algorithm are introduced. In comparison, the object-space algorithm works generally more efficiently and can produce continuous stroke trajectories with better appearance approximating that of hand-drawn illustrations. The image-space algorithm works better in the presence of noises in the geometry.

Schumann et al. evaluated the effectiveness of line drawings as an output means of CAD systems for architectural design [SSLR96]. Based on a poll of 54 architects participating in the user study, a conclusion was made that sketch drawings in CAD can help stimulate the design thinking of the architects. The same stimulation however is not always available with faithfully rendered photorealistic images.

2.5.2 Generating Painterly Rendering Animations from 3D Models

Meier introduced an algorithm which uses a 3D particle-based geometric model representation coupled with a 2D brush stroke generation method for producing painterly rendered animation [Mei96]. One feature of this algorithm is that it works in 3D geometry space and 2D screen space simultaneously. Like other geometry based methods, this algorithm also needs a geometric model of the scene to start with. A particle placer is first called to generate a particle representation of the model to be rendered. Clearly, this algorithm generally is also applicable to any point based model. Given the particles, through the traditional camera transformation from the world space to the screen space, the positions of these particles are transformed into positions on the screen space for placing 2D brush strokes onto the canvas. If the users have associated some stroke properties with the particles, such as the stroke colors, orientations, sizes, then brush strokes can be placed onto the 2D screen space canvas immediately; otherwise, a set of brush stroke property reference pictures will be needed, which can be generated through various shaders according to the input geometry model and taking into account the geometry, surface attributes and the lighting conditions. Either way, an additional brush texture image is needed to control the texture of the 2D strokes, which can be scanned from real world samples, manually drawn or produced by image processing packages, or procedurally generated. During the actual 2D stroke generation process, the algorithm follows a descendent order of the distances of the 2D strokes' corresponding particles in the 3D space to the viewpoint. In comparison, the latter method, i.e. to employ reference pictures for controlling the brush stroke attributes, gives the user a wide design space to tune the style of the generated painterly rendition in an intuitive and user friendly fashion. The results of the experiment also demonstrate that very different painting styles can be successfully achieved by using different brush texture images and painting parameters. One important smart trick employed in the generation process, capable of significantly enriching the handcrafted look of the painterly rendering result, is to introduce randomness into the animation parameters, in particular the brush stroke attributes. Special care is taken to ensure that the introduced randomness changes smoothly between frames so as not to destroy the temporal coherence of the resulting video. Except for this last point, this algorithm would not explicitly spend any effort on ensuring temporal coherence. Rather, this coherence is automatically taken care of by the very nature of the algorithm which is its structure for converting 3D particles into 2D brush strokes. Because of this structure, during the animation of the object the particles' movements naturally follow the motion of the geometry model, which leads to a corresponding motion of the brush strokes in the 2D screen space. This way of manipulating brush strokes not only makes the brush strokes appear to be always sticking to the objects during animation but also leads automatically to frame-to-frame coherence. Overall we consider this algorithm to be in essence a painterly rendering image generation method; its design is well suited for producing animations in painting styles.

2.5.3 Domain Specific Special-purpose Painterly Rendition Generation

There are also some domain specific efforts to generate painterly renditions. The algorithm for generating pen-and-ink illustration of trees introduced by Deussen and Strothotte [DS00] is an example. The motivation behind this algorithm comes from the wide application of tree illustration in architecture, landscaping and animation, and also from the unique challenges in rendering trees—because of a great many geometry primitives in a typical tree model, it is very hard for the traditional geometry-based illustration generation algorithms to handle this. During the pen-and-ink illustration generation process, their algorithm carries out a distinctive treatment between rendering tree skeletons and foliages. This is because there are orders of magnitude more geometric surfaces in representing foliages than in representing tree skeletons. Also, the screen space occupied by tree skeletons is much larger than that by foliages. Both factors suggest we should introduce a higher level of abstraction for illustrating foliages. The authors of [DS00] offer the following solution. For tree skeletons, they are rendered as silhouettes which are superimposed with crosshatching to indicate the shaded dark regions on the tree trunk and the main branches. Existent outline generation methods are employed to achieve this. For foliages they are rendered according to the depth differences. That is, first a depth-buffer is created by rendering all the foliages without tree skeletons. And then according to the discontinuities in the depth field, decisions can be made on whether a certain part of a foliage should be rendered. Choosing different difference thresholds in this decision step could lead to different levels of abstraction. The determination process based on the difference in the depth field can also lead to a natural support for level-of-abstraction if the depth values are used directly instead of being projected back to the eye coordinates. This is due to the well-known non-linear characteristic of the depth- buffer, i.e. depth difference tends to be small for far-away objects and larger for closer objects. Once it is decided to depict foliage in a certain area, some abstract drawing primitives are drawn on the canvas, which could be a disk, an ellipse or a polygon to represent the shape of a leaf. Using these abstract drawing primitives could further help achieve the abstract look of the resultant pen-and-ink illustration. The authors discussed an interesting failure during the design of their algorithm—"In our first experiments, we placed special textures on the leaves of our realistic tree models that looked like strokes. This is a fast and simple method, but the generated images never appeared like drawings." But once they switched to using abstract drawing primitives for depicting foliage, very satisfactory results were obtained. This suggests to us that there is a certain level of abstraction that has to be satisfied in generating a pen-and-ink illustration; otherwise the resulting image just will not work with the human perception system. Finally, shadowing effects are also added, in the process of which shadow regions are first detected using a software shadow detection method applied to the geometric model of the tree, and then dark regions are drawn or thicker lines are used for illustrating those regions in shadow.

The main advantage of this geometry-based tree illustration generation algorithm over the other image-based methods is in its superior spatial and temporal coherence, which makes the algorithm most suitable for the purpose of animation production. The paper also demonstrates, by using a tight difference threshold in generating abstract rendering of foliage, very faithful illustration of a tree model can be automatically created. For applications where such a high level of proximation to the real tree shapes is needed, the algorithm offers a huge saving in effort and time for the artist. If a series of such renderings is needed to tell a story, as needed for comic books or cartoon strips, the temporal and spatial coherence of the algorithm guarantees a possibility for automatic completion of the rendering task, which could be outrageously laborious if done by the human illustrators. Finally, the following properties of the algorithm are worth noting: 1) Because the pen-and-ink illustration generated by the algorithm is according to the tree geometry model, if a photorealistic rendition is needed, the difference between these two styles of rendition will not be significant. 2) During the pen-and-ink illustration generation process, significant model simplification, especially on the tree foliage part is carried out. 3) Photorealistic rendering by nature tends to cost much more than non-photorealitic rendering; for example, the lighting consumption calculation can be avoided in the latter. These three properties suggest that the pen-and-ink tree illustration generation algorithm is an ideal previewer for viewing tree models.

Kowalski et al.[KMN+99] introduced another special-purpose painterly rendering algorithm , which is suited for rendering fur, grass and trees in artistic style. This new algorithm can increase the visual complexity of the rendered target without demanding a correspondingly complicated geometric model. This offers a tremendous benefit for geometry-based painterly rendering for objects like fur, grass and trees whose geometric models could be extremely complicated even when we are interested in only a very limited precision. Also, visualizing in an artistic style can substantially speed up the rendering process which otherwise would spend much time in dealing with the complicated geometric models. In terms of rendering techniques, the key means used for achieving the art-based rendition is through mapping procedural stroke-based textures onto polyhedral models. That is, the geometric models for fur, grass and trees are first divided into surface patches to which procedural textures are interactively associated by the user. These procedural textures could be as simple as smooth-shading effects or wireframe effects, or as sophisticated as dithering or hatching. When placing the textures, a similar algorithm to what is used in [SWHS97] is employed for determining the position of the textures. This algorithm works by placing a procedural texture element first in the region that requests the densest distribution of textures. And then the expected distribution of texture elements is updated and the next texture element is put in the place that needs it the most at that moment. Through this greedy algorithm, a controlled screen-space density is achieved in placing textures. The texture elements can also scale their geometry and volume to maintain an expected screen-space size and relative density. What is interesting is that for the same texture element, it will be drawn in different details depending on the angle between the viewing direction and the surface normal. The variation of details include a texture drawn with outline edges, texture without outline, spine only, or nothing. Elements in a more orthogonal view will be drawn with more details. Such a tasteful idea improves considerably the visual charm of the resultant artistic rendering. Also, the authors paid attention to using different levels of details when drawing objects at different distances. A three-level hierarchy is introduced to realize this. When the camera is placed at a position near the objects, all the levels are drawn. When the camera zooms out, less details will be included, and so on. Doing this effectively gives a cleaner picture, especially when the scene is observed from far away, but presents enough details to look at when the scene is close by. Unfortunately the algorithm fails to achieve a good temporal coherence mostly due to its greedy approach in introducing and placing texture elements.

2.5.4 Efficient Painterly Rendition Generation

People have also endeavored to pursue efficient line drawing for large scale datasets for scientific and medical visualization applications. Markosian et al. [MKG$^+$97] contributed an early effort on achieving real-time non-photorealistic rendering. They modified the traditional Appel's hidden-line algorithm to realize very fast visibility determination which is the most time-consuming step hindering real-time non-photorealistic rendering for geometry models or volume datasets. They also introduced a fast randomized algorithm for finding silhouettes. The efficiency comes from the fact that once a silhouette edge in the geometry model is detected, by tracing the edge a complete silhouette curve could be easily and quickly derived. These two points in Markosian et al.'s paper inspired a later, more improved efficient non-photorealistic algorithm by Burns et al., which is capable of performing interactive line drawing for large volume data [BKR$^+$05]. The key observation that stimulated the design of Burns et al.'s efficient line drawing algorithm is that for a typical volume dataset of size $O(n)$, its contour would only have a length of $O(\sqrt[3]{n})$. Thus by tracing the contour lines and updating them iteratively, an exhaustive visit to all the voxels in the volume dataset could be avoided, thus significantly speeding up the overall algorithm. To implement this thinking, a seed-and-traverse line extraction framework is proposed, in which some seeds are first found and then traced to detect the entire lines of interest. A large portion of the seeding points are collected from the contour lines in the previous frame by exploiting the spatio-temporal coherence naturally exhibited between contour lines of adjacent frames. This is because despite the fact that the viewpoints for adjacent frames may change, which will lead to changes to the contours since they are view-dependent, contours of adjacent frames often intersect. By this observation, through visiting voxels on the contours of the previous frame, which is of time complexity $O(\sqrt[3]{n})$, it is likely that seeding points for the new contour in the new frame will be encountered. Also, two additional procedures are executed as a supplement to detect seeding points for those contours that do not observe temporal coherence well. One of them is a deterministic approach using an iterative gradient descent method and the other is a randomized approach essentially implementing a random sampling procedure for collecting the seeding points. In terms of stylistic rendering, a variety of types of lines are supported including silhouettes, suggestive contours and intersections with cutting planes. The exact appearance of a line is determined according to the type of the line, its positioning with respect to the isosurface, its visibility, its lengths, etc. Also, a lightweight visibility determination routine is introduced which works by tracing a ray from a vertex to the camera position. If the ray intersects any isosurface on its journey to the camera position, the vertex is marked as being occluded. The continuity property of the contour lines is utilized to execute visibility determination at a low resolution and only in regions where the contour lines' visibility changes, as detected in the low resolution calculation, will a high resolution visibility test be carried out. Overall, by working with sparse lines and avoiding enumerating all the voxels in the volume dataset, an efficient line drawing algorithm is made possible whose resultant rendition is superior in emphasizing important features in the dataset without presenting are overwhelming amount of visually straining information.

2.6 Special Support for Digital Painting

So far we are mostly concerned with the generation of paintings through computational approaches. But digital paintings also call for special support in their creation, representation and display.

2.6.1 Hardware Support for Digital Painting

Many of the virtual reality devices and technologies can be effectively utilized to enrich digital painting viewing and creation experiences. Examples of devices include haptic devices or resistive force feedback devices, six degrees-of-freedom input devices, graphics tablets, stereoscopic glasses, head mounted displays, virtual reality helmets providing 360-degree viewing scope, space balls and space mice for navigation. Quite a few research labs and companies have provided software and hardware prototypes and products which can be directly deployed for building user-friendly digital painting creation and viewing environments.

2.6.2 Multiresolutional Painting

The representation method of digital painting is a fundamental issue, which unfortunately is often overlooked. Currently, bitmap representation is still the dominant one in the industry. We notice however an important metaphor has been proposed for a while for digital paintings so that digital paintings would behave like real paintings in the physical world; it is the multiresolutional painting representation scheme and its associated operations. With this scheme, digital paintings no longer need to be confined to a specific resolution, which is one of the negative features of digital painting when compared to physical paintings.

Berman et al. [BBS94] studied the problem of multiresolutional painting representation and its associated operations. Most people wish to observe a painting at the finest possible resolution if they are close up and interested in a local region of the painting; meanwhile, they would not want to suffer from the overheads caused by excessively high resolution, especially in situations when they are more interested in a global view of the painting. A multi-resolution scheme therefore would best fit such variable expectations. To address the problem, Berman et al. turned to a Haar wavelet-based image decomposition method coupled with a sparse quadtree representation structure. The merits of this particular wavelet-based schema include: 1) a compact description of the target image at a high image compression rate, 2) a natural support for direct editing of compressed images without having to uncompress/compress, 3) a natural support for lazy evaluation in maintaining the consistency of the multiresolution image representation structure during image editing, which is much simpler to implement than the traditional image pyramid representation. Therefore, the algorithm they proposed achieves efficiency in terms of both space and time. Last but not least, they also proposed and implemented a feature called fractional-level zooming with which a painting can be viewed or edited under any arbitrary resolution. Perlin and Velho explored a similar idea of wavelet-based multiresolution painting at approximately the same time [PV92]. However, their method seems to be not as optimally tuned as Berman et al.'s algorithm.

References

[AMS97] Christopher G. Atkeson, Andrew W. Moore, and Stefan Schaal. Locally weighted learning. *Artificial Intelligence Review*, 11(1-5):11–73, 1997.

[BBS94] Deborah F. Berman, Jason T. Bartell, and David H. Salesin. Multiresolution painting and compositing. In *SIGGRAPH '94: Proceedings of the 21st Annual Conference on Computer Graphics and Interactive Techniques*, Orlando, FL, USA: ACM Press, pages 85–90, 1994.

[BKR⁺05] Michael Burns, Janek Klawe, Szymon Rusinkiewicz, Adam Finkelstein, and Doug DeCarlo. Line drawings from volume data. In *SIGGRAPH '05: ACM SIGGRAPH 2005 Papers*, Los Angeles, CA, USA: ACM Press, pages 512–518, 2005.

[DC90a] Debra Dooley and Michael F. Cohen. Automatic illustration of 3D geometric models: lines. In *SI3D '90: Proceedings of the 1990 Symposium on Interactive 3D Graphics*, New York, NY, USA: ACM Press, pages 77–82, 1990.

[DC90b] Debra Dooley and Michael F. Cohen. Automatic illustration of 3D geometric models: surfaces. *IEEE Computer Graphics and Applications*, 13(2):307–314, 1990.

[DFR04] Doug DeCarlo, Adam Finkelstein, and Szymon Rusinkiewicz. Interactive rendering of suggestive contours with temporal coherence. In *NPAR '04: Proceedings of the 3rd International Symposium on Non-photorealistic Animation and Rendering*, Annecy, France: ACM Press, pages 15–145, 2004.

[DFRS03] Doug DeCarlo, Adam Finkelstein, Szymon Rusinkiewicz, and Anthony Santella. Suggestive contours for conveying shape. In *SIGGRAPH '03: ACM SIGGRAPH 2003 Papers*, San Diego, CA, USA: ACM Press, pages 848–855, 2003.

[DS00] Oliver Deussen and Thomas Strothotte. Computer-generated pen-and-ink illustration of trees. In *SIGGRAPH '00: Proceedings of the 27th Annual Conference on Computer Graphics and Interactive Techniques*, New Orleans, LA, USA: ACM Press/Addison-Wesley Publishing Co. , pages 13–18, 2000.

[DS02] Doug DeCarlo and Anthony Santella. Stylization and abstraction of photographs. In *SIGGRAPH '02: Proceedings of the 29th Annual Conference on Computer Graphics and Interactive Techniques*, San Antonio, TX, USA: ACM Press, pages 769–776, 2002.

[FTP03] William T. Freeman, Joshua B. Tenenbaum, and Egon C. Pasztor. Learning style translation for the lines of a drawing. *ACM Transactions on Graphics*, 22(1):33–46, 2003.

[GG01] Bruce Gooch and Amy Gooch. *Non-Photorealistic Rendering*. A K Peters, Ltd., 2001.

[GGSC98] Amy Gooch, Bruce Gooch, Peter Shirley, and Elaine Cohen. A non-photorealistic lighting model for automatic technical illustration. In *SIGGRAPH '98: Proceedings of the 25th Annual Confer-

ence on Computer Graphics and Interactive Techniques, Orlando, FL, USA: ACM Press, pages 447–452, 1998.

[Hae90] Paul Haeberli. Paint by numbers: abstract image representations. In *SIGGRAPH '90: Proceedings of the 17th Annual Conference on Computer Graphics and Interactive Techniques*, Dallas, TX, USA: ACM Press, pages 207–214, 1990.

[Her98] Aaron Hertzmann. Painterly rendering with curved brush strokes of multiple sizes. In *SIGGRAPH '98: Proceedings of the 25th Annual Conference on Computer Graphics and Interactive Techniques*, Orlando, FL, USA: ACM Press, pages 453–460, 1998.

[Her01] Aaron Hertzmann. Paint by relaxation. In *CGI '01: Computer Graphics International 2001*, pages 47–54, Hong Kong, China: IEEE Computer Society, 2001. Also NYU Computer Science Technical Report, May 2000, NYU CS TR2000-801.

[Her02] Aaron Hertzmann. Fast paint texture. In *Proceedings of the 2nd International Symposium on Non-photorealistic Animation and Rendering (NPAR)*, Annecy, France: ACM Press, pages 91–97, 2002.

[Her03] Aaron Hertzmann. Tutorial: a survey of stroke-based rendering. *IEEE Computer Graphics and Applications*, 23(4):70–81, 2003.

[HP00] Aaron Hertzmann and Ken Perlin. Painterly rendering for video and interaction. In *NPAR '00: Proceedings of the 1st International Symposium on Non-photorealistic Animation and Rendering*, Annecy, France: ACM Press, pages 7–12, 2000.

[HZ00] Aaron Hertzmann and Denis Zorin. Illustrating smooth surfaces. In *SIGGRAPH '00: Proceedings of the 27th Annual Conference on Computer Graphics and Interactive Techniques*, New Orleans, LA, USA: ACM Press/Addison-Wesley Publishing Co., pages 517–526, 2000.

[IFP95] Victoria Interrante, Henry Fuchs, and Stephen Pizer. Enhancing transparent skin surfaces with ridge and valley lines. In *VIS '95: Proceedings of the 6th Conference on Visualization*, Atlanta, GA, USA: IEEE Computer Society, page 52, 1995.

[IHS02] Tobias Isenberg, Nick Halper, and Thomas Strothotte. Stylizing silhouettes at interactive rates: from silhouette edges to silhouette strokes. *Computer Graphics Forum (Proceedings of Eurographics)*, 21(3):249–258, 2002.

[IZ95] Lee A. Iverson and Steven W. Zucker. Logical/linear operators for image curves. *IEEE Transactions on Pattern Analysis and Machine Intelligence*, 17(10):982–996, 1995.

[JDA07] Tilke Judd, Fredo Durand, and Edward Adelson. Apparent ridges for line drawing. *ACM Transactions on Graphics*, 26(3):19, 2007.

[KDMF03] Robert D. Kalnins, Philip L. Davidson, Lee Markosian, and Adam Finkelstein. Coherent stylized silhouettes. In *SIGGRAPH '03: ACM SIGGRAPH 2003 Papers*, San Diego, CA, USA: ACM Press, pages 856–861, 2003.

[KMN⁺99] Michael A. Kowalski, Lee Markosian, Northrup J.D., Lubomir Bourdev, Ronen Barzel, Loring S. Holden, and John F. Hughes. Art-based rendering of fur, grass, and trees. In *SIGGRAPH '99: Proceedings of the 26th Annual Conference on Computer Graphics and Interactive Techniques*, Los Angeles, CA, USA: ACM Press/Addison-Wesley Publishing Co., pages 433–438, 1999.

[LFM96] Richard Lengagne, Pascal Fua, and Olivier Monga. Using crest lines to guide surface reconstruction from stereo. In *ICPR '96: Proceedings of the 1996 International Conference on Pattern Recognition*, Vienna, Austria: IEEE Computer Society, volume I, page 9, 1996.

[Lin94] Tony Lindeberg. *Scale-Space Theory in Computer Vision*. Norwell, MA, USA: Kluwer Academic Publishers, 1994.

[Lit97] Peter Litwinowicz. Processing images and video for an impressionist effect. In *SIGGRAPH '97: Proceedings of the 24th Annual Conference on Computer Graphics and Interactive Techniques*, Los Angeles, CA, USA: ACM Press/Addison-Wesley Publishing Co., pages 407–414, 1997.

[LS95] John Lansdown and Simon Schofield. Expressive rendering: a review of nonphotorealistic techniques. *IEEE Computer Graphics and Applications*, 15(3):29–37, 1995.

[Mei96] Barbara J. Meier. Painterly rendering for animation. In *SIGGRAPH '96: Proceedings of the 23rd Annual Conference on Computer Graphics and Interactive Techniques*, New Orleans, LA, USA: ACM Press, pages 477–484, 1996.

[MKG⁺97] Lee Markosian, Michael A. Kowalski, Daniel Goldstein, Samuel J. Trychin, John F. Hughes, and Lubomir D. Bourdev. Real-time nonphotorealistic rendering. In *SIGGRAPH '97: Proceedings of the 24th Annual Conference on Computer Graphics and Interactive Techniques*, Los Angeles, CA, USA: ACM Press/Addison-Wesley Publishing Co., pages 415–420, 1997.

[NM00] J.D. Northrup and Lee Markosian. Artistic silhouettes: a hybrid approach. In *NPAR '00: Proceedings of the 1st International Symposium on Non-photorealistic Animation and Rendering*, Annecy, France: ACM Press, pages 31–37, 2000.

[PV92] Ken Perlin and Luiz Velho. A wavelet representation for unbounded resolution painting. *Technical Report*, New York University, 1992.

[SABS94] Michael P. Salisbury, Sean E. Anderson, Ronen Barzel, and David H. Salesin. Interactive pen-and-ink illustration. In *SIGGRAPH '94: Proceedings of the 21st Annual Conference on Computer Graphics and Interactive Techniques*, Orlando, FL, USA: ACM Press, pages 101–108, 1994.

[SS02] Thomas Strothotte and Stefan Schlechtweg. *Non-Photorealistic Computer Graphics: Modeling, Rendering and Animation*. Morgan Kaufmann Publishers, 2002.

[SSLR96]   Jutta Schumann, Thomas Strothotte, Stefan Laser, and Andreas Raab. Assessing the effect of non-photorealistic rendered images in CAD. In *CHI '96: Proceedings of the SIGCHI Conference on Human Factors in Computing Systems*, Vancouver, Canada: ACM Press, pages 35–41, 1996.

[ST90]   Takafumi Saito and Tokiichiro Takahashi. Comprehensible rendering of 3-D shapes. In *SIGGRAPH '90: Proceedings of the 17st Annual Conference on Computer Graphics and Interactive Techniques*, Dallas, TX, USA: ACM Press, pages 197–206, 1990.

[Ste99]   Carsten Steger. Subpixel-precise extraction of watersheds. In *ICCV '99: Proceedings of the International Conference on Computer Vision*, Kerkira, Greece: IEEE Computer Society, volume 2, page 884, 1999.

[SWHS97]   Michael P. Salisbury, Michael T. Wong, John F. Hughes, and David H. Salesin. Orientable textures for image-based pen-and-ink illustration. In *SIGGRAPH '97: Proceedings of the 24th Annual Conference on Computer Graphics and Interactive Techniques*, Los Angeles, CA, USA: ACM Press/Addison-Wesley Publishing Co., pages 401–406, 1997.

[Wik07]   Wikipedia. http://en.wikipedia.org/wiki/digital_painting, last visited Oct. 13, 2007.

[WS94]   Georges Winkenbach and David H. Salesin. Computer-generated pen-and-ink illustration. In *SIGGRAPH '94: Proceedings of the 21st Annual Conference on Computer Graphics and Interactive Techniques*, Orlando, FL, USA: ACM Press, pages 91–100, 1994.

[WS96]   Georges Winkenbach and David H. Salesin. Rendering parametric surfaces in pen and ink. In *SIGGRAPH '96: Proceedings of the 23rd Annual Conference on Computer Graphics and Interactive Techniques*, New Orleans, LA, USA: ACM Press, pages 469–476, 1996.

[WV03]   John C. Whelan and Mahes Visvalingam. Formulated silhouettes for sketching terrain. In *Proceedings of Theory and Practice of Computer Graphics*, Birmingham, UK: Eurographics Association, pages 90–97, 2003.

[XLJP06]   Songhua Xu, Francis C.M. Lau, Hao Jiang, and Yunhe Pan. A novel method for fast and high-quality rendering of hair. In *EGSR'06: Proceedings of the 17th Eurographics Symposium on Rendering*, Nicosia, Cyprus: ACM Siggraph and Eurographics Association, pages 331–341 & 440, 2006.

Interactive Digital Painting and Calligraphy

This part consists of five chapters: Chapter 3—Chapter 7. The main theme is on how to construct a virtual brush system for digital artists to interactively create paintings and calligraphic artwork.

Chapter 3 provides a general picture on the virtual paintbrush research for interactive digital painting and calligraphy creation. It discusses the key elements in a physically-based digital painting environment, briefly overviews the state-of-the-art research in each subdiscipline, and brings out the objectives for our studies with respect to each of the constituent components of the virtual brush environment we intend to build.

Chapter 4 then presents the overall algorithmic framework of our virtual hairy brush system. It reveals the architecture of our system construction and introduces the basic simulation mechanisms we employ or develop for modeling brush geometry, simulating brush dynamics, emulating virtual pigment behaviors as well as acquiring user input into the system. This chapter also probes into the cooperative functioning between multiple working components in the virtual brush system. The chapter finishes with a comparison of the basic algorithmic design ideas we adopt in developing our virtual paintbrush system with other virtual brush models. Overall, this chapter lays down the foundational framework of our algorithm design and system development endeavors to bring forth an expressive and easy-to-use virtual paintbrush environment.

Following the framework set down in Chapter 4, Chapter 5—Chapter 7 then delve into the three key components of our virtual paintbrush system, with each chapter presenting some advanced algorithm design efforts for strengthening one particular component of the system: Chapter 5 focuses on how to improve the brush modeling realism and dynamics simulation performance of the system; Chapter 6 focuses on enhancing the virtual pigment behavior simulation in the system; Chapter 7 studies the way to provide a realistic, efficient and lightweight visual feedback on the runtime shapes of the virtual paintbrush's head bundle, which can grow into potentially highly sophisticated geometries. Various algorithm design strategies and engineering methods have been utilized and incorporated in these chapters to achieve the best attainable overall performance in our virtual paintbrush system design.

3

Introduction to Interactive Digital Chinese Painting and Calligraphy

3.1 Overview

In this part of the book, we propose a novel algorithmic framework for an advanced virtual brush to be used in interactive digital painting. The framework comprises the following components: a geometric model of the brush using a hierarchical representation that leads to substantial savings in every step of the painting process; fast online brush motion simulation assisted by offline calibration that guarantees an accurate and stable simulation of the brush's dynamic behavior; a new pigment model based on a diffusion process of random molecules that considers delicate and complex pigment behaviors at dipping time as well as during painting; and a user-adaptation component that enables the system to cater for the personal painting habits of different users. A prototype system has been implemented based on this framework. Compared with other virtual brushes, this new system is designed to present a realistic brush in the sense that the system accurately and stably simulates the complex painting functionality of a running brush, and therefore is capable of creating high-quality digital paintings with minute aesthetic details that can rival the real artwork. The advanced features also give rise to a high degree of expressiveness of the virtual brush that the user can comfortably manipulate.

In this chapter, we describe the architecture of the various components involved in a computational solution to digital Chinese painting and calligraphy. The four key elements constituting the digital painting and calligraphy process are painter, brush, ink and paper. Their interaction is illustrated in Fig. 3.1.

3.2 Background

Virtual brush is an important tool for interactive painting [Str86, HH90, HLW93, HL94, SABS94, ABL95, SN99, Pix00, WI00, BSLM01, KMM+02, XTLP02, CT02]. Smith has written a good survey on the early painting systems [Smi01]. These early systems offered 2D brushes for painting. The

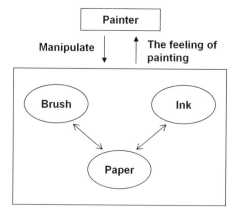

Fig. 3.1. The interaction of the four key elements of digital painting simulation.

newer painting systems are more sophisticated, which can for example automatically generate painterly rendering results based on some input reference images [Her98]. To provide a virtual brush that can mimic the real 3D brush for painting and calligraphy writing has become a popular area for research in recent years [WI00, BSLM01, XTLP02, CT02]. The researchers are attracted by the unique ability of a 3D virtual brush to generate expressive and realistic results through techniques such as physically-based modeling. Common to most existing 3D virtual brushes are three core components that implement the most essential functionalities of a 3D virtual brush: a brush geometry model, a brush motion simulator, and a pigment behavior model. The following subsections give an overview of existing work with regard to these three core components.

3.2.1 Previous Work

3.2.1.1 Virtual brush geometry models

One of the earliest models was by Strassmann [Str86], where brush strokes are created by sweeping a 1D brush bristle over a skeleton. It is effectively a 2D heuristic approach which is not natural to use for non-computer specialists. Wong and Ip's virtual brush is modeled as an inverse cone and can produce an elliptic drawing mark [WI00]. This represents a substantial improvement over Strassmann's in terms of usability. However, because of the need to manually specify an intricate set of parameters controlling the shape, density and opacity of the current brush drawing mark, the interactivity of Wong and Ip's system is limited. In the DAB project [BSLM01], a subdivision surface is wrapped around a spring-mass particle system skeleton to represent the brush geometry. One disadvantage of using a subdivision surface is that the splitting of the brush is very hard to model. To generate the subdivision surface to model the brush head, either interpolation or some approximating scheme is used. An interpolated brush head, however, often cannot deform smoothly because of the frequent occurrence of high curvature in the brush head surface, while approximation has the problem of properly placing control points to yield the desired surface. On top of all this, how to suitably anchor the control points of the surface to the mass particles is a non-trivial problem. In the work by Xu et al. [XTLP02], general sweeping is employed to establish the solid geometry model of each hair cluster. The problem however is that general sweeping is a time-consuming operation. At different stages of painting, much computation is needed to apply general sweeping operations to update the model. Also, the solid model requires a fair amount of memory for its internal representation, and after the brush is split many times, the demand for memory could become a bottleneck. In the work by Chu and Tai [CT02], a single hair bundle is modeled by a geometry model that is mathematically equivalent to that by Xu et al. [XTLP02]. Unlike the latter which simulates the spreading and splitting of the brush tip by a geometry approach, Chu and Tai used an alpha map to implement cluster modeling for the split brush. This results in an over simplification which limits the expressiveness and the amount of fine details that the brush is able to produce.

It appears that none of the above is sufficient to model a physical brush with a high degree of likeness to the brush's real behavior. One frequently occurring situation in reality, for example, is that of the brush splitting into a large number of hair clusters. To model this rather "chaotic" situation is out of reach for all the existing brush geometry models. According to many practising artists, such a high degree of splitting is very much desirable. We propose a hierarchical geometry model for a "realistic" brush; together with a fast rendering procedure, our model enables efficient simulation of the most complex effects of a real brush, such as brush splitting.

3.2.1.2 Virtual brush motion simulators

Simulating the motion and dynamic deformation of a real paintbrush is a tough problem because of the complex static geometry and dynamics of the modeled brush.

In DAB [BSLM01], the motion of the brush geometry is simulated by Newtonian dynamics using a pair of first-order differential equations and Aristotelian dynamics through a single first-order differential equation. Solving differential equations involves some tradeoff between system stability, computation efficiency and simulation accuracy. In fact the brush is a heavily damped system. When the penholder is motionless, the brush geometry stops deforming. Unfortunately, such a large damping force in Newtonian dynamics is hard to estimate. The authors of DAB therefore apply constraint satisfaction at the end of each step of motion simulation to ensure that the resultant brush geometry is a plausible configuration. This gives rise to the issue of simulation preciseness versus system stability. Unlike other classical motion simulation approaches which care a lot about simulation accuracy, the approach by Xu et al. [XTLP02] aims at providing a user with a customized virtual hairy brush. Their brush motion and brush geometry deformation are controlled by a set of "quality parameters" which, through a machine training module, can be customized for different users. These quality parameters affect the deformation process of a virtual hairy brush, and are not meant to be directly set or adjusted by the user. Unless the user can provide enough samples to train the system, he/she could only accept the default values for these quality parameters. The performance of the machine training process depends on the number of samples the user would input into the system. For a satisfactory customization result, a large number of samples is often needed. The dynamics of Chu and Tai's brush [CT02] are modeled as springs which are deformed through constrained energy minimization. This method of modeling can simulate small-scale deformation of the brush geometry but not large-scale bending or stretching due to the restriction of constrained energy minimization.

The simulation of the motion and dynamic deformation of our hierarchical virtual brush geometry model is performed through a collaboration between online and offline computations. We minimize on the amount of online computation, and the result is calibrated by an error calibration mechanism using a simulation error database that was constructed offline. Compared with other virtual brush systems, we can simulate the brush motion with high precision using just a small amount of computation on the fly.

3.2.1.3 Pigment behavior models

Pigment behavior simulation presents yet another challenge to virtual brush system designers. One approach to simulating the ink's behavior is through a cellular automaton [ZST+99]. A classic work on the pigment model is the computer-generated watercolor research contributed by Curtis et al. [CAS+97], which studies the complex interaction behind pigment mixing based on a shallow water model. Their approach can synthesize very realistic water color effects. During digital painting, the main loop of their algorithm iterates through several sub-processes simulating pigment behavior in a sequential manner. One sub-process will promote or restrain another sub-process. In a real painting process, however, these four sub-processes have subtle interaction, and therefore simulating the sub-processes separately would not necessarily add up to accurately simulating the pigment behavior. Another problem with their approach is that solving all the complex differential equations is too time-consuming for an interactive painting system. Other existing pigment behavior models include Lee's [Lee99] for black-white painting and Kunii et al.'s [LNH95] for diffused ink painting.

In Strassmann's hairy brushes [Str86], the color of brush strokes can be varied along the stroke's skeleton direction. In Wong's virtual brush [WI00], only monochrome calligraphic writing is supported. In DAB [BSLM01], a bidirectional, two-layer paint model is employed. They use essentially an additive compositive formula to mix the paint. In their paint representation, they assume that the paint surface contains two layers. One layer is completely wet where paint would transfer out and another is completely dry. This over-simplification of paint behavior makes the system incapable of achieving exquisite artistic effects demanded by the most seasoned painters. In Xu's virtual brush [XTLP02], a simple alpha blending strategy is employed to perform the pigment mixing.

Pigment mixing is a very important factor that contributes to the final results of painterly rendering and therefore deserves a very careful treatment. An ideal pigment behavior model should lead to fast response time in system implementation such as those described in [Str86, WI00, BSLM01, XTLP02], and highly realistic results as demonstrated in [CAS+97]. In our work we liken the complex pigment's behavior in a painting process to that of heat or moisture, and model the pigment's behavior as a diffusion process. We introduce a strategy to divide the overall computation into an offline and an online part, therefore solving the complex differential equations modeling the pigment's behavior accurately and stably in real time.

There are many other fancy features that previous virtual brush systems are capable of, such as the ability to do 3D painting [HH90, ABL95, Pix00]. The DAB system [BSLM01] has haptic feedback. The system by Wei et al. [WLSL92] uses an intelligent model to beautify the output. Chan et al. [CAC02] create 3D Chinese painting animation using existing commercial software packages. Way and Shih's system [WLS01] supports texture synthesis, with which beautiful rock textures in Chinese landscape painting can be created by a simple brush model based on some reference images.

3.2.2 Our Virtual Brush

The distinctive features of our design for a realistic virtual brush include: (1) hierarchical modeling of the complex geometry of real paintbrushes; (2) division of overall brush motion simulation into small online tasks and offline calibration; (3) modeling of pigment behavior at dipping time and during painting as a diffusion process subject to a certain physical condition, giving rise to a new expressive pigment model; and a strategy of solving the diffusion equations through a look-up table, which makes the numerical computation fast and stable; (4) a user manipulability adaptation component.

Compared with existent digital painting systems of virtual brushes, our newly designed virtual brush can accurately and stably simulate the motion of highly complex geometry of a running brush essential for generating large quantities of delicate but minute details to create high quality digital paintings comparable to real artworks. The advanced features of our system make it capable of generating more expressive digital artworks in a more user-friendly way.

References

[ABL95]   Maneesh Agrawala, Andrew C. Beers, and Marc Levoy. 3D paint-
           ing on scanned surfaces. In *SI3D '95: Proceedings of the 1995
           Symposium on Interactive 3D Graphics*, Monterey, CA, USA:
           ACM Press, pages 145–150 & 215, 1995.
[BSLM01]   Bill Baxter, Vincent Scheib, Ming C. Lin, and Dinesh Manocha.
           DAB: Interactive haptic painting with 3D virtual brushes. In
           *SIGGRAPH '01: Proceedings of the 28th Annual Conference on
           Computer Graphics and Interactive Techniques*, Los Angeles,
           CA, USA: ACM Press, pages 461–468, 2001.
[CAC02]   Ching Chan, Ergun Akleman, and Jianer Chen. Two methods
           for creating Chinese painting. In *Proceedings of Pacific Graphics
           2002*, Beijing, China: IEEE Computer Society, pages 403–412,
           2002.
[CAS+97]   Cassidy J. Curtis, Sean E. Anderson, Joshua E. Seims, Kurt W.
           Fleischer, and David H. Salesin. Computer-generated watercolor.
           In *SIGGRAPH '97: Proceedings of the 24th Annual Conference
           on Computer Graphics and Interactive Techniques*, Los Angeles,
           CA, USA: ACM Press/Addison-Wesley Publishing Co., pages
           421–430, 1997.
[CT02]   Nelson S.H. Chu and Chiew-Lan Tai. An efficient brush model for
           physically-based 3D painting. In *Proceedings of Pacific Graphics
           (PG '02)*, Beijing, China: IEEE Computer Society, pages 413–
           421, 2002.
[Her98]   Aaron Hertzmann. Painterly rendering with curved brush strokes
           of multiple sizes. In *SIGGRAPH '98: Proceedings of the 25th
           Annual Conference on Computer Graphics and Interactive Tech-
           niques*, Orlando, FL, USA: ACM Press, pages 453–460, 1998.
[HH90]   Pat Hanrahan and Paul Haeberli. Direct wysiwyg painting and
           texturing on 3D shapes. In *SIGGRAPH '90: Proceedings of the
           17th Annual Conference on Computer Graphics and Interactive
           Techniques*, Dallas, TX, USA: ACM Press, pages 215–223, 1990.
[HL94]   Siu-Chi Hsu and Irene H. H. Lee. Drawing and animation us-
           ing skeletal strokes. In *SIGGRAPH '94: Proceedings of the 21st
           Annual Conference on Computer Graphics and Interactive Tech-
           niques*, Orlando, FL, USA: ACM Press, pages 109–118, 1994.
[HLW93]   Siu-Chi Hsu, Irene H.H. Lee, and Neil E. Wiseman. Skeletal
           strokes. In *Proceedings of the 6th Annual ACM Symposium
           on User Interface Software and Technology*, Atlanta, GA, USA:
           ACM Press, pages 197–206, 1993.
[KMM+02]   Robert D. Kalnins, Lee Markosian, Barbara J. Meier, Michael
           A. Kowalski, Joseph C. Lee, Philip L. Davidson, Matthew Webb,
           John F. Hughes, and Adam Finkelstein. WYSIWYG NPR: draw-
           ing strokes directly on 3D models. In *SIGGRAPH '02: Pro-
           ceedings of the 29th Annual Conference on Computer Graphics*

and Interactive Techniques, San Antonio, TX, USA: ACM Press, pages 755–762, 2002.

[Lee99]   Jintae Lee. Simulating oriental black-ink painting. *IEEE Computer Graphics and Applications*, 19(3):74–81, 1999.

[LNH95]   Tosiyasu L. Kunii, Gleb V. Nosovskij, and Takafumi Hayashi. A diffusion model for computer animation of diffuse ink painting. In *Proceedings of Computer Animation*, Geneva, Switzerland: IEEE Computer Society, pages 98–102, 1995.

[Pix00]   Pixologic. Z-brush, http://pixologic.com, 2000.

[SABS94]   Michael P. Salisbury, Sean E. Anderson, Ronen Barzel, and David H. Salesin. Interactive pen-and-ink illustration. In *SIGGRAPH '94: Proceedings of the 21st Annual Conference on Computer Graphics and Interactive Techniques*, Orlando, FL, USA: ACM Press, pages 101–108, 1994.

[Smi01]   Alvy R. Smith. Digital paint systems: an anecdotal and historical overview. *IEEE Annals of the History of Computing*, 23(2):4–30, 2001.

[SN99]   Suguru Saito and Masayuki Nakajima.   3D physically-based brush model for painting. In *SIGGRAPH '99 Sketches, Conference Abstracts and Applications*, Los Angeles, CA, USA: ACM Press, page 226, 1999.

[Str86]   Steve Strassmann. Hairy brushes. In *SIGGRAPH '86: Proceedings of the 13th Annual Conference on Computer Graphics and Interactive Techniques*, Dallas, TX, USA: ACM Press, pages 225–232, 1986.

[WI00]   Helena T.F. Wong and Horace H.S. Ip. Virtual brush: a model-based synthesis of Chinese calligraphy. *Computers and Graphics*, 24(1):99–113, 2000.

[WLS01]   Der-Lor Way, Yu-Ru Lin, and Zen-Chung Shih.   The synthesis of rock textures in Chinese landscape painting. In *Proceedings of Eurographics 2001*, Manchester, UK: Blackwell, pages C123–C131, 2001.

[WLSL92]   X. Wei, S. Lu, M. Song, and B. Luo.   Computer pattern design and painting technique based on aesthetics knowledge. *Computer Aided Drafting, Design and Manufacturing*, 2(2):32–40, 1992.

[XTLP02]   Songhua Xu, Min Tang, Francis C.M. Lau, and Yunhe Pan.   A solid model based virtual hairy brush. *Computer Graphics Forum (Proceedings of Eurographics '02)*, 21(3):299–308 & 625, 2002.

[ZST+99]   Qing Zhang, Youetsu Sato, Junya Takahashi, Kazunobu Muraoka, and Norishige Chiba.   Simple cellular automaton-based simulation of ink behavior and its application to Suibokuga-like 3D rendering of trees. *Journal of Visualization and Computer Animation*, 10(1):27–37, 1999.

4

Basic Algorithmic Framework of a Virtual Hairy Paintbrush System

4.1 Overview

We propose a novel "e-brush" for calligraphy and painting, which meets all the criteria for a good e-brush. We use only four attributes to capture the essential features of the brush, and a suitably powerful modeling metaphor for its behavior. The e-brush's geometry, dynamic motions and pigment changes are all dealt with in a single model. A single model simplifies the synchronization between the various system modules, thus giving rise to a more stable system and lower costs. By a careful tradeoff between the complexity of the model and computation efficiency, more elaborate simulation of the e-brush's deformation and its recovery for interactive painterly rendering is made possible. We also propose a novel paper-ink model to complement the brush's model, and a machine intelligence module to empower the user to easily create beautiful calligraphy and painting. Despite the complexity of the modeling behind the scene, the high-level user interface has a simplistic and friendly design. The final results created by our e-brush can rival the real artwork.

4.2 Introduction

The problem of how to simulate Chinese calligraphy and paintings using the computer has attracted many researchers. A good method could produce calligraphic fonts or artwork that are useful in a wide variety of applications, and hence has a good market value. Among the many devices used in art or calligraphic creation, the hairy brush has for centuries been the most popular because of its versatility and special aesthetic and expressive power. It is therefore a meaningful pursuit for computer scientists to find a way to create an "e-hairy brush" that can effectively emulate a real brush. The pursuit is technically challenging because of the very complex structure and features of the hairy brush, especially when the brush is in motion during a calligraphy session. In fact the brush is not the only object that needs modeling and simulation, but also the paper and the ink.

A good e-brush system should meet the following criteria.

(1) Easy and natural to use: With a suitable input device, the user should be able to mimic the way he/she uses a real brush to produce an artwork. No user should be required to change his habits or to go through tedious adaptation in order to be able to use the brush. The most ideal virtual brush may even provide feedback to simulate a sense of touch resembling that of the real brush.

(2) Expressive power and realistic results: The results that can be produced by the system should be a close approximation to the equivalent real artwork, and therefore would appear to be realistic. The power of the brush lies in its ability to simulate a wide variety of effects and styles renderable by the real brush. It is reasonable to imagine that an e-brush can do more than what a real brush can do.

(3) Flexibility to fit the user and convenience: For the sophisticated user, the system should provide delicate controls for adjusting the different features and parameters of the e-brush. For others the system can provide a ready-to-use e-brush that needs no further tuning by most users. The system should also provide different brush types for the user to choose, as well as different types of paper and ink.

(4) Real-time response: A real brush gives real-time responses. If an e-brush is to rival a real one, it must respond instantaneously to the user's manipulation.

(5) Intelligent computer-aided art creation: To mimic the basic actions and features of a real brush requires certain intelligence on the part of the machine. A more powerful system can rely on artificial intelligence to implement features not present in any real brush, and thus could lead to results that surpass that of a real brush.

An e-brush system as we conceive it consists of three major components: an interactive input component to sample the user's input, a core component to simulate the dynamic behavior of the e-brush, and a component to render the generated result. The proper execution of these components relies on several models that are at the heart of the system, including a geometrical model of the brush, a dynamic model for the simulation, a pigment model for the continuous rendering of the ink mark at the brush tip, and a paper-ink model. Note that the challenge to produce realistic e-artwork lies not only in the modeling of the e-brush, but also the modeling of the paper and the ink [Lee01]. We add a fourth component—a machine-intelligent component, with which we offer easier and better manipulability for the user as well as more optimized results.

4.2.1 Overview of E-brush and Related Research

Some previous work has used cubic Bezier curves [Chu90, NTN93], cubic B-spline [Pha91] or skeletal strokes [HL94] to represent brush strokes, and combined strokes for doing calligraphy or painting. Hobby considered the problem of finding a discrete set of pixels that approximate the envelope of a convex brush shape with respect to a given trajectory [Hob85]. In his approach, a given brush shape is represented by a polygon. In [PF89], brush stroke boundaries are represented by circles of different diameters along a middle trajectory in the image space. A further step along this direction is reported in [AKL93], where the general sweeping boundary of a 2D curved object is used. Also, a brush touch function can be used to construct the shape of strokes [SYST89]. A structural method of using brush strokes to compose a character is discussed in [LK95]. Given the representation of a character, the technique of rasterization can then be used to generate the image of the character, to be used in applications such as desktop publishing [SZ95]. Systematic creation of large sets of characters ascribing to a certain style leads to typographic fonts. New font creation is indeed an interesting and challenging problem [Cou81]. Pan et al. employed an algebra of geometric shapes to generate new Chinese fonts. Shamir and Rappoport[SR97] have introduced a parametric method to compactly represent existing outline-based Oriental fonts [SR97]. Ip et al. discussed a method to encode Chinese calligraphic characters using automatic fractal shape coding [IWM94]. Models for generating realistic calligraphy are developed by Guo in [Guo95b, Guo95a].

Many discussions and research results for the "virtual brush" and its application and values can be found in [LW01a, YI90, YH84, YYI87, ZZST90, HY98]. The paper by Strassmann [Str86] presents a detailed analysis of the effects a virtual hairy brush can produce. Wong and Ip devised a virtual brush model for synthesizing Chinese calligraphic writings [WI00], in which the main working units are the cone and some ellipses. There exist many software approaches to modeling the brush [LW01b, LGE+99, HYH00, MHN+99, Lee97], of which most are physically based solutions. There are also hardware approaches, such as the one by Greene [Gre85].

Besides research on the e-brush, some elaborate ink diffusion models have been proposed to simulate different ink spreading effects [LNH95, ZST+99, KNV01, GK91]. Artificial intelligence, fuzzy logic, and knowledge-based engineering techniques have been found to be useful in equipping a virtual hairy brush to produce beautiful calligraphic artwork [NISL93, WLSL92, YH97].

With a good e-hairy brush model and a good paper-ink model, beautiful paintings can be generated in the same way as generating beautiful calligraphic artwork [PZ91]. Way et al. [WLS01] used a simple brush model to synthesize beautiful rock textures in Chinese landscape painting. With their method, the contours of the rocks and the areas to which textures are applied are manually supplied by the user using some existing image as reference. Many other papers have proposed similar e-brush approaches to tackle the problem of painterly rendering [Lee99, BSLM01, CAS+97, Her98, SN99, GEL00].

Simulating the hairy brush's various rendering effects falls into the research area of non-photorealistic rendering (NPR), of which a good survey can be found in the paper by Lansdown and Schofield [LS95]. Creating Chinese calligraphy or paintings by an e-hairy brush in real-time bears close resemblance to real-time generation of pen-and-ink illustrations in terms of both the goal and the problem-solving strategies [WS94, MKG+97]. The aesthetic effects pen and ink can produce can be emulated by using a virtual hairy brush with a fine brush tip; but the reverse is not that feasible. The complexity of a virtual hairy brush is obviously much greater than that of a pen or pencil, as the brush is much more powerful in artistic expression. This paper describes a complex virtual hairy brush and its associated paper-ink model and shows, despite the complexity, how the simulated brush can operate efficiently in real-time.

4.2.2 Our Work and Contributions

We developed an algorithmic software framework that can simulate the change of the physical conditions of a hairy brush, including the brush's geometric shape and its ink-related properties during the Chinese calligraphic writing process, where ink-related properties refer to the brush's degree of wetness and color. We have constructed an interactive software system implementing these algorithms which can be used to create calligraphic artwork fully electronically. Fig. 4.1 shows the overall architecture of our system.

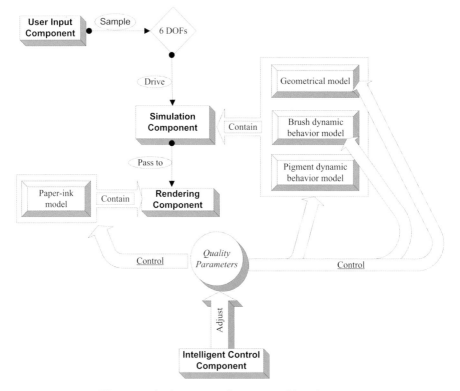

Fig. 4.1. Architecture of our virtual brush system

Our virtual hairy brush is closer to the real brush than other similar brushes because our e-brush can automatically determine both the geometric contour and the texture of its current drawing mark on the virtual paper at the same time. This process is done in real-time and no human intervention is necessary, which is not the case in other similar systems. The drawing mark in our model can be varied and of irregular shape, which is generated from any planar parametric curve instead of just an ellipse. This is a vital feature for achieving quality in an artist's work.

We introduce a useful concept called *writing primitive*, which is a hair cluster, to serve as the basic working unit of the virtual hairy brush. The cross section of each writing primitive as one indivisible entity intersecting the virtual paper plane and its ink-related information are computed only once during every time step. This makes real-time simulation of the hairy brush's writing and painting behavior possible in our system. We have implemented a prototype system to demonstrate the effectiveness of our algorithms in constructing a high-quality e-brush system.

By embedding ink-related information in the writing primitive's control axis, a single primitive can readily express reasonably complex, interesting and even mysterious distribution of the ink, including its color and wetness. In our proposed ink model, we use probabilities to create realistic effects to be used in rendering the current ink-mark, thus enabling our virtual hairy brush to simulate the drying and running effects of calligraphic artwork. Multiple gray levels, full-color paintings, dry brush writing effects and saturation effects can all be produced using this new ink model. All these writing effects contribute to the system's expressive power needed by computer-aided art creation.

We also introduce an inertia predictor to calculate the brush's virtual position based on its sampled position during the writing process. This inertia predictor simulates the acceleration of the virtual hairy brush, which gives the user the feeling of a real physical brush and helps to produce output that rivals real artwork. In addition to various ways that allow the user to manually edit various quality parameters of the virtual hairy brush, special optimization algorithms are built into the system to automatically customize these parameters to achieve better manoeuvrability of the brush and improved quality in the output.

According to the six Degrees of Freedom (DOF) of the hairy brush, which are sampled periodically, the computer can simulate the whole Chinese calligraphy process with high accuracy. The process can be performed with real-time response, as proven through experimentation. Since many of the geometrical and dynamic parameters of the brush can be automatically determined by the system, it is not necessary to store any bitmap image (for the brush's cross section) during the writing process. After completing the writing process, it is also not necessary to store the generated artwork in any standard format; a small file containing the changes of the virtual hairy brush's six degrees of freedom during the whole writing process is sufficient to reconstruct the full final image. Hence, the storage requirement of our approach is minimal.

Sect. 4.3 introduces and explains the concept of writing primitive. Sect. 4.4 presents the solid model of the virtual hairy brush. Sect. 4.5 discusses the sampling and processing of the brush's input. Sect. 4.6 discusses how the parameters in the parametric models of the e-brush are adjusted dynamically.

Sect. 4.7 presents the rendering of the brush's current ink mark at any time instant, namely the brush writing and painting process. Sect. 4.8 discusses how the brush and its quality parameters are configured by the system automatically. Sect. 4.9 gives an overview of the implemented system and showcases some examples of artwork created using the system. Sect. 4.10 presents the related work. Sect. 4.11.2 discusses some possible future extensions. Sect. 4.11.1 summarizes and concludes the paper.

4.3 Writing Primitives

We rely on the concept of *writing primitive*, which represents a hair cluster (i.e. a small bundle of hair), to reduce the complexity of the modeling and thus the computational requirement for the system. A virtual hairy brush consists of one or more writing primitives. Each writing primitive is described by a NURBS surface and is constructed through the general sweeping operation in CAD. The behavior of the virtual hairy brush is an aggregation of the behavior of all its writing primitives. This is in sharp contrast to with the approach used by Wong and Ip [WI00], where every hair is operated on; it is also different from the DAB system [BSLM01], where the whole brush head is modeled as one subdivision surface. The use of writing primitives does not diminish in any way the power of the virtual hairy brush in satisfactorily simulating all possible behavior of a real hairy brush including the branching out behavior. This is because the clustering of hair is a natural phenomenon and writing primitive appears to be a good model for capturing this phenomenon. In the physical clustering of hair, hair in the same bundle shares similar ink-related properties, which is also captured in our modeling. Our experimental results have confirmed the correctness of this approach in modeling the real brush, as well as the outstanding expressive power of our model. The artwork created using our system can be seen as better than those in the paper by Wong and Ip.

A writing primitive in the model is defined by its four attributes as shown in Fig. 4.2. taking the Based on these four attributes, the model is constructed through the general sweeping operation in CAD. This operation will construct

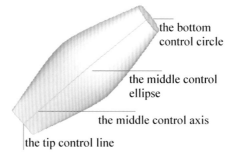

the bottom control circle

the middle control ellipse

the middle control axis

the tip control line

Fig. 4.2. A writing primitive and its four attributes

a NURBS sweeping surface by defined by curve of the writing primitive's middle control axis as its sweeping trajectory and the cross sections the user at initialization as the given profiles. Note that at the start of the writing process the brush consists of a single writing primitive. The general sweeping operation is implemented according to the minimized rotation frame algorithm by Maurer and Juttler [MJ99]. During the simulation, three of the four attributes (not including the bottom control circle) of the writing primitive will be dynamically adjusted according to the input data which describe the brush's current position in the 3D space. The bottom control circle never changes during the writing process.

All the input data are preprocessed to take into account the inertia of the hairy brush, which creates a realistic "feel" of the brush. We refer to the cross section of the intersection between a writing primitive and the virtual paper plane as the writing primitive's current drawing mark. For every time slice of the writing process, ink will be deposited according to the state of the current drawing mark. The union of the current drawing marks of all the writing primitives is the current mark made by the brush on the paper. The final artwork is the accumulation of such marks over all the time slices. Fig. 4.3 shows the state transitions of a writing primitive. The virtual hairy brush's working diagram is shown in Fig. 4.4. It will be explained in detail in Sect. 4.5—Sect. 4.7.

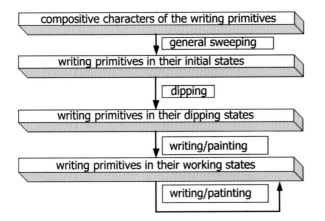

Fig. 4.3. State transitions of a writing primitives

4.4 The Model and the States

4.4.1 The Parametric Model of the Virtual Hairy Brush

Our model of a virtual Hairy Brush (**HB**) is in terms of the collection of writing primitives that the brush is composed of. Eq. (4.1) defines **HB**:

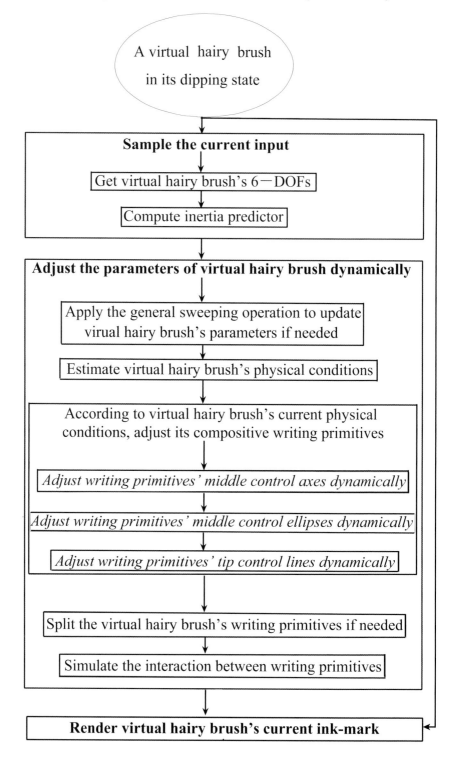

Fig. 4.4. Virtual hairy brush's working diagram

$$\begin{cases} \mathbf{HB} \triangleq (\mathbf{CWP}, \mathbf{Qp}) \\ \mathbf{CWP} \triangleq (\mathbf{WP}_1, \mathbf{WP}_2, \cdots, \mathbf{WP}_m) \\ \mathbf{Qp} \triangleq (\mathbf{Qp}^1, \mathbf{Qp}^2) \\ \mathbf{Qp}^1 \triangleq (e, tre, \nu, re, ie, sm) \\ \mathbf{Qp}^2 \triangleq (ren, \eta, ab, pw, dry) \end{cases} \tag{4.1}$$

The brush's writing primitives are denoted as $\mathbf{WP}_1, \mathbf{WP}_2, \cdots, \mathbf{WP}_m$. Each writing primitive $\mathbf{WP}_i$ $(i = 1, 2, \cdots, m)$, described by a NURBS surface, is constructed by the general sweeping operation in CAD. The number of $\mathbf{HB}$'s compositive writing primitives, m, will be dynamically adjusted by the system. There are several parameters for controlling the artwork style generated by the brush, the values of which are within $[0, 1]$. These parameters are called the quality parameters $\mathbf{Qp}$ of $\mathbf{HB}$, which are classified into two categories. The first category, $\mathbf{Qp}^1$, affects the created brush strokes' boundary. The second category, $\mathbf{Qp}^2$, affects the texture of the created brush strokes. Table 4.1 contains a complete list of these parameters. The meaning and detailed usage of these parameters and how they are configured will be explained later in the paper.

Table 4.1. Virtual hairy brush system's quality parameters

Name	Concise Meaning	Category	Usage
\multicolumn{4}{c}{Virtual Hairy Brush System's Quality Parameters}			
e	$\mathbf{HB}$'s degree of elasticity	$\mathbf{Qp}^1$	Eq. (4.12), Eq. (4.14)
tre	$\mathbf{HB}$'s threshold for splitting	$\mathbf{Qp}^1$	Eq. (4.20)
ν	$\mathbf{HB}$'s relocation factor	$\mathbf{Qp}^1$	Eq. (4.19)
re	$\mathbf{HB}$'s rotation coefficient	$\mathbf{Qp}^1$	Eq. (4.18)
ie	$\mathbf{HB}$'s elongation coefficient	$\mathbf{Qp}^1$	Eq. (4.18)
sm	ψ's degree of smoothness	$\mathbf{Qp}^1$	Eq. (4.14)
ren	$\mathbf{HB}$'s color rendering control factor	$\mathbf{Qp}^2$	Eq. (4.29)
η	$\mathbf{HB}$'s ink diffusion distance factor	$\mathbf{Qp}^2$	Eq. (4.22)
ab	ψ's absorbing ability	$\mathbf{Qp}^2$	Eq. (4.17), Eq. (4.26), Eq. (4.29)
pw	ψ's diffusion control factor	$\mathbf{Qp}^2$	Eq. (4.22)
dry	ψ's drying factor	$\mathbf{Qp}^2$	Eq. (4.26)
Notes	$\mathbf{HB}$ refers to the virtual hairy brush; ψ refers to the virtual paper. $\mathbf{Qp}^1$ are $\mathbf{HB}$'s quality parameters for shape; $\mathbf{Qp}^2$ are $\mathbf{HB}$'s quality parameters for texture.		

4.4.2 The Parametric Model of a Writing Primitive

The parametric model of a writing primitive $\mathbf{WP}_i$ $(i = 1, 2, \cdots, m)$ is defined as: $\mathbf{WP}_i \triangleq (\mathbf{C}_i, \mathbf{E}_i, \mathbf{L}_i, \mathbf{A}_i)$. To generate the parametric model of a writing primitive $\mathbf{WP}_i$ $(i = 1, 2, \cdots, m)$ through the general sweeping operation, a circle $\mathbf{C}_i$, an ellipse $\mathbf{E}_i$, and a line $\mathbf{L}_i$ are taken as the sweeping profiles, and an axis $\mathbf{A}_i$ is used as the sweeping trajectory. $\mathbf{C}_i, \mathbf{E}_i, \mathbf{L}_i, \mathbf{A}_i$ are called $\mathbf{WP}_i$'s bottom control circle, middle control ellipse, tip control line, and middle control axis, respectively (Fig. 4.2). Among these four attributes, $\mathbf{C}_i$ is a static attribute of $\mathbf{WP}_i$, that is, once $\mathbf{C}_i$ is initialized at the beginning, it remains unchanged during the whole process.

4.4.2.1 The bottom control circle of a writing primitive

The bottom control circle $\mathbf{C}_i$ of writing primitive $\mathbf{WP}_i$ is defined as:

$$\begin{cases} \mathbf{C}_i \triangleq (\mathbf{cen}_i, r_i, \mathbf{cori}_i) \\ \mathbf{cen}_i \triangleq (ccx_i, ccy_i, ccz_i) \\ \mathbf{cori}_i \triangleq (cox_i, coy_i, coz_i) \end{cases} \tag{4.2}$$

where $\mathbf{cen}_i$ is the coordinates of $\mathbf{C}_i$'s center, r_i its radius, and $\mathbf{cori}_i$, a 3-dimensional unit vector representing $\mathbf{C}_i$'s orientation. All the writing primitives of a brush share the same bottom control circle, and so this circle is also called the bottom control circle of the brush, denoted as $\mathbf{HB.C}$.

4.4.2.2 The tip control line of a writing primitive

The tip control line $\mathbf{L}_i$ of $\mathbf{WP}_i$ is defined as:

$$\begin{cases} \mathbf{L}_i \triangleq (len_i, \mathbf{mid}_i, \mathbf{lori}_i) \\ \mathbf{mid}_i \triangleq (mix_i, miy_i, miz_i) \\ \mathbf{lori}_i \triangleq (lox_i, loy_i, loz_i) \end{cases} \tag{4.3}$$

where len_i is the current length of $\mathbf{L}_i$, $\mathbf{mid}_i$ is $\mathbf{L}_i$'s midpoint, and $\mathbf{lori}_i$ a 3-dimensional unit vector representing $\mathbf{L}_i$'s orientation.

4.4.2.3 The middle control axis of a writing primitive

The middle control axis $\mathbf{A}_i$ is a cubic B-spline curve with interpolated key points $\mathbf{P}_{i,1}, \mathbf{P}_{i,2}, \cdots, \mathbf{P}_{i,n_i}$. Each of these points carries both geometric and ink-related information, including $\mathbf{P}_{i,j}$'s color in RGB and its degree of wetness. $\mathbf{P}_{i,j}$ is defined in Eq. (4.4):

$$\begin{cases} \mathbf{P}_{i,j} \triangleq (\mathbf{cc}_{i,j}, \mathbf{col}_{i,j}, wet_{i,j}, \mathbf{wv}_{i,j}, \mathbf{cv}_{i,j}, wr_{i,j}, cr_{i,j}) \\ \mathbf{cc}_{i,j} \triangleq (cx_{i,j}, cy_{i,j}, cz_{i,j}) \\ \mathbf{wv}_{i,j} \triangleq (wx_{i,j}, wy_{i,j}, wz_{i,j}) \\ \mathbf{cv}_{i,j} \triangleq (cx_{i,j}, cy_{i,j}, cz_{i,j}) \\ i = 1, 2, \cdots, m; j = 1, 2, \cdots, n_i \end{cases} \tag{4.4}$$

Here, $\mathbf{cc}_{i,j}$ is $\mathbf{P}_{i,j}$'s coordinates. $\mathbf{col}_{i,j}$ is $\mathbf{P}_{i,j}$'s color in RGB format. With this formulation, we can generate colorful calligraphic artwork and even create watercolor paintings. $wet_{i,j}$ is $\mathbf{P}_{i,j}$'s degree of wetness. For each $\mathbf{A}_i$, its first key point is always set at the center of the bottom control circle, and its last key point at the midpoint of the tip control line; that is $\mathbf{cc}_{i,1} \triangleq \mathbf{cen}_i, \mathbf{cc}_{i,n_i} \triangleq \mathbf{mid}_i$.

Each key point has four fields for specifying the point's ink-related information: *vector mode* wetness changing vector $\mathbf{wv}_{i,j}$, *vector mode* color changing vector $\mathbf{cv}_{i,j}$, *radiation mode* wetness changing factor $wr_{i,j}$ and *radiation mode* color changing factor $cr_{i,j}$. Based on these fields we can compute the ink-related information for any point $\mathbf{Q}$ on a plane perpendicular to the middle control axis $\mathbf{A}_i$ passing through $\mathbf{P}_{i,j}$. We allow two modes of ink distribution in the virtual hairy brush: the *vector mode*, in which ink is distributed according to the direction of a certain vector, and the *radiation mode*, in which ink is distributed radically. There is an ink-related texture function associated with each key point, which produces some hybrid effect contributed by these two distribution modes. Fig. 4.5 explains these two modes of ink distribution.

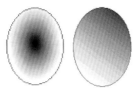

Fig. 4.5. Radiation (left) and vector (right) ink distribution modes

The contribution made by $\mathbf{P}_{i,j}$'s vector mode ink distribution is:

$$\begin{cases} \delta_v wet_\mathbf{Q} = wet_{\mathbf{P}_{i,j}} \times ((\mathbf{cc_Q} - \mathbf{cc_{P_{i,j}}}) \bullet \mathbf{wv}_{i,j}) \\ \delta_v \mathbf{col_Q} = \mathbf{col_{P_{i,j}}} \times ((\mathbf{cc_Q} - \mathbf{cc_{P_{i,j}}}) \bullet \mathbf{cv}_{i,j}) \end{cases}$$

where $\mathbf{cc_Q}$, $wet_\mathbf{Q}$ and $\mathbf{col_Q}$ are point $\mathbf{Q}$'s current coordinates in the 3D space, its degree of wetness, and its color, respectively; and $\mathbf{cc_{P_{i,j}}}$, $wet_{\mathbf{P}_{i,j}}$ and $\mathbf{col_{P_{i,j}}}$ are the corresponding values of point $\mathbf{P}_{i,j}$. Similarly for the contribution made by $\mathbf{P}_{i,j}$'s radiation mode ink distribution:

$$\begin{cases} \delta_r wet_\mathbf{Q} = wet_{\mathbf{P}_{i,j}} \times \|\mathbf{cc_Q} - \mathbf{cc_{P_{i,j}}}\| \times wr_{i,j} \\ \delta_r \mathbf{col_Q} = \mathbf{col_{P_{i,j}}} \times \|\mathbf{cc_Q} - \mathbf{cc_{P_{i,j}}}\| \times cr_{i,j} \end{cases}$$

Thus, $\mathbf{P}_{i,j}$'s ink-related texture function, which computes the hybrid effect contributed by both the point's vector mode and radiation mode ink distribution patterns, is defined as:

$$\begin{cases} wet_\mathbf{Q} \triangleq wet_{\mathbf{P}_{i,j}} + \delta_r wet_\mathbf{Q} + \delta_v wet_\mathbf{Q} \\ \mathbf{col_Q} \triangleq \mathbf{col_{P_{i,j}}} + \delta_r \mathbf{col_Q} + \delta_v \mathbf{col_Q} \end{cases},$$

or

$$\begin{cases} wet_\mathbf{Q} = wet_{\mathbf{P}_{i,j}} \times (1 + \|\mathbf{cc_Q} - \mathbf{cc_{P_{i,j}}}\| \times wr_{i,j} + (\mathbf{cc_Q} - \mathbf{cc_{P_{i,j}}}) \bullet \mathbf{wv}_{i,j}) \\ \mathbf{col_Q} = \mathbf{col_{P_{i,j}}} \times (1 + \|\mathbf{cc_Q} - \mathbf{cc_{P_{i,j}}}\| \times cr_{i,j} + (\mathbf{cc_Q} - \mathbf{cc_{P_{i,j}}}) \bullet \mathbf{cv}_{i,j}) \end{cases}.$$
$$(4.5)$$

Note that by vector mode ink distribution we mean that ink distribution can be characterized by a certain vector. Vector mode contribution is not necessarily positive. If the vector $\overrightarrow{\mathbf{ccp}_{i,j} - \mathbf{ccq}}$ is along the direction of the vector, the contribution will be positive; otherwise it could be negative. Please refer to Fig. 4.5 (right) for an illustration. Note also that only those $\mathbf{P}_{i,j}$s touching or just below or above the paper need to be evaluated in the virtual painting and writing process.

4.4.2.4 The middle control ellipse of a writing primitive

The middle control ellipse $\mathbf{E}_i$ of the writing primitive $\mathbf{WP}_i$ is defined as:

$$\begin{cases} \mathbf{E}_i \triangleq (a_i, b_i, loc_i, \mathbf{eori}_i) \\ \mathbf{eori}_i \triangleq (eox_i, eoy_i, oez_i) \end{cases} \tag{4.6}$$

where a_i is the length of $\mathbf{E}_i$'s major axis and b_i the length of $\mathbf{E}_i$'s minor axis. loc_i is $\mathbf{E}_i$'s location parameter, which indicates $\mathbf{E}_i$'s relative position along the middle control axis to which it belongs. $\mathbf{eori}_i$ represents $\mathbf{E}_i$'s minor axis's orientation.

4.4.3 The Three States of a Brush

A virtual Hairy Brush (**HB**) is assumed to have three possible states in its life cycle: the initial state, the dipping state, and the working state (Fig. 4.3).

4.4.3.1 The initial state of a virtual hairy brush

The initial state of the virtual Hairy Brush (**HB**) is when all of its compositive writing primitives are in their free states (Fig. 4.6).

Fig. 4.6. A writing primitive in its initial state

The three dynamic attributes of a writing primitive are simplest when in this state: the tip control line, the middle control axis and the middle control ellipse are reduced to a point, a straight line and a circle respectively. Varying the radius of the circle and its position along the middle control axis can result in a series of modeling effects, as shown in Fig. 4.7.

Fig. 4.7. Writing primitives with the middle control ellipse at different locations (left); writing primitives with different circle radii (right)

4.4.3.2 The dipping state of a virtual Hairy Brush

All the writing primitives of the virtual hairy brush shift to the dipping state after the brush is dipped into the ink bottle and before touching the paper. Through dipping, writing primitives acquire ink-related information which includes color and degree of wetness and is according to how the brush is dipped.

If $\mathbf{P}_{i,k}, \mathbf{P}_{i,k+1}, \cdots, \mathbf{P}_{i,n_i}$ are $\mathbf{WP}_i$'s key points that are soaked in ink, their color is simply set to the ink color. For the other key points, $\mathbf{P}_{i,l}$, $l = 2, 3, \cdots, k-1$, which are not soaked in ink, linear interpolations are applied to compute their individual colors $\mathbf{col}_{\mathbf{P}_{i,l}}$ with the assumption that $\mathbf{col}_{\mathbf{P}_{i,1}} \equiv 0$, which is the color code for pure white. Here we assume the paper is white. If that is not the case, we would substitute the color of the paper for pure white. The color distribution after dipping is depicted as:

$$
\begin{cases}
\mathbf{col}_{i,l} = \text{ink color} \quad (l = k, k+1, \cdots, n_i) \\
\mathbf{col}_{i,l} = \frac{\|\mathbf{cc}_{i,k} - \mathbf{cc}_{i,l}\| \times \mathbf{col}_{i,1} + \|\mathbf{cc}_{i,l} - \mathbf{cc}_{i,1}\| \times \mathbf{col}_{i,k}}{\|\mathbf{cc}_{i,k} - \mathbf{cc}_{i,1}\|} \\
(l = 2, 3, \cdots, k-1) \\
\mathbf{col}_{i,1} = 0
\end{cases}
\tag{4.7}
$$

Similarly for each key point's degree of wetness. We assume $wet_{\mathbf{P}_{i,1}} \equiv 0$, meaning that $\mathbf{P}_{i,1}$ is all dry; thus:

$$
\begin{cases}
wet_{i,l} = \text{the degree of wetness} \\
(l = k, k+1, \cdots, n_i) \\
wet_{i,l} = \frac{\|\mathbf{cc}_{i,k} - \mathbf{cc}_{i,l}\| \times wet_{i,1} + \|\mathbf{cc}_{i,l} - \mathbf{cc}_{i,1}\| \times wet_{i,k}}{\|\mathbf{cc}_{i,k} - \mathbf{cc}_{i,1}\|} \\
(l = 2, 3, \cdots, k-1) \\
wet_{i,1} = 0
\end{cases}
\tag{4.8}
$$

4.4.3.3 The working state of a virtual Hairy Brush

The working state of a virtual hairy brush is the "deformation" state of the brush. The brush deforms due to touching or being pressed against the paper. This varies the eccentricity of the middle control ellipse, the tip control line and the middle control axis, leading to a series of modeling effects, as shown in Fig. 4.8. The pressure against the paper may build up to the point where the brush hair will split, as shown in Fig. 4.9.

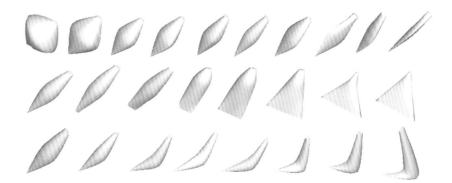

Fig. 4.8. Writing primitives with different ratios of major-to-minor axis length of the middle control ellipse (top row); writing primitives with different tip control line lengths (middle); writing primitives with different middle control axes (bottom)

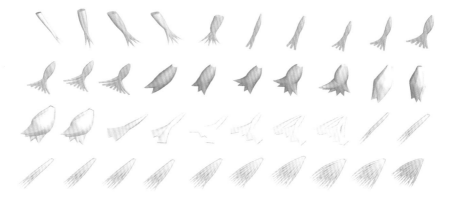

Fig. 4.9. Virtual brushes with hair split into several writing primitives

4.5 Sampling of the Input Data

During the writing process the brush's dynamic attributes are captured by sampling. Sampled input data are used to adjust the virtual brush dynamically. All such adjustments will preserve the validity (with respect to a real brush) of the parametric model. We need to first obtain the brush's six degrees of freedom. Assume that the sampled datum at time t is $\mathbf{Sam}^t \triangleq (x^t, y^t, z^t, d^t, q^t, r^t)$, where (x^t, y^t, z^t) is the center of $\mathbf{HB}$'s bottom control circle $\mathbf{HB.C}$ in the 3D space; d^t the degree of $\mathbf{HB}$'s sideways deflection; q^t the degree of $\mathbf{HB}$'s forward deflection; and r^t the degree of $\mathbf{HB}$'s rotation (Fig. 4.10).

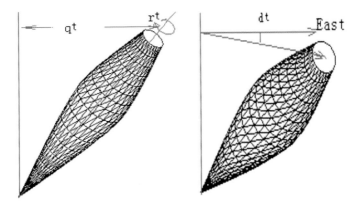

Fig. 4.10. The six degrees of freedom of an input sample

There are many ways to input a solid object's six degrees of freedom, such as using some special device [BSLM01]. A three-dimensional mouse, or a data glove or any other sensor that can take in the six degrees of freedom for a rigid body can also be used as the input hardware for the virtual hairy brush. Some other interesting methods have been introduced [ABL95, JIK+99].

To obtain the six degrees of freedom as input to our virtual brush system, we offer two methods. One method is keyboard plus mouse, and the other method is to use a tablet to obtain five out of six degrees and key pressing for the sixth degree, namely the rotation degree of the brush. The sixth degree is in fact the degree with the least changes, unless the artist is drawing very cursive brush strokes. The keyboard-mouse method is designed to allow for wide adaptability by ordinary home PC users. For the sampling of the six degrees of freedom using this method, please refer to Table 4.2 which shows the user actions and their corresponding effects.

Note that during the writing process not all of the virtual hairy brush's six degrees of freedom experience the same degree of changing. Under most circumstances, (x^t, y^t, z^t) will change much more frequently and sharply than d^t and q^t; r^t rarely changes. Our 3-button-mouse and keyboard hybrid input strategy offers an easy but effective way for the user to input (x^t, y^t, z^t); using the mouse to input d^t, q^t, r^t is a little more awkward but acceptable, as can be demonstrated by our experimental results. Of course, more expensive input devices such as the data glove or those with high dimensional sensors can certainly enhance the usability of the system.

Table 4.2. The 3-button-mouse and keyboard hybrid input method

User Action	Corresponding Effect
Moving the mouse	Generate the (x^t, y^t) coordinates
Scrolling the middle wheel of the mouse	Generates the z^t coordinate
Pressing key "q" with the little finger	Reduces the value of d^t
Pressing key "w" with the ring finger	Increases the value of d^t
Pressing key "e" with the middle finger	Reduces the value of q^t
Pressing key "r" with the index finger	Increases the value of q^t
Pressing key "c" with the thumb	Reduces the value of r^t
Pressing key "v" with the thumb	Increases the value of r^t
Pressing a key while the left button is pressed	The key is pressed twice
Pressing a key while the right button is pressed	The key is pressed four times

During the writing process, **HB**'s virtual position at time t, $\mathbf{S}^t \triangleq (sx^t, sy^t, sz^t, sd^t, sq^t, sr^t)$, is computed from the current sampled datum $\mathbf{Sam}^t$ together with an inertia predictor $\mathbf{M}^t = (mx^t, my^t, mz^t, md^t, mq^t, mr^t)$, using the following formula.

$$\mathbf{S}^t = wei_{sam} \times \mathbf{Sam}^t + (1 - wei_{sam}) \times \mathbf{M}^t \tag{4.9}$$

$\mathbf{M}^t$ comes from **HB**'s displacements in its last few sampling intervals $\mathbf{S}^{t-1}$, $\mathbf{S}^{t-2}, \cdots, \mathbf{S}^{t-n}$:

$$\mathbf{M}^t = \mathbf{Vel}^t \times dT + \mathbf{S}^{t-1} \tag{4.10}$$

$$\mathbf{Vel}^t = \frac{\sum_{k=1}^{el}(wei_k \times \frac{\mathbf{S}^{t-k} - \mathbf{S}^{t-k-1}}{dT})}{\sum_{k=1}^{el} wei_k} \tag{4.11}$$

Here $\mathbf{Vel}^t$ is a weighted sum representing an estimate of **HB**'s velocity, dT the length of a sampling interval and el the length of time over which our estimate is computed. wei_{sam} and the wei_ks are the relative weights given to the current sampled datum and the recent past velocities of the brush, respectively. A heavy wei_{sam} for instance means that the brush has a small inertia. This simple method to determine the position of **HB** turns out to be reasonable since the speed of the brush in real life rarely changes too abruptly, as can be easily observed when artists create Chinese calligraphic artwork using real physical brushes. By introducing an inertia predictor to influence the sampled position of the brush to yield its virtual position, the user can move the virtual hairy brush more continually to emulate the effect and enjoy the feeling of brush glidings and although it is a simple mouse that is used to create electronic calligraphic artwork, the system could still give the user the approximate feeling of a real physical brush in action. For the above formulation, the default parameter configuration is: $el = 4$; $wei_1 = 4$, $wei_2 = 2$, $wei_3 = 1$, $wei_4 = 1$; $wei_{sam} = 0.6$. These default values were obtained by experiments. Changing these values can yield different writing styles and feelings.

4.6 Dynamic Adjustments of the Brush

4.6.1 Estimating the Pysical Conditions of the Brush

Based on the sampled input data, the physical conditions of the virtual hairy brush are estimated at every time step. These conditions include the writing primitive $\mathbf{WP}_i$'s inner stress str_i^t at time t and the pressure of the primitive due to its interaction with the paper. The greater the inner stress, the more likelihood there is for the brush hair to split, and the pressure is the force per unit area as experienced by the virtual paper due to the inner stress of the brush. The parametric model of the e-brush is updated dynamically based on these estimates.

4.6.1.1 Estimating a writing primitive's current inner stress

Intuitively, the rigidity of $\mathbf{WP}_i$'s hair, $\mathbf{WP}_i$'s historical deformation, the wetness of $\mathbf{WP}_i$, and the size of the part of $\mathbf{WP}_i$ that is against the virtual paper plane ψ all have an effect on the value of str_i^t. We devised accordingly a formula to estimate str_i^t based on these factors:

$$str_i^t \triangleq (1-e) \times \frac{n_i}{\sum_{k=1}^{n_i} wet_{i,k}^t} \times \frac{S_i^t \times hei_i^t}{3} \times his_i^t \times \frac{\pi \times a_i^t \times b_i^t}{4} \qquad (4.12)$$

The term e which has a value between 0 and 1 represents the elasticity of **HB**'s hair, and hence $(1-e)$ indicates the rigidity of the hair. Since a_i^t and b_i^t are the lengths of $\mathbf{WP}_i$'s middle control ellipse $\mathbf{E}_i$'s major axis and minor axis at time t, respectively, the term $(\pi \times a_i^t \times b_i^t)/4$ is the area of $\mathbf{E}_i$. It is used to approximate $\mathbf{WP}_i$'s number of hair threads. The term $\sum_{k=1}^{n_i} wet_{i,k}^t/n_i$ is used to approximate $\mathbf{WP}_i$'s overall average degree of wetness, where n_i is the number of key points along the middle control axis $\mathbf{A}_i$ of the i-th writing primitive $\mathbf{WP}_i$. The reciprocal is used in the formulation since a wet brush will experience less force than a dry brush. S_i^t is the area of $\mathbf{WP}_i$'s cross section against the virtual paper ψ at time t approximated by the area of the section's smallest bounding box. hei_i^t is the distance between the cross section and the middle point $\mathbf{mid}_i$ of $\mathbf{WP}_i$'s tip control line. We use a cone to approximate the part of $\mathbf{WP}_i$ that is under ψ, which has a volume of $(S_i^t \times hei_i^t)/3$. The larger this volume is, the more it contributes to the inner stress.

The deformation of the brush also has a bearing on the inner stress, which can be viewed as the accumulated result of a series of per-time-step deformations since the starting of the writing process. The factor his_i^t represents this deformation factor in the formulation. It is decomposed into two parts: the displacement from the initial state, hdd_i^t, and shape deformation, hsd_i^t. And so his_i^t is defined as:

$$\begin{cases} his_i^t \triangleq hsd_i^t + hdd_i^t \\ hsd_i^t \triangleq \frac{a_i^t}{b_i^t} \times len_i^t \\ hdd_i^t \triangleq \frac{\sum_{j=2}^{n_i} (\|\mathbf{cc}_{i,j}^0 - \mathbf{cc}_{i,j}^t - \mathbf{mc}^t\| \times \|\mathbf{cc}_{i,j}^t - \mathbf{cc}_{i,j-1}^t\|)}{\sum_{j=2}^{n_i} \|\mathbf{cc}_{i,j}^t - \mathbf{cc}_{i,j-1}^t\|} \\ \mathbf{mc}^t \triangleq \mathbf{cc}_{i,1}^0 - \mathbf{cc}_{i,1}^t \end{cases} \qquad (4.13)$$

We use the ratio of middle control ellipse $\mathbf{E}_i$'s major axis' length to its minor axis' length, $\frac{a_i^t}{b_i^t}$, and $\mathbf{L}_i$'s length, len_i^t, to evaluate $\mathbf{E}_i$'s shape deformation due to past writing. hdd_i^t is a weighted sum of the displacement, $\|\mathbf{cc}_{i,j}^0 - \mathbf{cc}_{i,j}^t - \mathbf{mc}^t\|$, of each key point $\mathbf{P}_{i,j}$, where $\mathbf{cc}_{i,j}^0$ is $\mathbf{P}_{i,j}$'s coordinates when $\mathbf{WP}_i$ is at its initial free state, $\mathbf{cc}_{i,j}^t$ is $\mathbf{P}_{i,j}$'s coordinates at time t during writing, and $\mathbf{mc}^t$ is the accumulated displacement of $\mathbf{WP}_i$'s bottom control circle $\mathbf{C}_i$. Recall that $\mathbf{WP}_i$'s first key point ($j = 1$) is set as $\mathbf{C}_i$'s center, $\mathbf{cen}_i$. Here the weights are the difference of the relative positions of every pair of adjacent key points along the control axis $\mathbf{A}_i$. In our experiments we found this formula to be a good approximation of the behavior of a real brush. In comparison with the classical formulation in solid mechanics [LL86], this approximation formulation is simpler, which is helpful in reducing the computation time.

In our current design we use the term "elasticity" (e) to refer to an inherent physical property of the paintbrush, that is independent of the brush's wetness. During brush dynamics simulation we will then take into account the factor contributed by the brush's wetness. It is more or less a personal preference whether or not to include the wetness factor early in the elasticity equation or later in the dynamics simulation equation. Based on our study of material science, we adopt the current strategy because it seems more reasonable to model the elasticity as an essential material property of the brush hair.

4.6.1.2 Estimating the pressure due to interaction with the virtual paper

Given that we have a value for the inner stress, we can devise a formula to estimate $\mathbf{WP}_i$'s pressure γ_i^t due to interaction between a writing primitive and the virtual paper ψ. This pressure contributes directly to the degree of deformation of the brush during writing. It can be easily seen that fast movements of the virtual hairy brush, a high degree of inner stress of the current writing primitive $\mathbf{WP}_i$, and a coarse virtual paper can all severely deform $\mathbf{HB}$ (i.e. the middle control axes of the brush's compositive writing primitives). The formulation is as follows:

$$\gamma_i^t \triangleq \|\mathbf{Vel}^t\| \times str_i^t \times sm \times e, \qquad (4.14)$$

where $\mathbf{Vel}^t$ is the virtual hairy brush's velocity, str_i^t its inner stress, sm the virtual paper's degree of smoothness and e the e-brush's degree of elasticity.

4.6.2 Dynamic Adjustment of the Middle Control Axis

4.6.2.1 The current active point

During the writing process the intersection of the middle control axis $\mathbf{A}_i$ and the virtual paper ψ is the current active point. The current active point is inserted into $\mathbf{A}_i$'s series of key points dynamically. The point's ink-related information is computed from the neighboring points in $\mathbf{A}_i$ by linear interpolation Supposing at time t the active point being inserted into $\mathbf{A}_i$'s set of key points is $\mathbf{P}_{i,j}^t$, and $\mathbf{P}_{i,j+1}^t$ and $\mathbf{P}_{i,j-1}^t$ are its neighboring key points, we have:

$$
\begin{cases}
\mathbf{col}_{i,j}^t = \dfrac{\mathbf{col}_{i,j-1}^t \times \|\mathbf{cc}_{i,j+1}^t - \mathbf{cc}_{i,j}^t\| + \mathbf{col}_{i,j+1}^t \times \|\mathbf{cc}_{i,j}^t - \mathbf{cc}_{i,j-1}^t\|}{\|\mathbf{cc}_{i,j+1}^t - \mathbf{cc}_{i,j-1}^t\|} \\[2mm]
wet_{i,j}^t = \dfrac{wet_{i,j-1}^t \times \|\mathbf{cc}_{i,j+1}^t - \mathbf{cc}_{i,j}^t\| + wet_{i,j+1}^t \times \|\mathbf{cc}_{i,j}^t - \mathbf{cc}_{i,j-1}^t\|}{\|\mathbf{cc}_{i,j+1}^t - \mathbf{cc}_{i,j-1}^t\|}
\end{cases}
\tag{4.15}
$$

where $\mathbf{col}_{i,j}^t$ is $\mathbf{P}_{i,j}^t$'s color, $\mathbf{cc}_{i,j}^t$ is $\mathbf{P}_{i,j}^t$'s coordinates, and $wet_{i,j}^t$ is $\mathbf{P}_{i,j}^t$'s degree of wetness at time t.

4.6.2.2 Deformation of the middle control axis $\mathbf{A}_i$

The middle control axis $\mathbf{A}_i$ of $\mathbf{WP}_i$ changes form when subject to forces acting against the brush and the paper. A local reference frame is set up by taking $\mathbf{WP}_i$'s bottom circle $\mathbf{C}_i$ as the $X - Y$ plane, its center $\mathbf{cen}_i$ as the origin, and the brush shaft's direction as the Z-axis (Fig. 4.11).

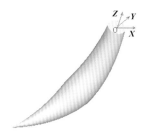

Fig. 4.11. A deformed writing primitive

If the current active point $\mathbf{P}_{i,j}$ travels a certain distance in the reference frame during time slice t, then all the key points that are underneath the virtual paper ψ will also travel the same distance, plus an additional displacement dis in the local reference frame. We estimate this distance to be proportional to the product of $\mathbf{HB}$'s elasticity and $\mathbf{WP}_i$'s current pressure, namely $dis = e \times \gamma_i^t$. Note that by using a time slice which is reasonably small, it is safe to assume that this active point remains to be the true active point for the duration covered by the time slice.

4.6.2.3 Recovery of the middle control axis $\mathbf{A}_i$

As an elastomer, a writing primitive $\mathbf{WP}_i$ will recover in a certain fashion once the outer force exerted on it is released, such as when the brush is partially or completely lifted. Each time that the virtual hairy brush $\mathbf{HB}$ is lifted, every key point on each of $\mathbf{HB}$'s compositive writing primitives will change its place in the 3D space, that is all the key points' z components will increase by a certain amount. The higher the virtual brush is lifted, the more intense the current writing primitive's inner stress would be, and so would be the recovery. That is, for every key point $\mathbf{P}_{i,j}$ $(i = 1, 2, \cdots, m; j = 1, 2, \cdots, n_i)$ along $\mathbf{A}_i$ which is deformed, an additional vertical displacement will be exerted to recover its previous deformation:

$$\gamma_i^t \times |sz^{t+1} - sz^t| \times tr(sz^{t+1} - sz^t) \tag{4.16}$$

where $cz_{i,j}^t$ is $\mathbf{P}_{i,j}$'s coordinates' z component, γ_i^t is $\mathbf{WP}_i$'s pressure against the virtual paper ψ at time t, and the term $|sz^{t+1} - sz^t|$ is the amount by which the virtual hairy brush $\mathbf{HB}$ is lifted between the time t and $t+1$; $tr()$ is the truncation function, which is defined as

$$tr(x) \triangleq \begin{cases} 0 \ (x < 0) \\ 1 \ (x \geqslant 0) \end{cases}.$$

We have made a simplification in our modeling, which combines the flexibility and the "springiness" of the brush into the single concept of elasticity. The decision was based on the observation that having the distinction between flexibility and springiness would make very minor differences in the final output.

4.6.2.4 Dynamic djustment of the wetness

During the writing process, $\mathbf{HB}$'s degree of wetness will be dynamically updated. Suppose the intersecting point, between the middle control axis $\mathbf{A}_i$ and the virtual paper plane ψ, namely the current active point, is inserted into $\mathbf{A}_i$'s key points' sequence and denoted as $\mathbf{P}_{i,j}$. The degree of wetness of all the key points on $\mathbf{A}_i$ will decrease by a certain amount because of their contact with or proximity to the paper, which is estimated to be proportional to the product of ψ's ink absorbing ability ab and $\mathbf{WP}_i$'s current pressure γ_i^t against ψ:

$$wet_{i,j \pm s}^{t+1} = wet_{i,j \pm s}^t - ab \times \gamma_i^t \times \frac{1}{2^{s+d}} \tag{4.17}$$

where $d = \begin{cases} 2 \ (s \in \mathbf{N}^+) \\ 1 \ (s = 0) \end{cases}$ and $(j \pm s) \in [1, n_i]$.

In our current design, the color of $\mathbf{HB}$ is assumed to be constant throughout the virtual writing and painting process. We plan to add a mechanism to dynamically vary the color of the brush in our future work.

4.6.3 Dynamic Adjustment of the Middle Control Ellipse

The deformed virtual hairy brush has an orientation which is determined by the orientation of the middle control ellipse. Our formulation for the latter is based on the phenomenon that if $\mathbf{HB}$'s moving direction is the same as the orientation of writing primitive $\mathbf{WP}_i$'s minor axis $\mathbf{eori}_i^t$ at time t, further writing movements will rotate the ellipse by a certain angle $\mathbf{rot}_i^t$. If the moving direction does not coincide with the orientation of the minor axis, this movement will increase the length of $\mathbf{WP}_i$'s major axis a_i^t; the amount of increase is denoted by $\mathbf{inc}_i^t$. $\mathbf{inc}_i^t$ and $\mathbf{rot}_i^t$ are defined as:

$$\begin{cases} \mathbf{rot}_i^t = re \times \gamma_i^t \times (\mathbf{Vel}^t \bullet \mathbf{eori}_i^t) \\ \mathbf{inc}_i^t = ie \times \gamma_i^t \times \|\mathbf{Vel}^t \times \mathbf{eori}_i^t\| \end{cases} \tag{4.18}$$

where re and ie are $\mathbf{HB}$'s rotation and elongation coefficients respectively. Since writing primitive $\mathbf{WP}_i$'s number of hair threads, approximated by $\mathbf{E}_i$'s area, $(\pi \times a_i^t \times b_i^t)/4$, is a constant if $\mathbf{WP}_i$ does not split during its writing process, $\mathbf{E}_i$'s minor axis' length b_i^t can be determined given a certain value for its major axis' length a_i^t.

The middle control ellipse $\mathbf{E}_i$'s position loc_i^t within the middle control axis $\mathbf{A}_i$ may also vary during the writing process. We assume from intuition that the ideal position of the middle control ellipse should be such that it divides the key points of the middle control axis into two equal groups, because at this location the ellipse's profile has the maximum capacity to control the writing primitive's geometric modeling characters. Since the speed at which the ellipse can relocate is limited by the mechanical and flowage properties of the virtual hairy brush, the actual position of the middle control axis is a linear interpolation of its ideal position (based on the ellipse's ideal location) and its previous position. This is depicted as:

$$loc_i^{t+1} = \nu \times loc_i^t + (1 - \nu) \times \frac{1}{n_i} \sum_{j=1}^{n_i-1} \frac{\sum_{k=1}^{j} \|\mathbf{cc}_{i,k+1}^{t+1} - \mathbf{cc}_{i,k}^{t+1}\|}{\sum_{k=1}^{n_i-1} \|\mathbf{cc}_{i,k+1}^{t+1} - \mathbf{cc}_{i,k}^{t+1}\|}. \tag{4.19}$$

Here ν is the relocation factor, its default value is $\nu = 0.75$. And $\mathbf{cc}_{i,k}^t$ is the coordinates of $\mathbf{WP}_i$'s key point $\mathbf{P}_{i,k}$ at time t. The complex summation term is used to estimate the ideal position of the middle control ellipse. Here we use the term $\|\mathbf{cc}_{i,k+1}^{t+1} - \mathbf{cc}_{i,k}^{t+1}\|$ to approximate the distance between the middle control axis $\mathbf{A}_i$'s two neighboring key points $\mathbf{P}_{i,k+1}$ and $\mathbf{P}_{i,k}$ at time $t + 1$. Thus, the sum $\sum_{k=1}^{j} \|\mathbf{cc}_{i,k+1}^{t+1} - \mathbf{cc}_{i,k}^{t+1}\|$ is the distance of key point $\mathbf{P}_{i,j+1}$ from the the center of the bottom control circle of the brush, $\mathbf{HB.C}$. The fraction $\frac{\sum_{k=1}^{j} \|\mathbf{cc}_{i,k+1}^{t+1} - \mathbf{cc}_{i,k}^{t+1}\|}{\sum_{k=1}^{n_i-1} \|\mathbf{cc}_{i,k+1}^{t+1} - \mathbf{cc}_{i,k}^{t+1}\|}$ indicates key point $\mathbf{P}_{i,j+1}$'s position along $\mathbf{A}_i$. According to the assumption about the ideal position of the middle control ellipse, this position actually is the arithmetic mean of all the key points' positions along $\mathbf{A}_i$. Notice that $\mathbf{HB.C}$'s position along $\mathbf{A}_i$ is always zero.

4.6.4 Dynamic Adjustment of the Tip Control Line

The tip control line of a writing primitive $\mathbf{WP}_i$ is assumed to be a single point in its initial state. It changes into a real line during writing. The line's elongation and rotation are simulated by employing the same strategy as is applied to the middle control ellipse $\mathbf{E}_i$—that is, the tip control line $\mathbf{L}_i$ will increase in length by the amount of $\mathbf{inc}_i^t$ and be rotated by the same amount of $\mathbf{rot}_i^t$ as for the major axis of the middle control ellipse $\mathbf{E}_i$. The tip control line does not have a direct effect on the current ink mark during writing in our modeling, but it will define the shape of the end of a stroke, at the time when the brush is about to leave the paper.

4.6.5 Splitting of the Virtual Hairy Brush

There is a threshold tre which specifies the extent to which $\mathbf{WP}_i$ can be deformed before splitting of the hair occurs. When this threshold is reached or exceeded, the current writing primitive will split into several smaller writing primitives. This simulates the "branching out" behavior of the virtual hairy brush during the writing process. Specifically, if writing primitive $\mathbf{WP}_i$'s current inner stress str_i^t becomes greater than tre, $\mathbf{WP}_i$ will split into

$$k = \lfloor \frac{str_i^t}{tre} \rfloor \tag{4.20}$$

new writing primitives $\mathbf{WP}_i^1, \mathbf{WP}_i^2, \cdots, \mathbf{WP}_i^k$.

Each of the new writing primitives, $\mathbf{WP}_i^j$ ($j = 1, \cdots, k$), has a number of hair threads which is equal to $1/k$ of $\mathbf{WP}_i$'s total number. Note that in the virtual hairy brush, we use the area of the middle control ellipse $(\pi \times a_i^t \times b_i^t)/4$ and the length of the tip control line len_i^t to compute the number of hair threads. Therefore the lengths of the middle control ellipse's major axis $a_i^{t,j}$ and minor axis $b_i^{t,j}$ of each of the new writing primitives $\mathbf{WP}_i^j$ are set to $1/\sqrt{k}$ of $\mathbf{WP}_i$'s original values ($j = 1, 2, \cdots, k$) and the tip control line's length $len_i^{t,j}$ is set to $1/k$ of the original value. That is:

$$\begin{cases} a_i^{t,j} = \frac{a_i^t}{\sqrt{k}} \\ b_i^{t,j} = \frac{b_i^t}{\sqrt{k}} \quad (j = 1, 2, \cdots, k). \\ len_i^{t,j} = \frac{len_i^t}{k} \end{cases} \tag{4.21}$$

At the beginning, the virtual hairy brush $\mathbf{HB}$ contains only one writing primitive, and so $m = 1$. During the writing process the number of $\mathbf{HB}$'s compositive writing primitives may increase because of the split operation. A brush with one writing primitive is probably good enough for official scripts, but for cursive scripts the brush must split into at least a dozen of primitives in order to achieve the necessary effects.

During the split operation every new writing primitive generated, $\mathbf{WP}_i^j$ ($j = 1, \cdots, k$), has the same number of key points as the original one, $\mathbf{WP}_i$, with coordinates at a certain distance from $\mathbf{WP}_i$'s. This distance is proportional to the amount of $\mathbf{WP}_i$'s current inner stress exceeding the split threshold tre, and the direction of this distance is assumed random. Therefore for each key point $\mathbf{P}_{i,l}$ ($l = 1, 2, \cdots, n_i$) in $\mathbf{WP}_i$, there is a corresponding key point $\mathbf{P}_{i,l}^j$ in $\mathbf{WP}_i^j$ ($j = 1, 2, \cdots, k$). The coordinates of $\mathbf{P}_{i,l}$ and $\mathbf{P}_{i,l}^j$ have the following relationship: $\mathbf{cc}_{\mathbf{P}_{i,l}^j} = \mathbf{cc}_{\mathbf{P}_{i,l}} + \mathbf{S}_{\mathbf{P}_{i,l}^j}$, where $\mathbf{S}_{\mathbf{P}_{i,l}^j}$ is determined by $\mathbf{S}_{\mathbf{P}_{i,l}^j} = \mathbf{rand} \times (str_i^t - tre) \times tr(str_i^t - tre)$, and $\mathbf{rand}$ is a random unit vector in the 3D space.

4.6.6 Ink Flowage between Writing Primitives

Although each primitive has full control over its behavior during the writing process, due to reciprocity in mechanics and ink flowage there could be interaction between writing primitives that are close to each other. To simulate this interaction, we allow each key point's degree of wetness to be affected by its neighboring key points if the distance separating them is within the ink diffusion distance factor η. Linear interpolation is used to compute one key point's current degree of wetness based on its previous value and the average degree of wetness of those neighboring key points. That is formulated as:

$$wet_{i,k}^{t+1} = wet_{i,k}^t \times (1 - pw) + \frac{\sum_{j=1,j\neq i}^m \sum_{l=1}^{n_j} (wet_{j,l}^t \times tr(\eta - \|\mathbf{cc}_{j,l}^t - \mathbf{cc}_{i,k}^t\|))}{\sum_{j=1,j\neq i}^m \sum_{l=1}^{n_j} tr(\eta - \|\mathbf{cc}_{j,l}^t - \mathbf{cc}_{i,k}^t\|)}$$
$$\times pw, \quad (i = 1, 2, \cdots, m; k = 1, 2, \cdots, n_i). \tag{4.22}$$

Here pw is the diffusion control factors of virtual hairy brush **HB**; $wet_{i,k}^t$ is key point $\mathbf{P}_{i,k}$'s degree of wetness and $\mathbf{cc}_{i,k}^t$ is its coordinates at time t; η is the ink diffusion distance factor, and $tr()$ is the truncation function.

4.7 The Writing Process

At time t, each of **HB**'s writing primitives will intersect with the virtual paper plane to yield a cross section. The drawing operations are executed taking into account the writing primitives' ink-related information. The following paragraphs outline the algorithm for this process—the virtual hairy brush's real-time writing/painting algorithm.

The algorithm begins with a given writing primitive $\mathbf{WP}_u$ constructed by the general sweeping operation. The generated sweeping surface is a NURBS surface denoted by $SS_u(s,t)$; s and t are the parameters of this parameterized surface, whose values are within $[0, 1]$. The direction of s is the same as that of $\mathbf{WP}_u$'s middle control axis. The algorithm intersects $SS_u(s,t)$ with the virtual paper plane ψ to get an intersecting curve cur_u that encloses an area which is the current ink mark (Fig. 4.12). It can be easily seen that by our intersection operation the contour of our drawing mark is not always (as a matter of fact, it seldom is) an ellipse. The more deformation our brush tip experiences, the more different our drawing mark would be from an ellipse.

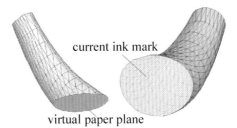

current ink mark

virtual paper plane

Fig. 4.12. The virtual paper plane and its drawing mark

Each point $\mathbf{V}_{u,v}$ on cur_u is projected onto $\mathbf{WP}_u$'s middle control axis $\mathbf{A}_u$ to obtain the point $\hat{\mathbf{V}}_{u,v}$. The ink-related information of the two nearest key points $\boldsymbol{\delta}_{u,v}^1, \boldsymbol{\delta}_{u,v}^2$ on $\mathbf{A}_u$ to $\hat{\mathbf{V}}_{u,v}$ is then used to compute $\hat{\mathbf{V}}_{u,v}$'s ink-related information by linear interpolation, as follows:

$$
\begin{cases}
\mathbf{col}_{\hat{\mathbf{V}}_{u,v}} = \dfrac{\mathbf{col}_{\boldsymbol{\delta}_{u,v}^2} \times \|\mathbf{cc}_{\boldsymbol{\delta}_{u,v}^1} - \mathbf{cc}_{\hat{\mathbf{V}}_{u,v}}\| + \mathbf{col}_{\boldsymbol{\delta}_{u,v}^1} \times \|\mathbf{cc}_{\hat{\mathbf{V}}_{u,v}} - \mathbf{cc}_{\boldsymbol{\delta}_{u,v}^2}\|}{\|\mathbf{cc}_{\boldsymbol{\delta}_{u,v}^1} - \mathbf{cc}_{\boldsymbol{\delta}_{u,v}^2}\|} \\[2ex]
wet_{\hat{\mathbf{V}}_{u,v}} = \dfrac{wet_{\boldsymbol{\delta}_{u,v}^2} \times \|\mathbf{cc}_{\boldsymbol{\delta}_{u,v}^1} - \mathbf{cc}_{\hat{\mathbf{V}}_{u,v}}\| + wet_{\boldsymbol{\delta}_{u,v}^1} \times \|\mathbf{cc}_{\hat{\mathbf{V}}_{u,v}} - \mathbf{cc}_{\boldsymbol{\delta}_{u,v}^2}\|}{\|\mathbf{cc}_{\boldsymbol{\delta}_{u,v}^1} - \mathbf{cc}_{\boldsymbol{\delta}_{u,v}^2}\|}
\end{cases}
\tag{4.23}
$$

$\mathbf{V}_{u,v}$'s ink-related information is derived from $\hat{\mathbf{V}}_{u,v}$'s by following $\hat{\mathbf{V}}_{u,v}$'s texture function [Eq. (4.5)]:

$$
\begin{cases}
wet_{\mathbf{V}_{u,v}} = wet_{\hat{\mathbf{V}}_{u,v}} \times (1 + \|\mathbf{cc}_{\mathbf{V}_{u,v}} - \mathbf{cc}_{\hat{\mathbf{V}}_{u,v}}\| \times wr_{u,v} + (\mathbf{cc}_{\mathbf{V}_{u,v}} - \mathbf{cc}_{\hat{\mathbf{V}}_{u,v}}) \cdot \mathbf{wv}_{u,v}) \\
\mathbf{col}_{\mathbf{V}_{u,v}} = \mathbf{col}_{\hat{\mathbf{V}}_{u,v}} \times (1 + \|\mathbf{cc}_{\mathbf{V}_{u,v}} - \mathbf{cc}_{\hat{\mathbf{V}}_{u,v}}\| \times cr_{u,v} + (\mathbf{cc}_{\mathbf{V}_{u,v}} - \mathbf{cc}_{\hat{\mathbf{V}}_{u,v}}) \cdot \mathbf{cv}_{u,v})
\end{cases}
\tag{4.24}
$$

And for any pixel $\boldsymbol{\tau}$ on the virtual paper plane enclosed by the curve cur_u, it must lie uniquely on a certain line segment, $\overline{\mathbf{V}_{u,v}\hat{\mathbf{V}}_{u,v}}$. Its ink-related information is computed based on $\mathbf{V}_{u,v}$'s and $\hat{\mathbf{V}}_{u,v}$'s ink-related information:

$$
\begin{cases}
\mathbf{col}_{\boldsymbol{\tau}} = \dfrac{\mathbf{col}_{\hat{\mathbf{V}}_{u,v}} \times \|\mathbf{cc}_{\mathbf{V}_{u,v}} - \mathbf{cc}_{\boldsymbol{\tau}}\| + \mathbf{col}_{\mathbf{V}_{u,v}} \times \|\mathbf{cc}_{\boldsymbol{\tau}} - \mathbf{cc}_{\hat{\mathbf{V}}_{u,v}}\|}{\|\mathbf{cc}_{\mathbf{V}_{u,v}} - \mathbf{cc}_{\hat{\mathbf{V}}_{u,v}}\|} \\[2ex]
wet_{\boldsymbol{\tau}} = \dfrac{wet_{\hat{\mathbf{V}}_{u,v}} \times \|\mathbf{cc}_{\mathbf{V}_{u,v}} - \mathbf{cc}_{\boldsymbol{\tau}}\| + wet_{\mathbf{V}_{u,v}} \times \|\mathbf{cc}_{\boldsymbol{\tau}} - \mathbf{cc}_{\hat{\mathbf{V}}_{u,v}}\|}{\|\mathbf{cc}_{\mathbf{V}_{u,v}} - \mathbf{cc}_{\hat{\mathbf{V}}_{u,v}}\|}
\end{cases}
\tag{4.25}
$$

Denote the point inside the volume of the virtual hairy brush and that coincides with the pixel $\boldsymbol{\lambda}_{u,v}$ on $\boldsymbol{\psi}$ as $\boldsymbol{\tau}_{u,v}$. $\boldsymbol{\lambda}_{u,v}$'s new degree of wetness is linear-interpolated from $\boldsymbol{\lambda}_{u,v}$'s previous value with $\boldsymbol{\tau}_{u,v}$'s degree of wetness and by using $\boldsymbol{\psi}$'s absorbing ability factor ab as the interpolation weight. A drying factor dry is introduced to automatically reduce each pixel's degree of wetness periodically until it reaches 0. That is,

$$
wet_{\boldsymbol{\lambda}_{u,v}}^{t+1} = (1 - ab) \times wet_{\boldsymbol{\lambda}_{u,v}}^t + ab \times wet_{\boldsymbol{\tau}_{u,v}}^t - dry.
\tag{4.26}
$$

If the degree of wetness exceeds the upper bound of virtual paper $\boldsymbol{\psi}$'s degree of wetness, saturation takes place. We assume that saturation would only affect $\boldsymbol{\lambda}_{u,v}$'s eight neighboring pixels on $\boldsymbol{\psi}$. The degree of wetness of a pixel will increase if it is not saturated. The increased amount is proportional to the unsaturated degree. That is, $\boldsymbol{\lambda}_{i,j}$, which is one of $\boldsymbol{\lambda}_{u,v}$'s eight neighboring pixels on $\boldsymbol{\psi}$, will have its degree of wetness increased according to the following formulation.

$$
\begin{aligned}
wet_{\boldsymbol{\lambda}_{i,j}}^{t+1} = wet_{\boldsymbol{\lambda}_{i,j}}^t &+ \frac{(1 - wet_{\boldsymbol{\lambda}_{i,j}}^t) \times tr(1 - wet_{\boldsymbol{\lambda}_{i,j}}^t)}{\varrho_{u,v}^t} \times (wet_{\boldsymbol{\lambda}_{u,v}}^t - 1) \\
&\times tr(wet_{\boldsymbol{\lambda}_{u,v}}^t - 1)
\end{aligned}
\tag{4.27}
$$

where $wet_{\boldsymbol{\lambda}}^t$, a real number between 0 and 1, is point $\boldsymbol{\lambda}$'s degree of wetness at time t, and $\varrho_{u,v}^t = \sum_{g=u-1}^{u+1} \sum_{h=v-1}^{v+1} (1 - wet_{\boldsymbol{\lambda}_{g,h}}^t) \times tr(1 - wet_{\boldsymbol{\lambda}_{g,h}}^t)$, indicates the total degree of unsaturation that $\boldsymbol{\lambda}_{u,v}$'s eight neighboring pixels have attained. Note that $tr(1 - wet_{\boldsymbol{\lambda}_{g,h}}^t)$ is non-zero only when the point $\boldsymbol{\lambda}_{g,h}$

is not saturated. Note that it is possible that after one pass of simulated ink diffusion, there could still be some points that are over-saturated. This situation would occur if the ink mark originally deposited on the paper is too wet. Thus, in our simulation an iterative diffusion process is employed, which stops only when all the points on the paper become unsaturated.

The rendering of the current ink-mark is based on a unique ink model we propose. The current color of the pixel $\boldsymbol{\lambda}_{u,v}$ is the linear interpolation of $\boldsymbol{\lambda}_{u,v}$'s previous color and $\boldsymbol{\tau}_{u,v}$'s color, as follows.

$$\mathbf{col}_{\boldsymbol{\lambda}_{u,v}}^{t+1} = \mathbf{col}_{\boldsymbol{\tau}_{u,v}}^{t} \times Cr_{u,v}^{t} + \mathbf{col}_{\boldsymbol{\lambda}_{u,v}}^{t} \times (1 - Cr_{u,v}^{t}) \tag{4.28}$$

where $Cr_{u,v}^{t}$, the interpolation weight, is a random number, which has the value of either 0 or $wet_{\boldsymbol{\lambda}_{u,v}}^{t}$ based on the following probabilities.

$$\begin{cases} P\{Cr_{u,v}^{t} = 0\} = 1 - min(ren \times ab \times \gamma_i^t, 1) \\ P\{Cr_{u,v}^{t} = wet_{\boldsymbol{\lambda}_{u,v}}^{t}\} = min(ren \times ab \times \gamma_i^t, 1) \end{cases} \tag{4.29}$$

where ren is **HB**'s color rendering control factor, ab is the virtual paper ψ's absorbing ability, and γ_i^t is the pressure due to the interaction between the writing primitive and the virtual paper plane. We use this formulation to simulate the dry brush drawing effect and the running style effect.

In the above discussions, for simplicity, to tackle the problem of mixing pigments in full color painting, we adopt directly the RGB color model as our active working color space. In some very rare circumstances, this might not lead to the best results, for the simple reason that the R, G, B channels in the physical world are not really independent of each other (see [ISO] for more details). But this problem is easy to solve: we first convert RGB-formatted ink color to HSV-formatted ink color; in the color space of HSV, we separately process the H, S, V channels using the same procedures for the R, G, B channels described above; we finally convert the synthesized results from HSV-formatted ink color back to RGB-formatted ink color for rendering.

4.8 Customizing the Brush

4.8.1 Quality Parameters

In real life, brushes having soft hair tend to branch out easily during writing. Some brushes have a good deal of hair and tend to suck in more ink and cause serious saturation during the writing process, while other brushes have rather long hair and their tip tends to get deformed and rotated easily to a great extent. For our virtual hairy brush, a number of quality parameters can be set to simulate these different kinds of brush character. What comes out as the final electronic artwork from using the virtual hairy brush can be much affected by the values of these parameters. Similarly, the virtual paper has a set of quality parameters to be assigned a value for simulating different kinds of paper.

All the quality parameters $\mathbf{Qp}$ are classified into two categories. The first category, $\mathbf{Qp}^1 = (e, \, tre, \, \nu, \, re, \, ie, \, sm)$, can affect the brush strokes' boundaries while the second category, $\mathbf{Qp}^2 = (ren, \, \eta, \, ab, \, pw, \, dry)$, can affect the brush strokes' texture. Different combinations of possible values for these quality parameters of the virtual hairy brush would result in an e-brush with different qualities. Please refer to Fig. 4.1 for the concise meaning of each of these parameters.

To ease the task of selecting the appropriate values to achieve the desired quality, our implemented system offers a set of predefined quality configurations in a library for the user to choose from. This is similar to what happens in reality when a calligrapher chooses the most suitable real hairy brush from many brushes in his collection or in a shop, some of which could have been contributed by the users themselves. Others are prefabricated based on empirical knowledge provided by real-life calligraphers and painters. After choosing or creating a certain quality configuration, the end user can write/paint with the chosen or created virtual hairy brush. He can change his decision later and choose another new configuration until he is satisfied with the e-brush and the created artwork. Although not implemented in the current prototype, it is possible to allow an artwork to be automatically transformed using a new configuration because all the inputs leading to the creation of the artwork are already recorded in a file.

The implemented system provides a window in which the user can adjust the above parameters visually. If he feels that the virtual hairy brush dries too quickly and the final artwork should have more versatile color layers, he can increase the value of the color rendering control parameter ren. If he feels that the virtual hairy brush deforms too slowly, he can increase the values of the parameters ν, re and ie which govern the deformability of the brush. And if the virtual hairy brush recovers too quickly from deformation, he can decrease the value of the elasticity parameter e. To increase the tendency of brush splitting, he can assign a small value to tre, the splitting threshold. If his strokes are fast so that the brush tends to brush out more easily, he may need to adjust the parameters pw and ab which control the diffusion and absorption abilities of the paper, since fast movements of the brush leave little time for the paper to diffuse or absorb the ink, and hence the proper setting of these parameters is important for any desired effect. Of course the user can save all this trouble of assigning values to the parameters by simply accepting an offered configuration.

4.8.2 Configuring the Brush with Machine Intelligence

In addition to user-created configurations, the system can configure a brush automatically. To enable the computer to adjust the quality parameters of the virtual hairy brush as well as those for the virtual paper automatically, a special procedure needs to be carried out to train the computer. The training samples consist of brush strokes being painted within boundaries specified by the training module. The procedure is similar to a beginner starting to learn how to use a hairy brush in real life, referred to as the "MiaoHong" process in

Chinese calligraphy. The number of training samples can be set by the user. Of course, the more samples used the better would be the resulting quality of the brush. Simple artwork such as the one in Fig. 4.17 can be rendered after a few minutes of training.

Let $S^i[len][wid]$ and $C^i[len][wid]$ be two matrices where each of the elements is the RGB color code of a pixel of the virtual paper ψ. The first matrix corresponds to the i-th sample of n training samples and the second matrix the i-th user-generated result. Figs. 4.13 and 4.14 show some examples of real training samples.

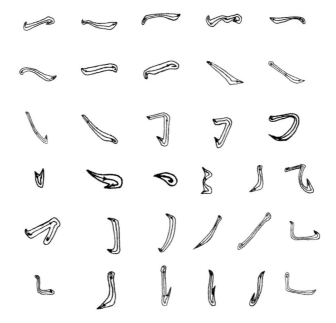

Fig. 4.13. Some selected training samples for the first category of quality parameters

We define a target function ϑ to indicate the difference between the system's specified training samples and the user-created images using the virtual hairy brush:

$$\vartheta \triangleq \sum_{i=1}^{n} \vartheta^i \triangleq \sum_{i=1}^{n} \sum_{p=1}^{len} \sum_{q=1}^{wid} (S^i[p][q] \bigotimes C^i[p][q]), \qquad (4.30)$$

where the operator $\bigotimes$ is defined as $(r_1, g_1, b_1) \bigotimes (r_2, g_2, b_2) \triangleq |r_1 - r_2| + |g_1 - g_2| + |b_1 - b_2|$. All the quality parameters of the virtual hairy brush contribute to ϑ. Hence with a certain set of initial values for all the quality parameters, a user can create a collection of facsimile images after the training sample images using our virtual hairy brush, based on which the corresponding ϑ can be computed. Thus, the problem of determining a good set of values

Fig. 4.14. Some selected training samples for the second category of quality parameters

to configure the virtual hairy brush is reduced to the problem of finding a configuration which can minimize or nearly minimize ϑ, which is a typical optimization problem. We devised and used an optimization algorithm based on the Steepest Descent Algorithm [Lue03] in nonlinear programming to find the needed solution, as described below.

We use ordered training procedures to compute the optimal configuration of **HB**'s quality parameters **Qp**. Firstly, we need to train and determine all the first-category quality parameters $\mathbf{Qp}^1$, followed by the second-category parameters $\mathbf{Qp}^2$. Like the quality parameters, the training samples are divided into two classes. The first class of samples are used to train the e-brush to draw brush strokes with proper stroke boundaries, and so parameters that have to do with the texture of the brush stroke are ignored, namely $\mathbf{Qp}^2$. Hence, to determine $\mathbf{Qp}^1$, our virtual brush simulates neither drying brush effect nor diffusion effect; that is, all the pixels on the virtual paper that are covered by the ink mark at a certain simulated time are rendered completely dark. After the algorithm yields the value for $\mathbf{Qp}^1$, the value for $\mathbf{Qp}^2$ are computed, this time with $\mathbf{Qp}^1$ being assigned the value derived from the previous computation.

Because the values of all the quality parameters of the virtual hairy brush share the same range of $[0, 1]$, we can view this problem as a minimization problem with its feasible solution space being a unit cube in a 6-dimensional space. We equally divide the edges of the cube to decompose the cube into subcubes and take every resultant grid point (at a corner of a subcube) as a possible initial point; so each initial point's coordinates in the 5-dimensional space are in the form of $\mathbf{X}^0 = (d_1/d, d_2/d, \cdots, d_6/d)$, where $d \in N$ is the number of parts an edge is divided into, and $d_i = 0, 1, \cdots, d$ $(i = 1, 2, \cdots, 6)$. With $\mathbf{X}^0$ as the initial point, we use the Steepest Descent Algorithm [Lue03] to find a satisfactory solution that minimizes $\vartheta(\mathbf{X}^0)$. That is,

(1) Set $k = 0$. Compute $\mathbf{y}^k = -\nabla\vartheta(\mathbf{X}^k)$;
(2) If $\|\mathbf{y}^k\| < \varepsilon$, the algorithm stops, where ε is the error bound;
(3) Determine λ_k, such that $\vartheta(\mathbf{X}^k + \lambda_k \times \mathbf{y}^k) = min(\mathbf{X}^k + \lambda \times \mathbf{y}^k)$, $\lambda \geqslant 0$;
(4) Let $\mathbf{X}^{k+1} = \mathbf{X}^k + \lambda_k \times \mathbf{y}^k$; $k = k + 1$; go to Step 2.

The value of $\nabla\vartheta(\mathbf{X}^k)$ is approximated by ϑ's differential at the point $\mathbf{X}^k$. That is, we disturb the position of $\mathbf{X}^k$ along the coordinate system's axis x_i by a short distance $\triangle x_i$ and run the algorithm for the virtual hairy brush to yield $\vartheta(\mathbf{X}^k + \triangle x_i)$. The differential of $\vartheta(\mathbf{X}^k)$ can then be approximated by $\vartheta(\mathbf{X}^k + \triangle x_i)/\triangle x_i$. After taking several $(d_1/d, d_2/d, \cdots, d_6/d)$, $d_i = 0, 1, \cdots, d$ $(i = 1, \cdots, 6)$, as the initial point $\mathbf{X}^0$, we can determine an $\mathbf{X}$ $(= (d_{i,1}/d, d_{i,2}/d, \cdots, d_{i,6}/d))$ which yields the nearly minimum $\vartheta(\mathbf{X})$. We then take $[(d_{i,1} - 1)/d, (d_{i,1} + 1)/d] \times [(d_{i,2} - 1)/d, (d_{i,2} + 1)/d] \times \cdots \times [(d_{i,6} - 1)/d, (d_{i,6} + 1)/d]$ as a new cube, and re-run the above procedure to search for a smaller ϑ, until meeting a solution that satisfies the user's specified error bound.

Of course the user can adjust the the parameters of the configuration if he feels that the result from the above procedure still falls short of his demand. Any of the preset configurations in the system's library can be used as the initial point for the optimization procedure so that a solution to the problem can be obtained at much more quickly and accurately. In this sense, all the above strategies to determine the quality parameters for the virtual hairy brush can be combined to achieve better performance and results.

4.9 System Implementation and Experiment Results

Fig. 4.15 shows a screen shot of the implemented system in action, where there is one Window responsible for displaying the current sampled input and the history of all the sampled inputs (Window 8); one for the current drawing mark (Window 3); one for the current writing mark imprinted on the paper (Window 1). There are several additional windows for displaying the 3D model of the virtual hairy brush in action including: one for the part of the virtual brush penetrating the virtual paper (Window 2); one for the complete solid model of the virtual brush in the 3D space (Window 4); one for the 3D model of the virtual brush in silhouette form (Window 6); one for the part of the virtual brush which is above the virtual paper (Window 5) and one for the part that is below (Window 7). There are several other optional windows which can be displayed by the user's choice. They include a window to display the current control parameters derived from the input, one for the parameter values automatically assigned to the writing primitives

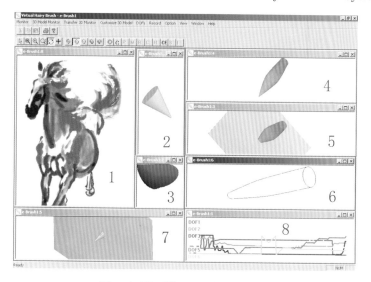

Fig. 4.15. The running system

by an internal algorithm, and one for the configuration of current quality parameters.

Fig. 4.16—Fig. 4.18 show some real artwork digitized from calligraphy samples together with the imitation artwork created by our virtual hairy brush. We highlight using red circles a few spots that are the result of the dry brush effect in our design; such an effect is difficult to achieve in other e-brush projects. These samples prove that very realistic-looking calligraphic artwork can be generated by our virtual hairy brush. If carefully tuned, the simulation's result can be nearly indistinguishable from the original one to a human viewer. By fiddling with the quality parameters and the input data for the brush's six degrees of freedom, users can create interesting calligraphy fully electronically. It is well known that to imitate an original calligraphic artwork is a nontrivial task. With our electronic environment however, such an imitation task becomes relatively easy. The system offers a friendly user interface, which supports adjusting the quality parameters and the input data dynamically to achieve whatever delicate effect the user desires. Fig. 4.19— Fig. 4.22 show a series of computer artwork created using the virtual hairy brush.

Although these figures show only imitation artwork generated by our virtual brush, the real imitation that our design and implementation have set out to achieve is to imitate the manipulability, aesthetic features and expressive power of traditional hairy brushes. A person who has mastered our virtual brush should be able to create high-quality calligraphic artwork as can be done by a real brush.

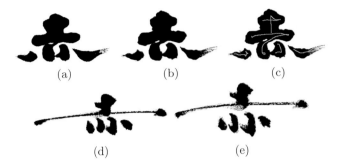

Fig. 4.16. Real artwork (a), (d) and imitations (b), (e). The brush's trajectories at (b) are highlighted at (c)

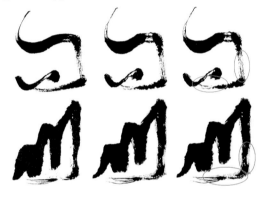

Fig. 4.17. Real artwork (left column) vs. imitation (middle column). And in the right column, the rich and fine details of the dry brush effect produced by our virtual brush are enclosed by red ellipses

4.10 Related Work

Pure hardware approaches such as Greene's [Gre85] tend to be expensive and not easily applicable in all environments. The method by Pan *et al.* [PMZS97] can only generate new fonts from existing ones. The method by Way and Shih [WLS01] requires the user to specify the contour and the parameters of the object to be painted via a reference image or figure, which deviates from the way traditional artists perform their painting tasks.

In the following we make a detailed comparison with two projects that in many ways are closest among all related work to our work—the first one is the DAB system by Baxter et al. [BSLM01], a painting system based on a deformable 3D brush model and with an intuitive haptic interface; the second work is the "virtual brush" by Wong and Ip [WI00], a model-based approach to synthesizing realistic Chinese calligraphic writings. We also survey briefly several other e-brush systems.

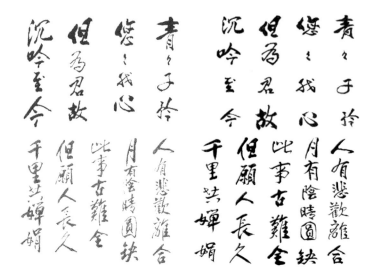

Fig. 4.18. Two Chinese love poems: real artwork (left) vs. imitation (right)

Fig. 4.19. Pinasters (left) and stones (right)

4.10.1 DAB

Although DAB is a complex system [BSLM01], it cannot capture all the complex physical properties and conditions of a hairy brush and its ink distribution, which are necessary for simulating Chinese calligraphy and painting. DAB relies on a special device with a 6-DOF input and a 3-DOF force output that implements a haptic feedback. The device is expensive and therefore this limits its wide application. In comparison, either a tablet or a keyboard-and-mouse strategy would suffice as an input method for our e-brush prototype. These simple methods, when coupled with the simulation of brush stroke inertia and a machine intelligence component, provide a suitable level of comfort and manipulatbility for the user. DAB's complex algorithms require the use of powerful hardware to give real-time response. Our e-brush system can achieve interactive response on an ordinary PC due to a carefully picked tradeoff between the quality of the final rendering and computation efficiency.

In DAB a layer carries only one color and blending of colors happens when different layers interact. Our e-brush employs a more direct approach,

Fig. 4.20. A running horse

Fig. 4.21. Orchid

with the pigment model being an integral part of the e-brush, which makes it possible to simulate highly complex ink distribution patterns within the e-brush volume. This enables the user to create more elaborate and complex blends in a more natural manner than DAB.

DAB's one-color-per-layer strategy limits the richness of the output texture. It seems not at all easy to improve on this, such as by adding ink-related information to DAB's simple particle-system model or its complex subdivision model. DAB needs to integrate a new, elaborate pigment model in order

Fig. 4.22. Bamboos

to generate varied-texture output. In our model, ink-related information is naturally and inherently embedded in the e-brush, which makes possible the efficient and powerful rendering of ink marks with complex textures. We have also designed a new pen-and-ink model to render the brush's footprint, which is probabilistic and considers the pressure on the virtual paper, the inner stress of the e-brush, and the wetness of both the brush and the virtual paper. This should be much better that DAB's simple alpha blending. Besides, our e-brush is tuned to optimal performance in handling paint representation, paint mixing and the drying of the canvas.

DAB uses two separate models—a subdivision surface mesh wrapped around a spring-mass particle system skeleton for the basic motion and behavior of the brush head, and a deformable mesh skinned around this skeleton for the actual shape of the head—which leads to the synchronization problem of how to properly anchor the control points of the subdivision surface relative to the mass particles. To have a tradeoff between the ease to place the control points and the modeling ability makes DAB only capable of supporting four styles of brushes used in oil-like painting. In comparison, we use four compositive attributes and a suitably powerful modeling metaphor, the general sweeping operation, to model our e-brush. Thus, our e-brush is much simpler than DAB's as we use only one model to cover the geometrical shape, the dynamic behavior, and pigment changes. The result is a simulated brush capable of expressing all kinds of brush tips, and better efficiency.

DAB likens the brush tip to a piece of cloth, and uses cloth simulation to construct the brush surface. In order to solve the mesh at the brush tip, DAB relies on an approximated implicit integration method. This poses two problems: modeling with cloth is not the best choice as far as approximating the reality is concerned, and solving for cloth can make the system unstable. To maintain stability, modeling accuracy has to be sacrificed. In our modeling, by relying on the concept of writing primitives and choosing the general sweeping operation as the modeling metaphor, our e-brush can readily simulate almost all kinds of brush heads and their deformation, including splitting of the brush tip. The general sweeping operation also has an advantage in terms of the running system's stability. Hence, our e-brush is more stable, efficient, and expressive than DAB's.

The simulation of our e-brush's dynamics and its visual effects incurs less cost than DAB. This is due to our combining the geometrical modeling, dynamic behavior and paint blending all into a single model which is evaluated only once per time slice. Because of the reduced complexity of the e-brush simulation, we could use the saved time and resources to perform a more delicate simulation of the brush's dynamic deformation behavior. The simulated deformation of our virtual brush can be simulated to deform in a variety of ways and to a large extent, which is not the case with DAB.

4.10.2 Virtual Brush by Wong and Ip

The virtual brush model by Wong and Ip [WI00] also offers a feasible means for artists to produce Chinese calligraphic characters electronically. Their method, however, is inconvenient to use because of an intricate set of interrelated parameters for controlling the shape, density and opacity of the current drawing mark. These parameters need to be specified manually by the user, thus limiting the interactivity of the system. More specifically, the user needs to specify the profiles for seven parameters to control the brush motion dynamic model, and another three parameters to control the ink deposition—a total of ten profiles. Only two of these profiles, the stroke's trajectory in the X and Y directions, can be sampled by a mouse or a digitizing pen; so there are eight profiles to be input manually. Whereas in our approach there are many input devices that can take in the six degrees of freedom of a solid object, and no profile needs to be supplied by the user. For instance, MacKenzie [Mac95] discusses input devices that can capture six degrees of freedom for brush/paint systems. Ware and Baxter [WB89] describe a model for converting hand position and orientation into six useful variables for computer input and its application in an experimental computer paint program.

Other than the input parameters for the brush's six degrees of freedom, several parameters have been introduced in our design for controlling the virtual brush's quality, whose values can be automatically set via an optimization algorithm. Although our e-brush model is more elaborate than that of Wong and Ip, all the modeling details and quality parameters of the e-brush can be hidden from the end user. The user can in fact use the e-brush in the same way he/she uses the traditional hairy brush. We can therefore say that our e-brush is simpler and easier to manipulate than the e-brush by Wong and Ip. But because of the more complex model we use behind the scenes and the automatically tunable quality parameters we introduce, we can achieve better output results with our e-brush.

Referring to the examples in Figs. 4.17 and 4.18, it may be possible for an experienced artist to produce a similar artistic calligraphy result using the system described in [26]. But, as we have already explained, that will take a much greater effort because of the need to adjust many parameters that control the shape as well as the texture of the strokes. In comparison, our brush is much more "usable"—it is easy to use yet sufficiently expressive. Users can conveniently manipulate our e-brush by controlling its six DOFs, using either a tablet pen or the keyboard plus a mouse.

Although [WI00] provides an extensive library of pre-set stroke parameters through a convenient panel, during the digital painting process these parameters are visible to, and need to be adjusted by the end users. Also, some of those parameters are not quite intuitive. In comparison, our e-brush hides all the complex parameters and only requires the six DOFs input from the user. The quality parameters associated with our e-brush all have an intuitive meaning and are therefore easy to adjust by the user. A machine training module can further make the quality parameter tuning process intelligent and most convenient to the user.

4.10.3 Other Virtual Brush Models

The very recent work by Chu and Tai [CT02] proposes a virtual brush which is very similar to ours. The geometrical aspects of their brush are essentially the same as those in an early report of our work [XTLP02]. They however use simple blending for paint mixing, which severely restricts the richness of the resulting e-paintings. They model the dynamics of the e-brush as springs which are deformed through constrained energy minimization. This way of modeling can only simulate small-scale deformation of the e-brush but not large-scale bending or stretching, due to the restriction of constrained energy minimization. For the same reason, spreading and splitting of brush tips cannot be simulated physically in their system. [CAC02] presents two methods to create Chinese paintings. One of them creates 3D Chinese painting animation using existing commercial software packages. Their second method is based on a simple strategy in which many bristles which are arranged randomly within a circular area constitute the brush tip. As a result only a small number of modeling effects are possible using this method. There is no formal ink model being proposed for their system. The water in each brush bristle is directly used as the transparency for the generated brush strokes, and so both the shapes and the textures of the strokes produced by their system appear stiff and artificial. Their results are far less expressive than the real artwork.

4.11 Conclusion and Future Work

4.11.1 Summary and Conclusion

In this chapter, by modeling the hairy brush using a few writing primitives which work independently, a real-time virtual hairy brush system has been implemented for creating artwork by the computer. Measured against the criteria presented at the beginning of this chapter, our e-brush is easy to use, and people can more or less treat the e-brush like a traditional brush. With the support of an input component and a machine intelligence component, it is quite comfortable and easy to manipulate. The output samples show that indeed our e-brush can generate more expressive and realistic rendering results than all the previous e-brush systems. The machine intelligence component allows different levels of automation in controlling the e-brush to be enabled. Fast response time is guaranteed due to the use and efficient implementation of writing primitives and our e-brush can offer more functionalities than traditional brushes and other e-brushes via the machine intelligence component.

Like the virtual hairy brush itself, the proposed ink model is also physically-based, which blends wetness, ink color and the current inner stress of the brush with rendering probabilities, and reduces all the complex interactions to a set of simple equations. Compared to [CAS+97], where complex differential equations are used, our model is computationally efficient. The ink model is integrated into the e-brush system so that much of the computation can also be used in computing for the ink model.

With the ink-related information that is lodged in the writing primitive's control axis, a single primitive can readily express complex, interesting and even mysterious distribution of the ink, color and wetness. Together with the use of rendering probabilities, our brush can achieve the effects of multiple gray levels, colorful painting, dry brush writing and saturation.

During the writing process the simulation takes into account the acceleration of the virtual hairy brush, producing an effect that emulates the manipulation of a real physical brush.

Although the system provides methods to manually edit a collection of parameters that can affect the rendering and the final result, it is not necessary for the user to interactively input values for these parameters. All that is needed from the user is the series of six degrees of freedom of the hairy brush, based on which the computer can simulate the whole writing process. This leads to an efficient system operable in real-time, and which is easy to use for the user. Since most of the handwriting's geometrical and dynamic parameters can be automatically tuned by the system on the fly, little storage space is required to keep track of state information.

4.11.2 Future Work

A real brush operates in a fashion that is orders of magnitude more complex than which that can be modeled by a computer. Features that can be added in future versions to further enhance the modeling include dynamic merging of writing primitives, repeated dipping effects and more user's control of the brush during writing. Other features requiring longer-term effort include mapping of 2D calligraphic artwork to 3D and feature extraction of real artwork. We explain some of these in the following.

(1) **More delicate modeling.** It includes making the elasticity of our brush hair a variable rather than a constant in our system, and adopting a more sophisticated model for hair splitting rather than the current random splitting since the probability of hair strands on the outside splitting should be larger than that of the inner ones.

(2) **Multiple dipping effects.** In the current design dipping operations only take place before the first time the virtual hairy brush touches the paper plane. In real life, an artist may dip the brush either partially or completely multiple times. Partial dipping would cause local changes in the brush's wetness and color.

(3) **More control.** Another problem with the current prototype is that, once the simulation is on its way, the number of key points on the middle control axis would keep increasing, which is not quite in line with the real case where an artist may caress a deformed brush to restore its shape. A variety of interfaces are required to allow the user to control and edit the writing primitive's geometry, as well as its color and its degree of wetness, as the linear interpolation in the current design, is just one of many possibilities.

(4) **Hair merging.** In the current virtual hairy brush model, writing primitives will split into several smaller ones, which simulates the branching out of the hair in a real writing process. In real life, branched-out hair bundles may merge together later. Such a feature is not in the current implementation.

(5) **3D writing effects.** Many famous Chinese calligraphic artwork creations are chiseled in monuments. How to map 2D calligraphy work into 3D is an interesting research problem. So is the problem of directly creating 3D calligraphic artwork.

(6) **Automatic imitation.** Pattern recognition and machine learning mechanisms can equip the system with the ability to duplicate existing artwork fully automatically, and in the process to extract useful components such as the brush's path and the thicknesses of the strokes. These components will then be useful in automatic imitation of calligraphic artwork or computer-assisted calligraphy.

References

[ABL95] Maneesh Agrawala, Andrew C. Beers, and Marc Levoy. 3D painting on scanned surfaces. In *SI3D '95: Proceedings of the 1995 Symposium on Interactive 3D Graphics*, pages 145–150 & 215, Moterey, CA, USA: ACM Press, 1995.

[AKL93] Jae-Woo Ahn, Myung-Soo Kim, and Soon-Bum Lim. Approximate general sweep boundary of a 2D curved object. *CVGIP: Graph Models Image Process*, 55(2):98–128, 1993.

[BSLM01] Bill Baxter, Vincent Scheib, Ming C. Lin, and Dinesh Manocha. DAB: Interactive haptic painting with 3D virtual brushes. In *SIGGRAPH '01: Proceedings of the 28th Annual Conference on Computer Graphics and Interactive Techniques*, Los Angeles, CA, USA: ACM Press, pages 461–468, 2001.

[CAC02] Ching Chan, Ergun Akleman, and Jianer Chen. Two methods for creating Chinese painting. In *Proceedings of Pacific Graphics 2002*, Beijing, China: IEEE Computer Society, pages 403–412, 2002.

[CAS+97] Cassidy J. Curtis, Sean E. Anderson, Joshua E. Seims, Kurt W. Fleischer, and David H. Salesin. Computer-generated watercolor. In *SIGGRAPH '97: Proceedings of the 24th Annual Conference on Computer Graphics and Interactive Techniques*, Los Angeles, CA, USA: ACM Press/Addison-Wesley Publishing Co., pages 421–430, 1997.

[Chu90] Yap S. Chua. Bézier brushstrokes. *Computer-Aided Design*, 22(9): 556–573, 1990.

[Cou81] Philippe Coueignoux. Character generation by computer. *Computer Graphics and Image Processing*, 16(3):240–269, 1981.

[CT02] Nelson S.H. Chu and Chiew-Lan Tai. An efficient brush model for physically-based 3D painting. In *Proceedings of Pacific Graphics (PG '02)*, Beijing, China: IEEE Computer Society, pages 413–421, 2002.

[GEL00] Arthur D. Gregory, Stephen A. Ehmann, and Ming C. Lin. Intouch: interactive multiresolution modeling and 3D painting with a haptic interface. In *VR '00: Proceedings of the IEEE Virtual Reality 2000 Conference*, New Brunswick, NJ, USA: IEEE Computer Society, page 45, 2000.

[GK91] Qinglian Guo and Tosiyasu L. Kunii. Modeling the diffuse paintings of sumie. In *Modeling in Computer Graphics (Proceedings of IFIP)*, Tokyo, Japan: Springer-Verlag, pages 329–338, 1991.

[Gre85] Richard Greene. The drawing prism: a versatile graphic input device. In *SIGGRAPH '85: Proceedings of the 12th Annual Conference on Computer Graphics and Interactive Techniques*, San Francisco, CA, USA: ACM Press, pages 103–110, 1985.

[Guo95a] Qinglian Guo. Generating realistic calligraphy words. *IEICE Transactions on Fundamentals of Electronics, Communications and Computer Sciences*, E78-A(11):1556–1558, 1995.

[Guo95b] Qinglian Guo. Rendering calligraphy words with 'Kasure' variations. In *Proceedings of the Sixth International Conference on Human-Computer Interaction (HCI '95)*, Tokyo, Japan: Cambridge University Press, pages 129–134, 1995.

[Her98] Aaron Hertzmann. Painterly rendering with curved brush strokes of multiple sizes. In *SIGGRAPH '98: Proceedings of the 25th Annual Conference on Computer Graphics and Interactive Techniques*, Orlando, FL, USA: ACM Press, pages 453–460, 1998.

[HL94] Siu-Chi Hsu and Irene H. H. Lee. Drawing and animation using skeletal strokes. In *SIGGRAPH '94: Proceedings of the 21st Annual Conference on Computer Graphics and Interactive Techniques*, Orlando, FL, USA: ACM Press, pages 109–118, 1994.

[Hob85] John D. Hobby. *Digitized Brush Trajectories*. PhD Thesis, Stanford University, (also *Technical Report* STAN-CS-85-1070), 1985.

[HY98] Kazuyuki Henmi and Tsuneo Yoshikawa. Virtual lesson and its application to virtual calligraphy system. In *Proceedings of IEEE International Conference on Robotics and Automation*, Leuven, Belgium: IEEE Computer Society, pages 1275–1280, 1998.

[HYH00] Seiichiro Hangai, Shinji Yamanaka, and Takayuki Hamamoto. Writer verification using altitude and direction of pen movement. In ICPR'00: *Proceedings of the International Conference on Pattern Recognition*, Barcelona, Spain: IEEE Computer Society, volume 3, pages 479–482, 2000.

[ISO] ISO10526. Joint ISO/CIE standard ISO 10526: 1999/CIE S005/E-1998 CIE standard illuminants for colorimetry.

[IWM94] Horace H.S. Ip, Helena T.F. Wong, and Florence Y. Mong. Fractal coding of Chinese scalable calligraphic fonts. *Computers and Graphics*, 18(3):343–351, 1994.

[JIK+99] David Johnson, Thomas V. Thompson Ii, Matthew Kaplan, Donald Nelson, and Elaine Cohen. Painting textures with a haptic interface. In *VR '99: Proceedings of the IEEE Virtual Reality*, Houston, TX, USA: IEEE Computer Society, page 282, 1999.

[KNV01] Toshiyasu L. Kunii, Gleb V. Nosovskij, and Vladimir L. Vecherinin. Two-dimensional diffusion model for diffuse ink painting. *International Journal of Shape Modeling*, 7(1):45–58, 2001.

[Lee97] Jintae Lee. Physically-based modeling of brush painting. *Computer Networks and ISDN Systems*, 29(14):1571–1576, 1997.

[Lee99] Jintae Lee. Simulating oriental black-ink painting. *IEEE Computer Graphics and Applications*, 19(3):74–81, 1999.

[Lee01] Jintae Lee. Diffusion rendering of black ink paintings using new paper and ink models. *Computers and Graphics*, 25(2):295–308, 2001.

[LGE+99] Ming C. Lin, Arthur Gregory, Stephen Ehmann, Stephan Gottschalk, and Russ Taylor. Contact determination for real-time haptic interaction in 3D modeling, editing and painting. In

Proceedings of the Fourth PHANTom Users Group Workshop, Dedham, MA, USA: ACM Press, 1999.

[LK95] Soon-Bum Lim and Myung-Soo Kim. Oriental character font design by a structured composition of stroke elements. *Computer Aided Design,* 27(3):193–207, 1995.

[LL86] L.D. Landau and E.M. Lifshitz. *Course of Theoretical Physics 7: Theory of Elasticity.* Oxford: Pergamon Press, 1986.

[LNH95] Tosiyasu L. Kunii, Gleb V. Nosovskij, and Takafumi Hayashi. A diffusion model for computer animation of diffuse ink painting. In *Proceedings of Computer Animation,* Geneva, Switzerland: IEEE Computer Society, pages 98–102, 1995.

[LS95] John Lansdown and Simon Schofield. Expressive rendering: a review of nonphotorealistic techniques. *IEEE Computer Graphics and Applications,* 15(3):29–37, 1995.

[Lue03] David G. Luenberger. *Linear and Nonlinear Programming.* Springer, 2nd edition, 2003.

[LW01a] Jiunn-Shyan Lee and Chung-Ming Wang. Computer-generated calligraphy: a precise calligraphic learning system. In *Proceedings of E-Learning and Continuing Professional Education,* Chiayi, Taiwan, China, pages (I): 167–172, 2001.

[LW01b] J.S. Lee and C.M. Wang. Toward a physically-based model for monochromatic ink rendering. In *CVGIP 2001: CD-ROM Proceedings of 14th IPPR Conference on Computer Vision, Graphics, and Image Processing,* Pingtung, Taiwan, China, 2001.

[Mac95] Scott I. MacKenzie. Input devices and interaction techniques for advanced computing. *Virtual environments and advanced interface design,* eds. W. Barfield, and T.A. Furness III, Oxford University Press, pages 437–470, 1995.

[MHN⁺99] Junji Mano, Lifeng He, Tsuyoshi Nakamura, Hiroshi Enowaki, Atsuko Mutoh, and Hidenori Itoh. A method to generate writing-brush-style Japanese Hiragana character calligraphy. In *Proceedings of IEEE International Conference on Multimedia Computing and Systems,* Florence, Italy: IEEE Computer Society, volume 1, pages 787–791, 1999.

[MJ99] Christoph Maurer and Bert Juttler. Rational approximation of rotation minimizing frames using pythagorean-hodograph cubics. *Journal of Geometry and Graphics,* 3(2):141–159, 1999.

[MKG⁺97] Lee Markosian, Michael A. Kowalski, Daniel Goldstein, Samuel J. Trychin, John F. Hughes, and Lubomir D. Bourdev. Real-time nonphotorealistic rendering. In *SIGGRAPH '97: Proceedings of the 24th Annual Conference on Computer Graphics and Interactive Techniques,* Los Angeles, CA, USA: ACM Press/Addison-Wesley Publishing Co., pages 415–420, 1997.

[NISL93] Tsuyoshi Nakamura, Hidenori Itoh, Hirohisa Seki, and Todd Law. A writing system for brush characters using neural recognition and fuzzy interpretation. In *Proceedings of International Joint*

Conference on Neural Networks, Nagoya, Japan: IEEE Computer Society, pages 2901–2904, 1993.

[NTN93] Tomoyuki Nishita, Shinichi Takita, and Eihachiro Nakamae. A display algorithm of brush strokes using Bézier functions. In CGI'93: Proceedings of CG International, Lausanne, Switzerland: Springer-Verlag, pages 244–257, 1993.

[PF89] K.C. Posch and W.D. Fellner. The circle-brush algorithm. ACM Transactions on Graphics, 8(1):1–24, 1989.

[Pha91] Binh Pham. Expressive brush strokes. CVGIP: Graph. Models Image Process., 53(1):1–6, 1991.

[PMZS97] Zhigeng Pan, Xiaohu Ma, Mingmin Zhang, and Jiaoying Shi. Chinese font composition method based on algebraic system of geometric shapes. Computers and Graphics, 21(3):321–328, 1997.

[PZ91] Yunjie Pang and Huixiang Zhong. Drawing Chinese traditional painting by computer. In Proceedings of the IFIP TC5/WG5.10 Working Conference on Modeling in Computer Graphics, Tokyo, Japan: Springer-Verlag, pages 321–328, 1991.

[SN99] Suguru Saito and Masayuki Nakajima. 3D physically based brush model for painting. In SIGGRAPH '99 Sketches, Conference Abstracts and Applications, Los Angeles, CA, USA: ACM Press, page 226, 1999.

[SR97] Ariel Shamir and Ari Rappoport. Quality enhancements of digital outline fonts. Computers and Graphics, Special Issue on Graphics in Electronic Printing and Publishing, 21(6):713–725, 1997.

[Str86] Steve Strassmann. Hairy brushes. In SIGGRAPH '86: Proceedings of the 13th Annual Conference on Computer Graphics and Interactive Techniques, Dallas, TX, USA: ACM Press, pages 225–232, 1986.

[SYST89] M. Shiono, O. Yoshimura, H. Sanada, and Y. Tezuka. Generation of brush written Kanji patterns using brush touch function controlled by three dimensional motion of brush core. Trans. IEICE Japan, J72-D-11(1):76–84, 1989.

[SZ95] Lejun Shao and Hao Zhou. A new contour fill algorithm for outlined character image generation. Computers and Graphics, 19(4):551–556, 1995.

[WB89] Colin Ware and Curtis Baxter. Bat brushes: on the uses of six position and orientation parameters in a paint program. ACM SIGCHI Bulletin, 20:155–160, 1989.

[WI00] Helena T.F. Wong and Horace H.S. Ip. Virtual brush: a model-based synthesis of Chinese calligraphy. Computers and Graphics, 24(1):99–113, 2000.

[WLS01] Der-Lor Way, Yu-Ru Lin, and Zen-Chung Shih. The synthesis of rock textures in Chinese landscape painting. In Proceedings of Eurographics 2001, Manchester, UK: Blackwell, pages C123–C131, 2001.

[WLSL92] X. Wei, S. Lu, M. Song, and B. Luo. Computer pattern design and painting technique based on aesthetics knowledge. *Computer Aided Drafting, Design and Manufacturing*, 2(2):32–40, 1992.

[WS94] Georges Winkenbach and David H. Salesin. Computer-generated pen-and-ink illustration. In *SIGGRAPH '94: Proceedings of the 21st Annual Conference on Computer Graphics and Interactive Techniques*, Orlando, FL, USA: ACM Press, pages 91–100, 1994.

[XTLP02] Songhua Xu, Min Tang, Francis C.M. Lau, and Yunhe Pan. A solid model based virtual hairy brush. *Computer Graphics Forum (Proceedings of Eurographics '02)*, 21(3):299–308 & 625, 2002.

[YH84] Toshinori Yamasaki and Tetsuo Hattori. Training system for well writing of Chinese characters based on their local structure. *IEICE Trans. Japan*, J67-D(4):442–449, 1984.

[YH96] Toshinori Yamasaki and Tetsuo Hattori. Computer calligraphy-brush written kanji formation based on the brush-touch movement. In *IEEE International Conference on Systems, Man, and Cybernetics*, Vancouver, Canada: IEEE Computer Society, pages 1736–1741, 1996.

[YH97] Toshinori Yamasaki and Tetsuo Hattori. Computer calligraphy-brush written Kanji formation based on the calligraphic skill knowledge. *IEICE Transactions on Information and Systems (Special Issue on Educational System using Multimedia and Communication Technology)*, E80-D(2):170–175, 1997.

[YI90] Toshinori Yamasaki and Seiji Inokuchi. Computer coaching for beautiful handwriting of Japanese characters in elementary school. In *WCCE90: Proc. 5th World Conf. on Computers in Education*, Sydney, Australia: Australia Computer Society, pages 725–728, 1990.

[YYI87] Toshinori Yamasaki, Masahiro Yamamoto, and Seiji Inokuchi. CAI system for acquiring good writing skills based on the analysis of pen speed. *IEICE Trans. Japan*, J70-D(11):2071–2076, 1987.

[ZST+99] Qing Zhang, Youetsu Sato, Jun ya Takahashi, Kazunobu Muraoka, and Norishige Chiba. Simple cellular automaton-based simulation of ink behavior and its application to Suibokuga-like 3D rendering of trees. *Journal of Visualization and Computer Animation*, 10(1):27–37, 1999.

[ZZST90] J. Zeng, X. Zhang, H. Sanada, and Y. Tezuka. A computer generation-model of brush-used handwritten Chinese characters and its applications in education. In *Computer Processing of Handwriting*, ed. Plamondon R. Leedham, World Scientific Publishing Co., pages 363–400, 1990.

5

Performance Enhanced Virtual Hairy Paintbrush System

5.1 Overview

This chapter presents a new approach to modeling a 3D physical paintbrush, based on which an interactive painting system has been developed. Compared with existent brush-based painting systems, our new system can accurately and stably simulate the complex painting functionality of a running brush using a modest amount of system resources. The detailed modeling empowers the user to create high-quality digital paintings with delicate aesthetic details that can rival real artwork. With the amount of details to be modeled, we have to rely on a hierarchical modeling approach, dividing the modeling tasks to on-line and off-line computations, and a powerful pigment model that is fully integrated into the brush model. These optimizations and special components make the system operable in real time, fully interactive, and easy to manipulate.

5.2 Introduction

A long cherished dream of both scientists and artists since the birth of digital computers is to be able to use the computer to produce beautiful art. With the ever increasing power of modern computers, the computer as a serious artistic tool is now within reach for many. The more powerful the computer would becomes, the more that can be done in perfecting the artistic effects achievable through advanced computing techniques. The recent hot pursuit of Non-Photorealistic Rendering (NPR) is one major effort to capitalize on the power and flexibility of today's computers for art creation that can surpass what is possible by human artists with conventional means. One major research area in the NPR field is emulation by pen-and-ink [SABS94] which has wide applicability and could lead to powerful expression in many situations. In the genre of Chinese art forms, the brush takes the place of the pen, and the computerization of a paintbrush (and the ink) for interactive painting or calligraphy is a very attractive goal. A brush is many times more complex than a pen, and hence the problem presents a huge challenge for the interested computer scientists. We describe our solution to the problem in this chapter.

Smith [Smi01] has written a good survey on the early painting systems. More recently, several researchers have successfully implemented a virtual brush (or "e-brush") that can mimic a real 3D brush for painting and calligraphy through physically-based modeling [WI00, BSLM01, CT02]. Compared with many existing 2D virtual brushes, which often require the user to specify the contour's control points and the texture of painted strokes (e.g. [Str86]), these 3D brushes are more natural to use, especially for non-computer specialists. A guiding principle for the design of an e-brush is that it must present itself as a familiar tool to the traditional human artist, because "presenting a system that requires the designer to adapt, distract, or place attention outside of the actual task will hinder the creative process to which the designer can come up with ideas" [HSS02]. With the e-brush we have implemented, the user will not be required to specify any control point or to adjust any parameter for the texture, but can operate the brush in more or less the same way as a physical brush.

In a good virtual brush design, each step of the painting process should be simulated in high realism. Here simulation refers to both the production of strokes on the virtual canvas and the continuous visual display of the running brush. The latter is necessary if the user is to be able to feel the presence of a brush in order to have full control over it and to manipulate the brush as in real life. An even more perfect virtual brush should also provide a haptic interface, like what is done in [BSLM01]. Apart from research on virtual brushes for 2D painting, designing e-brushes for 3D painting appears to be a promising area [HH90, ABL95, Pix00, KMM+02].

In this chapter we describe a new e-painting system with improved system design aiming at better performance. We particularly focus on the modeling aspects—the geometry and the dynamics of the paintbrush. Our modeling of the paintbrush stands out among existing approaches because of its unique ability to capture the highly complex geometry of a physical brush as well as its dynamic behavior during painting with great accuracy. Our modeling approach pays special attention to many very fine details that are called for by the creation of high quality digital paintings. Because of these very fine details, the system presents a "realistic" simulation of the physical brush to the user who would operate it like a real brush and expect the output to be as good as a real one.

Compared with the brush based painting system design that we've studied in Chapter 4, this chapter delves further into the underlying detailed modeling of various essential aspects of the realistic paintbrush. The level of details being addressed here is useful not only to those who want to implement a similar system, but also others who develop painting systems of different kinds, as well as those working in the more general area of NPR and physically-based modeling. Besides the low-level details, we also provide in-depth analyses and discussion to justify several high-level design decisions, and experimental results to demonstrate their effectiveness.

The chapter is organized as follows. Sect. 5.3 and Sect. 5.4 present our realistic modeling of the geometry and the dynamics of the brush respectively. Sect. 5.5 gives an overview of the new e-painting system we developed based on our modeling. Sect. 5.6 compares our system with other e-brush based painting systems. Sect. 5.7 concludes the chapter and discusses possible future tasks.

5.3 Modeling the Paintbrush's Geometry

One of the earliest paintbrush models was by Strassmann [Str86], in which brush strokes are created by sweeping a 1D brush bristle over a skeleton, and the color, width and wetness of the brush can be varied. Wong and Ip's virtual brush [WI00] is modeled as an inverse cone which can produce an elliptic drawing mark. In the DAB project [BSLM01], a subdivision surface is wrapped around a spring-mass particle system skeleton to emulate the brush surface. Most recently, Chu and Tai [CT02] use a geometrically-based approach to model an un-split brush tip and an alpha map to model a split brush tip. None of these models however is powerful enough to model a physical brush to a high degree of likeness to the physical brush's real geometry. In particular, the common situation in which a brush splits into a large number of hair bundles appears to be out of the reach of all these existing models. According to many practising artists, a feature for modeling such a high degree of splitting is very desirable. The novel e-brush modeling method we propose here can effectively deal with this and other difficult problems using little memory and CPU resources.

To model a paintbrush with the granularity of a single hair strand which is done in Wong and Ip's system [WI00] is inefficient because a typical real brush may consist of thousands,or even tens of thousands of individual hair strands. To overcome this inefficiency, in Chapter 4 we have introduced our first effort at increasing the brush system's modeling capability with careful consideration of the consumption of system resources by modeling a brush as clusters of brush hair. This approach however can only handle the case of a brush splitting into a small number of hair clusters but not one with heavy splitting.

In this chapter we propose a hierarchical brush geometric model. At a lower level of the hierarchy, hair strands whose position and geometry in 3D space are close to each other are gathered together and modeled as one *hair macro*. At the upper level, disjoint hair macros whose geometries are similar are classified into the same *cluster of hair macros*. The motivation behind having multiple levels is to eliminate as much as possible the redundancy in representing and simulating the brush hair. In real actions, a brush can easily split into thousands of disjoint clusters of hair threads. Cluster-based modeling alone,as introduced in Chapter 4, is not sufficient to deal with the highly chaotic geometry of the brush. It can be easily observed that even in such a situation there exist only a few sharply distinctive geometries among all the geometries of hair clusters. We call these distinct geometries *primitive geometries.* With these primitive geometries, the geometries of all the hair clusters can be approximately derived via simple affine transformations. Fig. 5.1 shows some complex brush geometries of our virtual brush. Based on this two-level hierarchical representation, our virtual brush model can efficiently represent the complex geometry as well as simulate the dynamic behavior of real paintbrushes having thousands of disjoint hair clusters.

Fig. 5.1. Some complex brush geometries of our virtual brush

5.3.1 Three-layer Hierarchical Modeling

Our realistic modeling of the paintbrush geometry is organized as a three layered hierarchy: the lowest layer consists of *hair macros*, which are clusters of hair threads; the intermediate layer consists of clusters of hair macros; the highest layer is the whole brush tip bundle.

Hair strands whose positions in the 3D space are close to each other and whose geometries are similar, are modeled together as one *hair macro* which is a single, aggregative representation of both the geometry and dynamics of these hair threads. A hair macro is the smallest granularity in our modeling. Hence. the overall modeling capability of our virtual brush derives from the modeling power of a hair macro. A formal definition for our geometric model of a hair macro is given as Eq. (5.1). We construct the model of a hair macro **H** through the general sweeping operation in CAD, *GeneralSweeping*($\cdot$), by moving a variable ellipse $E(t)$ along a 3D trajectory, $K(t)$. We call the trajectory "the skeleton of **H**", which is represented as a 3D B-spline. The generated skinning surface is the surface of **H** while the swept volume is the interior volume of **H**. During the sweeping operation we ensure that the sweeping ellipse $E(t)$ always lies on the normal plane of the sweeping trajectory $K(t)$, i.e. $E(t)|_{t=t_0} \perp K(t)|_{t=t_0}$. See Fig. 5.2 for the illustration of a hair macro in its initial geometry, and a deformed hair macro.

$$\begin{cases} \mathbf{H} & \triangleq GeneralSweeping\Big(E(t), K(t)\Big) \ (0 \leqslant t \leqslant 1) \\ E(t) \triangleq \{(x,y)|x = L(t)\nu\cos\big(w+\theta(t)\big) \\ \quad y = S(t)\nu\sin\big(w+\theta(t)\big)(0 \leqslant \nu \leqslant 1, 0 \leqslant w < 2\pi)\} \end{cases}, \quad (5.1)$$

$$\mathbf{H} \triangleq Modeling\big(K(t), S(t), L(t), \theta(t)\big) . \quad (5.2)$$

$E(t)$ is a variable ellipse in that the lengths of its major axis $L(t)$, minor axis $S(t)$ and its orientation $\theta(t)$ (on the normal plane of its sweeping trajectory) can all be varied during sweeping. Thus, given three B-splines,

$S(t)$, $L(t)$ and $\theta(t)$, we can uniquely determine an $E(t)$ $(0 \leqslant t \leqslant 1)$. We can also rewrite Eq. (5.1) as Eq. (5.2), which means that by four B-splines, $\big(K(t)$, $S(t)$, $L(t)$, $\theta(t)$ $\big)$, the geometry of a hair macro, $\mathbf{H}$, can be presented parametrically. This representation makes it easy and intuitive for end users to tailor the geometry of a hair macro and further customize their virtual brush if the users so choose. Fig. 5.2 (a) shows the graphical user interface to be used for this purpose.

The general sweeping operation we adopted is a suitably powerful modeling metaphor, which meets the demand for modeling long furry objects. Our representation is simple to generate and capable of capturing all kinds of geometries that a paintbrush may have, as is demonstrated in Fig. 5.2(a). In comparison, although the subdivision surface mesh employed in [BSLM01] is a more powerful modeling metaphor in general, unlike our general sweeping operation, it is not specifically customized for the modeling of brush hair. Therefore, in spite of its being more sophisticated than our method, it cannot deal with some of the more extreme cases, such as heavily deformed brush hair.

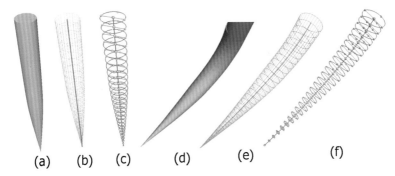

Fig. 5.2. (a to c)An initial hair macro: (a) when shaded; (b) as a wireframe with the sweeping trajectory highlighted; (c) as a series of profiles of the sweeping ellipse, which are in red. (d to f)A deformed hair macro: (d) when shaded; (e) wireframe; (f) profiles of the sweeping ellipse

General sweeping, however, is a time-consuming operation. Moreover, the internal solid models of all the hair macros together could take up a substantial amount of space, especially in situations when the brush is split into many small hair bundles. Consideration of system response time and memory resources calls for a strategy to eliminate as much as possible the redundancy in representing and simulating the brush hair. We introduce the idea of *hair macro cluster* to group disjoint hair macros,whose geometries are similar into one single,modeling unit. This is a reasonable move because it can be easily observed in real life when a brush is split into numerous disjoint hair strands or clusters, there will only be a limited number of sharply distinctive geometries among the clusters. Note that the grouping considers only the geometries but not the physical positions of the hair macros in the 3D space. Given a macro hair cluster and the geometry of any individual hair macro in the cluster, the geometries of all the remaining hair macros of the cluster can be easily derived via simple affine transformations. This design gives rise to a brush geometry model that is compact in memory, and enables fast simulation of the brush's actions.

Fig. 5.3 shows two examples of complex brush geometry modeled using our three-layer hierarchy. Fig. 5.4 shows the brush modeling when one, two, or three layers in the hierarchy are in effect.

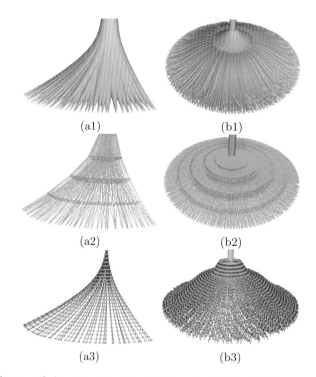

(a1)   (b1)

(a2)   (b2)

(a3)   (b3)

Fig. 5.3. (a1 to a3) A split virtual brush when shaded, in wireframes, and in terms of profiles of the sweeping ellipses respectively; (b1 to b3) a brush that is heavily splitting

5.3.2 Real-time Visual Display of the Brush

Visual feedback is important for any interactive system. In a painting session the user needs to feel the physical presence of the brush in order to manipulate it at will. To provide a good visual feedback could require a huge amount of computation because of the highly complex geometry of a realistic virtual brush. Our hierarchical modeling provides a solution to efficiently tackle the problem. As discussed previously, we only need to explicitly model the geometry of one hair macro for each hair macro cluster, from which all other geometries belonging to the same cluster can be derived. Thus all the hair macros in a cluster share the same data structure, and one tessellation process

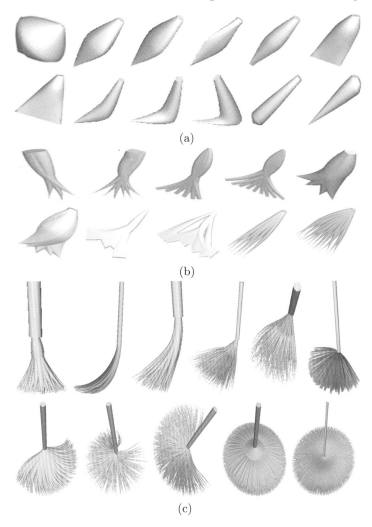

Fig. 5.4. Brush geometry modeling on three levels: (a) using only the top level—
the whole brush tip bundle; (b) using two levels—the top level and the "hair macro"
level; (c) using all three levels

being applied to the geometry of one hair macro is sufficient for tessellating
all the hair macros in the cluster (by applying the same affine transformation
as mentioned before).

We also make sure that modeling satisfies the preconditions necessary for
taking advantage of the hardware acceleration facility through the "Display
Lists" feature in OpenGL. The time-consuming commands for rendering the
geometries of the hair macros would therefore be optimized by the driver
as the affine transformations can be pre-computed. With the hierarchical
modeling approach and hardware acceleration, our virtual brush can achieve

real-time visual feedback of the complex geometry of the brush using a reasonably small amount of memory and CPU time.

5.4 Modeling the Paintbrush's Dynamic Behavior

Simulating the dynamics of a real paintbrush, which includes the brush's deformation due to outer force, recovery from deformation when the force vanishes, splitting due to inner stress, etc., is a non-trivial problem because of the complexity of the brush's geometry and the physical principles that underlie the brush's behavior. In the DAB project [BSLM01], the motion of the brush geometry is simulated through a pair of first-order differential equations. The dynamics of Chu and Tai's brush [CT02] are modeled as springs whose deformation is via constrained energy minimization. In spite of all these efforts, what would be a good model of brush dynamics that supports realistic, efficient, and stable brush motion simulation using a reasonable amount of system resources remains not completely answered.

Our design of the virtual brush system offers a highly detailed dynamic modeling of the behavior of a physical paintbrush. The modeling is divided into two phases. The first phase consists of on-line computation of the computationally inexpensive and input-sensitive physical processes, such as brush deformation due to brush pressing. We adopt the approach of using a "phenomenal model" which simulates the dynamics of a changing object based on observations, instead of by the highly complex underlying physical laws that govern the changes. It proves to be a highly economical approach when we have to model a large number of brush features. The result is fast simulation of a sufficiently detailed model of the brush. With this observational modeling approach, however, we compromise some degree of modeling accuracy. And so in the second phase, off-line data are used to calibrate and refine the on-line simulated results. These data come from a simulation error calibration database constructed from off-line acquired ground truth about simulation errors. Our design represents a balance between a complete on-line based approach and one that is at the other extreme. The former demands a huge amount of runtime resources in order to achieve real-time response; the latter could result in a database which is too large to manage. This "observation model plus calibration database" approach achieves high realism for the brush dynamics being simulated as well as interactivity with little incurred computational cost. Fig. 5.5 shows the dynamic deformation of a primitive geometry. Fig. 5.6 shows a series of simulated dynamic deformations of our virtual brush.

During painting, the geometry of the paintbrush is deformed due to the outer force arising from friction between the brush and the paper. Brush deformation is modeled in the first phase of the two-phase modeling, in two different parts: deforming of hair macro due to brush-paper collision and deforming of hair macro due to the brush's inner stress.

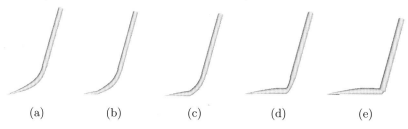

(a)   (b)   (c)   (d)   (e)

Fig. 5.5. Dynamic deformation of a primitive geometry during painting

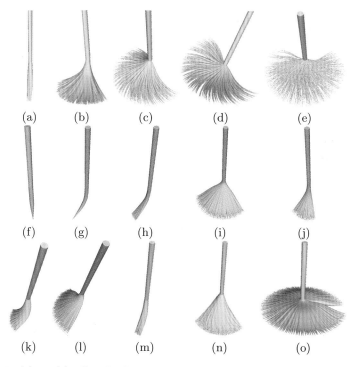

(a)   (b)   (c)   (d)   (e)

(f)   (g)   (h)   (i)   (j)

(k)   (l)   (m)   (n)   (o)

Fig. 5.6. (a) to (e)—Simple dynamic deformation of the virtual brush: (a) the initial geometry, (b) pressed down, (c) rotated, (d) tilted, (e) further pressed down and rotated. (f to o) A more sophisticated virtual brush deformation process: (f) the initial brush; (g) pressed down before splitting is simulated; (h) after splitting is simulated; (i) rotated and further pressed down; (j) lifted a bit with some split brush strands merging; (k) tilted; (l) further rotated and pressed down; (m) further lifted to the initial brush position; (n) pressed down again; (o) completely pressed down to the virtual paper with some rotation

5.4.1 Deformation due to Brush-paper Collision

5.4.1.1 Deformation of skeleton

The main constraint to observe here is that the brush's skeleton cannot penetrate the virtual paper. During brush painting or writing, if some part of a skeleton $K(t)$ penetrates the virtual paper ψ at an intersecting point $K_o(t_p)$ between the original skeleton $K_o(t)$ and the virtual paper ψ, we would deform $K_o(t)$ by replacing it with a new curve $K_n(t)$ to satisfy the above constraint. The deformation scheme is expressed mathematically as Eq. (5.3) and illustrated by Fig. 5.7.

$$K_n(t) \triangleq K_{pro}(t) \times (1 - rfc) + K_{ro}(t) \times rfc, \tag{5.3a}$$

$$K_{pro}(t) \triangleq \begin{cases} Pro\big(K_o(t), \psi\big) & \text{when } K_o(t) \text{ is below } \psi \\ K_o(t) & \text{otherwise} \end{cases}, \tag{5.3b}$$

$$t_p = \max\{t | K_o(t) \text{ is below } \psi\}, \tag{5.3c}$$

$$K_{ro}(t) \triangleq \begin{cases} K_o(t) & t_p \leqslant t < 1 \\ Rot\big(K_o(t), K_o(t_p), \phi_{min}\big) & 0 \leqslant t < t_p \end{cases}, \tag{5.3d}$$

$$\phi_{min} \triangleq \arg\min_\phi \Big(\forall P \in \{Rot\big(K_o(t), K_o(t_p), \phi\big) | \\ 0 \leqslant t < t_p\} \Rightarrow P \text{ is above } \psi \Big), \tag{5.3e}$$

$$K_o(t) \leftarrow Smooth(K_n(t)). \tag{5.3f}$$

$K_n(t)$ is the linear interpolation between $K_o(t)$'s projected version K_{pro} and its rotated version K_{ro} [Eq. (5.3a)]. The weight rfc used in the above interpolation is essentially a coefficient representing the degree of rigidity-flexibility of the material used for the brush hair [Cal99]. K_{pro} is computed by simply projecting any point on $K_o(t)$ that is below the virtual paper ψ onto the plane of ψ [Eq. (5.3b)]. To compute $K_{ro}(t)$, we need to first detect the intersecting point $K_o(t_p)$ between $K_o(t)$ and ψ. In Eq. (5.3c), we define this point to be the closest point below the virtual paper ψ to $K_o(1)$, if the point exists. Here $K_o(1)$ is the bottom of the skeleton, i.e. the tip of the penholder. Then the rotated version K_{ro} can be computed by rotating $K_o(t)|_{0 \leqslant t < t_p}$ around $K_o(t_p)$ through a minimum angle ϕ_{min} to make all the points on the skeleton come on top of the virtual paper ψ [Eqs. (5.3d) and (5.3e)]. At last, before replacing $K_o(t)$ with the new skeleton $K_n(t)$, we first smooth $K_n(t)$ by applying a B-spline curve fitting to ensure a smooth transition of the curvature of $K_n(t)$ [Eq. (5.3f)].

We also model the kinking up of a hair macro due to large friction induced by high stress which is according to classic Newton force. The larger the friction, the slower the hair macro will move. This non-uniform displacement will cause local prolongation and compression of the hair macro's skeleton, which when it becomes too severe will lead to kinking up of the skeleton, as shown in Fig. 5.8. To simulate this, we introduce additional curvature to the skeleton so that the arc length of the skeleton is the skeleton's original length and the chordal length is its squeezed length.

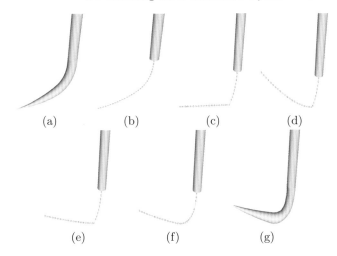

Fig. 5.7. Skeleton deformation of the virtual brush: (a) a hair macro penetrating the virtual paper; (b) its corresponding skeleton; (c) the projected skeleton, (d) the rotated skeleton; (e) the interpolated version of the skeleton; (f) the new skeleton after smoothing, which is completely above the virtual paper; (g) the deformed hair macro with the new skeleton

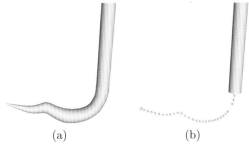

Fig. 5.8. (a) A kinked-up hair macro; (b) its corresponding skeleton

5.4.1.2 Deformation of sweeping ellipse

Recall that the geometry model of a hair macro is constructed by sweeping a variable ellipse along a trajectory. When the brush is deformed, the profiles of the variable ellipse touching the paper will also be deformed. We apply minimization to the areas of the parts of the deformed profiles that are under the virtual paper plane, with the hard constraint that the profiles' areas cannot change. These areas could change at a later stage in the modeling when we take into account the inner stress. We minimize the areas concerned for the simple reason that the physical brush cannot go under the canvas; minimizing gives us the best approximation to what would happen in reality. Eq. (5.4) is a brief mathematic representation of this deformation.

$$\begin{cases} \min \sum_i Area\Big(UnderPaper(Profile_i)\Big) \\ \text{subject to :} \\ \forall\, Profile_i : Area(Profile_i) \equiv \text{Constant} \end{cases} \qquad (5.4)$$

Here $Profile_i$ is the i-th profile of the sweeping ellipse of a certain hair macro. $UnderPaper(Profile_i)$ computes the part of the profile $Profile_i$ that is under the virtual paper plane. Operator $Area(\cdot)$ computes the area of a planar shape.

5.4.2 Deformation due to Inner Stress

Once the hair macro is deformed due to collision between the brush and the paper, inner stress will develop inside the hair macro. Because we model the geometry of a hair macro explicitly, its volume is computable. Based on the volumes of the initial and the deformed geometry of a hair macro, we can estimate the inner stress of the macro. This inner stress will then give rise to further deformation of the geometry of the macro, in the form of distension and splitting of the hair macro.

5.4.2.1 Estimating the inner stress

From Eq. (5.1) we notice any point in a certain profile $E(t)|_{t=t_0}$ of the variable ellipse $E(t)$ can be determined by the pair (ν, w) under a given $L(t_0)$, $S(t_0)$ and $\theta(t_0)$. Accordingly, we set up a local planar elliptical polar coordinate system for $E(t_0)$ by taking the major and minor axes of $E(t_0)$ as two axes of the coordinate system, and the center of $E(t_0)$ as its origin. We can then establish a point to point correspondence between the un-deformed profile of $E(t_0)$ and its deformed counterpart in the new local coordinate system. We use the subscripts "u" and "d" to refer to the un-deformed and deformed items respectively during the brush deformation. Then the correspondence rule we adopted can be stated as: two points (ν_u, w_u) in $E_u(t_0)$ and (ν_d, w_d) in $E_d(t_0)$ are correlated if and only if $\nu_u = \nu_d$ and $w_u = w_d + \tau(t_0)$, where τ is a parameter to be determined later. By this correspondence, we can then estimate the local inner stress $\rho(\nu_d, w_d)$ around point (ν_d, w_d) on $E_d(t_0)$ with Eq. (5.5).

$$\rho(\nu_d, w_d, \tau(t_0)) \triangleq \begin{cases} \tan\left(\max\left(k_1(1 - \frac{\nu_u}{\nu_d}), -\frac{\pi}{2}\right)\right) & \text{when } \nu_d \leqslant \nu_u; \\ \tan\left(\min\left(k_2(1 - \frac{\nu_u}{\nu_d}), \frac{\pi}{2}\right)\right) & \text{otherwise.} \end{cases} \tag{5.5}$$

Based on this point-wise stress estimation, we can derive the formulae to evaluate the average inner stress $\rho(E_d(t))$ of the ellipse $E_d(t)$ as Eq. (5.6). Here by our design, $\tau(t)$ is supposed to be a number between $[0, 2\pi)$ in order to minimize the absolute value of $\rho(E_d(t))$.

$$\rho(E_d(t)) \triangleq \min_{\tau(t)\in[0,2\pi)} \left(\frac{\int_{E_d(t)} \rho(\nu_d, w_d, \tau(t))d\nu_d\,dw_d}{\int_{E_d(t)} d\nu_d\,dw_d} \right). \tag{5.6}$$

Integrating the point-wise stress throughout the volume of the hair macro can further lead to the estimated average inner stress $\rho(\mathbf{H}_d)$ of the deformed hair macro $\mathbf{H}_d$ as given by Eq. (5.7).

$$\rho(\mathbf{H_d}) \triangleq \int_0^1 \rho(E_d(t))\mathrm{d}t. \qquad (5.7)$$

A positive ρ suggests that the stress is inward, which will compress the geometry of the hair macro; whereas the negative ρ suggests that the stress is outward and will dilate the hair macro; zero ρ means the hair macro is in its steady geometry. If only $\rho \neq 0$, stress-driven brush deformation tends to reduce the current inner stress of the virtual brush through brush geometry deformation.

5.4.2.2 Distension of hair macro

Although the volume of a hair macro is determined mainly by the number of hair strands in the macro, there is another factor, the *phenomenal distensibility* of the hair macro, which will affect the volume. A high degree of phenomenal distensibility suggests that the hair strands are not very densely packed inside the hair macro. Obviously, distensibility is a function of the inner stress of a hair macro. For a hair macro, if its phenomenal distensibility increases (resp. reduces), all of the sweeping ellipse profiles of this hair macro will increase (resp. reduce) in size. For simplicity we model the degree of distensibility β as a function of the stress in the hair macro $\mathbf{H}$ as follows:

$$\beta(\mathbf{H}) \triangleq \frac{1}{2} - \frac{1}{\pi} \arctan(k_3 \times \rho(\mathbf{H})). \qquad (5.8)$$

Since $\rho(\mathbf{H})$'s range is the whole real number axis $(-\infty, +\infty)$, the range of $\beta(\mathbf{H})$ is $(0, 1)$. Here k_3 is a positive coefficient controlling the sensitivity of the distensibility to the inner stress. For each hair macro $\mathbf{H} = Modeling(K(t), S(t), L(t), \theta(t))$, if its phenomenal distensibility grows from $\beta_1(\mathbf{H})$ to $\beta_2(\mathbf{H})$, $\mathbf{H}$'s parametric representation will change to $\mathbf{H}'$, as defined in Eq. (5.9).

$$\begin{cases} \mathbf{H}' \triangleq Modeling(K(t), S'(t), L'(t), \theta(t)) \\ S'(t) \triangleq (\beta_2(\mathbf{H})/\beta_1(\mathbf{H}))S(t) \\ L'(t) \triangleq (\beta_2(\mathbf{H})/\beta_1(\mathbf{H}))L(t) \end{cases} \qquad (5.9)$$

5.4.2.3 Splitting of hair macro

If there is a part inside the volume of a hair macro, whose stress is above the threshold of a maximum tolerable inner stress, the hair macro will split. Splitting of the hair macro takes place in a stress-descending order if multiple parts of the virtual brush meet the splitting criterion simultaneously. Split hair macros could merge again if their inner stress starts to come down. In the current version of our modeling, merging however is controlled through user interaction, mimicking the way the user caresses a physical brush to merge some split hair. Fig. 5.9 shows some brush motion simulation results with and without brush splitting.

More formally, if there exists a point in a hair macro, whose stress is above the threshold of a maximum tolerable inner stress, the hair macro $\mathbf{H}$ will split.

According to the way we compute the stress in **H**, discussed in Sect. 5.4.2.1, the distribution of the stress within **H** is continuous. This means if there exists one such point in **H** whose stress is greater than the splitting threshold, it is likely that the neighbouring points are also above the threshold. Therefore our splitting procedure works on groups of points. For one specific sweeping ellipse we need first of all to separate those points, whose stress is above the threshold, from the other points. If the number of connected points whose stress is above the threshold is very small, there will be no splitting. This is the effect of physical attraction between neighbouring hair threads. After the small group elimination, real splitting operation comes into the picture. The separated point groups will become two ellipses, the centers of which are the centroids of each group. To determine the lengths of major and minor axes of the ellipse, we impose two constraints: the area of the ellipse should be equal to the area of the group before splitting, and the ratio of the major axis to minor axis of the ellipse is equal to the ratio of the length to width of the bounding box of the point group. The orientation of the major axis of the new ellipse is determined by the principal axis of the group. Splitting the hair macro takes place in a stress-descending order if multiple point groups meet the splitting criterion. After splitting **H** at the largest average stress point group, the stress inside **H** is recomputed. Splitting continues as long as the splitting condition holds.

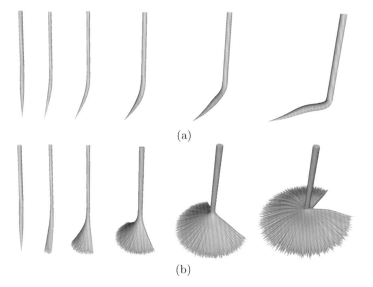

(a)

(b)

Fig. 5.9. A brush deforming when being pressed down continuously: (a) with no splitting of hair; (b) with splitting

5.4.2.4 Recovery from deformation

To simulate recovery from deformation, we model the material of the hair macro as a kind of hybrid elastic-rigid material. According to studies in material science [Cal99], the deformed hair macro will recover to a certain degree, which ranges from full recovery in the case that the material is purely flexible to no recovery at all if the material is completely rigid. In our computation model we determine the recovery extent based on the amount of inner stress of the hair macro and the hair macro's inherent threshold of elasticity and threshold of rigidity. Using the estimated recovery extent as the weight, we can then simulate the brush's recovery by interpolating its original undeformed geometry and its current deformed geometry. The above process is described in Eq. (5.10).

$$
\begin{aligned}
&\mathbf{H}_\mathrm{r} \leftarrow \big(\mathbf{H}_\mathrm{d} \times (1 - extent) + \mathbf{H}_\mathrm{u} \times extent\big), \\
&extent = \begin{cases}
1 & Stress(\mathbf{H}_\mathrm{d}) < thre^\mathrm{ela}; \\
0 & Stress(\mathbf{H}_\mathrm{d}) > thre^\mathrm{rig}; \\
\frac{thre^\mathrm{rig} - Stress(\mathbf{H}_\mathrm{d})}{thre^\mathrm{rig} - thre^\mathrm{ela}} & \text{otherwise.}
\end{cases}
\end{aligned}
\tag{5.10}
$$

Here $\mathbf{H}_\mathrm{r}$ is the geometry that a hair macro will recover to; $\mathbf{H}_\mathrm{d}$ is its deformed geometry before recovery; $\mathbf{H}_\mathrm{u}$ is the hair macro's initial (un-deformed) geometry; $extent$ is the recovery extent, which is determined by the current inner stress, $Stress(\mathbf{H}_\mathrm{d})$, of $\mathbf{H}_\mathrm{d}$ as well as the hair macro's inherent thresholds of elasticity, $thre^\mathrm{ela}$, and rigidity, $thre^\mathrm{rig}$.

5.4.3 Calibrating the On-line Results

To ensure the accuracy of our simulation of the brush dynamics with respect to a physical brush, we calibrate the fast on-line simulation results in the second phase of the modeling. The procedure relies on data from a "simulation error database", whose records came from sampling using a real brush. Since the deformation of our virtual brush's geometry is according to the six degrees of freedom (DOFs) of the input, the database is indexed by the differential of the virtual brush's six DOFs between two consecutive simulation time slices and the current brush geometry. The content of each record in the database is the corresponding transformation of the virtual brush's current geometry. Our brush deformation database operates at the level of a hair macro in our three-level hierarchy. This reduces substantially the number of different cases that need to be separately sampled and stored in the database. To further reduce the size of the calibration database, we assume the effects that all the six DOFs have on the brush geometry are independent. As a result, the whole calibration database is divided into many small sections, each of which being responsible for calibrating the part of the deformation caused by variation of only one specific DOF. It turned out that a modest number of records (40) is enough to perform a satisfactory calibration for improving the on-line simulation results in our system.

Compared with traditional physically-based approaches to model the brush dynamics through numerical computation, there are two important advantages of our on-line plus off-line modeling approach. First, we do not have to model those extremely complicated physical processes of a brush's dynamics. Second, we can avoid the very time-consuming and probably unstable numerical computation for solving differential equations on the fly if some truly powerful but complex equations can be established to model all the underlying detailed dynamics governing the brush's behavior.

More formally, since the deforming of a hair macro's geometry is according to the six DOFs of the input, the database is indexed by: 1) the differential of the virtual brush system's six DOFs between the current and the previous simulated time slice, which is denoted as $\partial \mathbf{D}$; 2) the current geometry of the hair macro $\mathbf{H} \triangleq Modeling\big(K(t), S(t), L(t), \theta(t)\big)$ [Eq. (5.2)]. The content of each record in the database is the corresponding transformation $\mathbf{T}$ on $\mathbf{H}$'s current geometry, namely $K(t), S(t), L(t), \theta(t)$. When collecting records to establish the calibration database, we choose the samples in such a way that no two similar brush dynamic deformation processes are sampled and stored.

The above keywords to index the database have many dimensions. We construct a manageable database by taking advantage of the inter-relationships among the fields of the keywords. The product of $L(t_0)$ and $S(t_0)$ reflects the area of the ellipse $E(t_0)$, and hence the number of hair strands in the hair macro under a certain distensibility. If the hair macro will not split, $S(t_0)$ can be computed from $L(t_0)$. Thus we can use four control points to represent the geometry deformation on $L(t)$ and four control points for $K(t)$. We also assume there is no inter-relationship between the dynamic deformations on $K(t)$ and $L(t)$, i.e. changing either one of the two splines will not have any direct effect on the other spline. This assumption comes from the observation that there is only a weak relationship between deformations on $L(t)$ and $K(t)$ during a real brush's deformation. As a result, the whole database can be divided into two sub-databases: $\mathbf{DL}$ for calibrating the simulated dynamic deformation on $L(t)$, and $\mathbf{DK}$ for calibrating the simulated deformation on $K(t)$. For simplicity we ignore the possible but minute deformation on the brush geometry introduced by the x, y displacement of the virtual brush. So only four of the six DOFs will affect the brush's geometry deformation process. We also assume that the effects these four DOFs have on the brush geometry are separable. Thus $\mathbf{DL}$ and $\mathbf{DK}$ are further divided into four sections, each of which is used to calibrate the error in the simulation of the geometry's dynamic deformation under the change of one DOF. For each of the sections in $\mathbf{DL}$ and $\mathbf{DK}$, the index words are of low dimensions: one dimension for the varied DOF and the remaining dimensions for the control points of $L(t)$ in $\mathbf{DL}$ or $K(t)$ in $\mathbf{DK}$.

During database retrieval we find several records in the database whose distances to the input index are within a certain threshold. The contents of the retrieved records are interpolated using the distances between the indices of the retrieved records and the input index as the weights. For database retrieval, the distance between two splines is defined to be the sum of the Euclidian distances of their corresponding four control points.

With the way we organize the database as described above, the database in our prototype implementation contains a modest number of records (40).

This number of records is already sufficient for performing a satisfactory calibration to correct/improve the online simulation results.

5.5 E-painting System based on Realistic Virtual Brush Modeling

We have built a complete working e-brush system based on the modeling strategies just described. Compared with other virtual brushes, this new system is designed to present a realistic brush in the sense that the system accurately and stably simulates the complex painting functionality of a running brush, and therefore is capable of creating high-quality digital paintings with minute aesthetic details that can rival the real artwork.

5.5.1 Additional Components of Our New Painting System

Other than brush modeling, the system has also incorporated a novel pigment model and a user manipulability improving component. As these two components are not the focus of this chapter, we will only give an overview in the following.

5.5.1.1 A novel pigment model

During painting, the contour of the current ink mark left by virtual brush on virtual paper can be computed by intersecting the geometrical models of these two virtual objects. To produce a good texture for the ink mark, a pigment model is required. A number of pigment models for digital painting have been proposed [Sma91, Lee99, ZST+99, Coc91], but they are either not well embedded into a 3D virtual paintbrush, or were developed earlier and therefore could only produce some very coarse painting results. A recent pigment model is contributed by [CAS+97]. It is however too slow to be used in interactive painting because of the need to solve heavy differential equations on the fly. Other pigment models that can be found in existent virtual brush systems are too simplistic: they either simply transfer ink values from the penetrating brush tip onto the ink mark area [CT02], or apply alpha blending in the above ink transformation to simulate glazing effects [BSLM01].

For our system, we devise a new pigment model that is best for expressive Oriental painting. The prominent feature of this new pigment model is that it is completely and seamlessly integrated into our realistic virtual brush model: we store both the local ink color and the wetness at each control point of the geometry model of our virtual brush. When generating the ink mark, each point in the ink mark is painted using a color which is a linearly interpolated result between the ink mark's original color on the paper and the color of the point on the brush surface contacting this ink mark. The interpolation weight is a random number, whose distribution is controlled by the current inner stress of the hair macro, the local wetness around the painted pixel, as well as the quality parameters (explained in the next section) of the virtual brush. This probability-based pigment model allows us to simulate the dry brush effect, the running style effect and the ink saturation effect. These are important aesthetic effects that can contribute significantly to the expressiveness of the painting system.

5.5.1.2 User manipulability improving component

As with any real brush, it can happen that the user would feel unsatisfied with their creations using the virtual brush. Instead of training the user, our virtual brush system has the unique feature of training the brush. This is done through an intelligent *user manipulability improving component*. This component applies an additional transformation to the user's input before the system commits to the final painting result.

The idea behind the design of this component is as follows. Our virtual brush carries with it a collection of beautiful strokes and the input for creating these strokes. The user can choose among these "known" brush strokes not for his/her own strokes, but use them as training samples. For each selected sample, the user would then use our virtual brush to produce a stroke as close to the sample as possible. The system then applies a numerical analysis to compute a transformation from the user's input to that of the sample stroke. The derived transformation is the "personal habitual bias" of the user. Later, when the user paints using our virtual brush, his/her input will firstly go through the transformation of his personal habitual bias. Thus, it is the transformed input rather than his original input that drives the virtual brush to paint.

The system input used to paint one stroke by our virtual brush is essentially a six-dimensional curve, where each dimension is the profile of one DOF for the geometry of the virtual brush with respect to a certain time during painting. This is denoted as $D(t) = \{D_1(t), D_2(t), D_3(t), D_4(t), D_5(t), D_6(t)\}$. We also denote the standard input to create the brush stroke as $I(t) = \{I_1(t), I_2(t), I_3(t), I_4(t), I_5(t), I_6(t)\}$. We then derive a third six-dimensional curve to capture the user painting bias, i.e. $B(t) = \{B_1(t), B_2(t), \cdots, B_6(t)\}$, which comes from dividing the value of each point in $I(t)$ against the corresponding point in $D(t)$, namely $B_i(t_j) \triangleq I_i(t_j)/D_i(t_j)$ $(i = 1, 2, \cdots, 6)$ and t_j is one simulation time epoch. For $B_i(t)$'s we apply piecewise degree-3 Bézier curve fitting. Suppose $B_i(t)$ is fitted using n segments of a Bézier curve, $F_i(t) = \{F_i^1(t), F_i^2(t), \cdots, F_i^n(t)\}$. We also use the segmentation result to segment the input profile of $D_i(t)$ into $D_i(t) = \{D_i^1(t), D_i^2(t), \cdots, D_i^n(t)\}$. A set of mapping relationships M_i can thus be collected, where $M_i \triangleq \{(D_i^j(t), F_i^j(t))|j = 1, 2, \cdots, n\}$, which is the extracted i-th component of the user's personal habitual bias.

Applying this extracted painting bias is simple. With a new user input $D_i^{\text{new}}(t)$, we search the collected mapping relationships M_i to find the closest matching record, say $D_i^{\text{close}}(t)$ with the complete mapping relationship pair being $(D_i^{\text{close}}(t), F_i^{\text{close}}(t))$. Then, $D_i^{\text{new}}(t)$ is multiplied by $F_i^{\text{close}}(t)$ to achieve the user painting bias correction. To better strengthen the functionality of this user manipulability improving component, we retrieve several closest matching pairs and then use linear interpolation to derive the specific painting correction pair by taking the discrete curve similarities of the first fields of the retrieved pairs to $D_i^{\text{new}}(t)$ as the interpolation weights. The definition of curve similarity is taken from [HOCS02].

5.5.2 The Running System

Figs. 5.10 (a to b) show two screen shots of the GUI of the running system. (a) was taken when the user was customizing the geometry of the hair macro—the skeleton as well as the profiles of the sweeping ellipse. (b) shows a painting in the making, with some closeup views as (c to d).

Figs. 5.11 and 5.12 give two examples of e-paintings created using our improved virtual brush system design, which are imitations of real paintings. Although the simulation attends to many fine details, our virtual brush running on a PC with 256 M memory and an AMD Duron 1.2 GHz processor can respond interactively to user commands. Currently, we use a WACOM pen on a tablet to get the position, the pressure (used as the brush's vertical displacement), and the tilt of the virtual brush; and keyboard input to get the remaining two DOFs. The rational behind using the vertical displacement of the brush as the pressure term is because the more displacement a brush experiences, the more inner pressure it will develop. A better input device in the future should provide some degree of haptic feedback.

5.6 Related Work

5.6.1 Wong & Ip's System

Wong and Ip's system [WI00] simulates the painting functionality of a real brush with granularity of a single hair thread. As a typical paintbrush can have hundreds or thousands of hair strands, the responses of their system tend to be too slow for interactive painting. Moreover, their system relies on an intricate set of parameters to control the shape, density and opacity of the brush's ink mark, all of which need to be manually specified through user interaction. Thus it is at best a semi-interactive system, and not natural to use for the human artists. And the ink mark generated by their system is always an elliptical blot.

In comparison, we use writing primitives instead of individual hair strands to serve as the basic working units in the virtual hairy brush. In general, a single primitive is probably enough for regular scripts, official scripts and most running scripts and perhaps a dozen or so for cursive scripts. Hence our software needs to handle only a small number of writing primitives most of the time. As a result, our system operates comfortably in real-time mode because of the hierarchical modeling of the paintbrush geometry and hardware acceleration we employ. Our system is natural to use and is a genuine

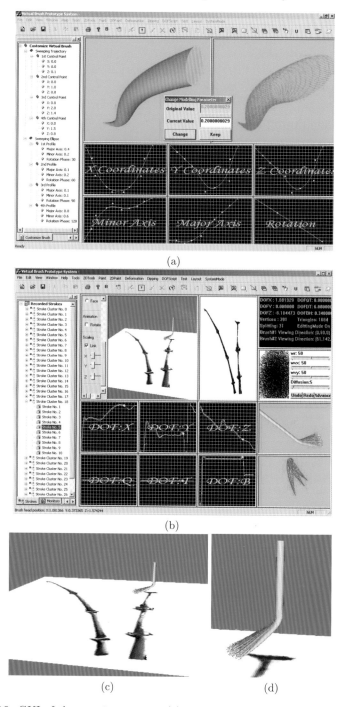

Fig. 5.10. GUI of the running system: (a) the running system—user customizing the virtual brush; (b) the running system—bamboos being painted; (c & d) closeup views of (b)

Fig. 5.11. "Spring garden" by the virtual brush

Fig. 5.12. "Summer water lily" by the virtual brush

interactive system in which the determination of both the painted stroke contour and its texture is fully automatic. The ink mark rendered by our virtual brush can be varied and of irregular shape, in order not to limit the creativity of the artist.

5.6.2 The DAB System

The brush geometry model in the DAB system [BSLM01] can represent some of the most common types of brushes typically used in oil painting, but not all the possible types. Their system is weak in modeling the splitting of a paintbrush. They use two separate models to model the brush geometry and the brush dynamics: a particle system skeleton to simulate the basic brush motion, and a deformable mesh to model the actual shape of the brush head surface. Synchronizing the running of the two models is a non-trivial problem. Their brush dynamics modeling is based on a pair of differential equations, and to solve these equations involves some tradeoff between system stability, computation efficiency and simulation accuracy.

In our system, the brush geometric model we use is very powerful, which can capture literally almost all the possible brush geometries with little memory consumption, and the rendering of the model is fast. Our brush's geometry model dynamics model and the pigment model are designed to be closely knitted together, and hence there is no synchronization problem between these models. Because of the division of work into on-line and off-line computations in modeling the brush's dynamics, our system performs the simulation accurately, operates stably, and requires a modest amount of system resources.

5.6.3 Chu & Tai's System

Chu and Tai [CT02] use an explicit geometrical modeling approach for the un-split brush tip, which is mathematically equivalent to the clustered modeling strategy as reported in one of our previous publications [XTLP02]. To model the split brush, unlike our fully geometrically-based approach, they use an alpha map. This results in an over-simplification which limits the expressiveness and the amount of fine details that the brush is able to produce. For the brush dynamics, their modeling through brush energy minimization can simulate small-scale deformation of the brush geometry but not large-scale bending or stretching due to the restriction of constrained energy minimization. In fact, large-scale deformation of brush geometry is a frequent phenomenon in watercolor painting and Oriental painting.

Chu and Tai's system gives a somewhat awkward support for mimicking the dry brush effect and simulating brush splitting. The alpha map is central to their production of 2D expressive painting results. It is used to control which parts of the brush tuft are dry, and to specify which parts of the brush tip are split. Computing the alpha map automatically is challenging which Chu and Tai did not attack. Loading a pre-stored alpha map from a texture database will miss the power of user control on the texture of painted strokes. The idea however was published more than ten years ago [HLW93, HL94] and perfectly implemented in a commercial paint system [Cre]. The other possible choice would be to rely on the user to control the alpha map for the desired texture of the strokes to be painted. In any case, Chu and Tai's system lacks the needed support for the very important dry brush and brush splitting effects that occur frequently in Oriental painting.

In comparison, our system offers an explicit modeling of the highly complex paintbrush geometry to support creation of even the minutest details in a generated e-painting. Our hybrid observational-model-calibration-database modeling of the brush dynamics provides an accurate simulation of the paintbrush in motion, which includes splitting, stretching, bending to any extent. A variety of paintbrush effects are supported owing to the realistic modeling of the virtual brush as well as the seamlessly embedded pigment model. As a result no mandatory user interaction is required for generating aesthetic textures for the painted strokes.

5.7 Conclusion and Future Work

We have presented the design of a powerful painting system based on realistic modeling of the paintbrush. The amount of details being modeled necessitates the many time or space optimizations that we have introduced into the design. The result is a high degree of realism in every simulation step. Here is a summary of the unique features of our modeling approach: 1) Clustered and hierarchical modeling is used to minimize redundant representations and computations, and together with hardware acceleration, the model is easily renderable in real-time; 2) Division of the modeling into on-line tasks and off-line calibration makes possible an accurate and stable simulation of the brush's motion using little computational resources; 3) Our virtual brush can automatically determine both its geometric contour and the texture of its ink mark on the virtual paper without any human intervention; 4) Other features such as the pigment model and the user manipulability adaptation component make the virtual brush system a powerful one and natural to use for creating high-quality e-artwork.

There are still many interesting problems to be addressed on further enhancing the components in this virtual brush-based painting system design. One of them is that of choosing the appropriate samples for the brush motion calibration database that can enumerate all the possible motions a painting brush could experience without repetitive sampling. For the currently employed pigment model, only water-soluble pigment is simulated. An obvious future task would be to extend the model to cover oil painting and maybe other kinds of painting by following Small's [Sma91] and Cockshott's [Coc91] pioneering approaches. For the user manipulability improving component, finding the features that distinguish good input leading to visually pleasing brush strokes from bad input could help establish a mechanism to perform auto-beautification.

Although we have gone after a detailed modeling of the paintbrush, a real brush operates in a fashion that is orders of magnitude more complex than what is currently simulated. Features that can be added in the future versions include repeated dipping effects and more user's control of the brush during painting. Other features requiring longer-term effort include support for 3D painting (such as oil painting), and vectorization of painting results. The latter could lead to many interesting applications such as animation of e-paintings.

References

[ABL95]   Maneesh Agrawala, Andrew C. Beers, and Marc Levoy. 3D paint-
           ing on scanned surfaces. In *SI3D '95: Proceedings of the 1995
           Symposium on Interactive 3D Graphics*, Monterey, CA, USA:
           ACM Press, pages 145–150 & 215, 1995.

[BSLM01]   Bill Baxter, Vincent Scheib, Ming C. Lin, and Dinesh Manocha.
           DAB: Interactive haptic painting with 3D virtual brushes. In
           *SIGGRAPH '01: Proceedings of the 28th Annual Conference on
           Computer Graphics and Interactive Techniques*, Los Angeles,
           CA, USA: ACM Press, pages 461–468, 2001.

[Cal99]   Jr William D. Callister. *Materials Science and Engineering: An
           Introduction.* John Wiley & Sons, Inc., 1999.

[CAS+97]   Cassidy J. Curtis, Sean E. Anderson, Joshua E. Seims, Kurt W.
           Fleischer, and David H. Salesin. Computer-generated watercolor.
           In *SIGGRAPH '97: Proceedings of the 24th Annual Conference
           on Computer Graphics and Interactive Techniques*, Los Angeles,
           CA, USA: ACM Press/Addison-Wesley Publishing Co., pages
           421–430, 1997.

[Coc91]   Malcolm Tundle Cockshott. *Wet and sticky: a novel model for
           computer-based painting.* PhD thesis, Computing Science Depart-
           ment (Research Report 91/R20), University of Glasgow, 1991.

[Cre]   Creature House Ltd. Expression (software). First released in
           October 1999. http://www.creaturehouse.com/, Hong Kong.

[CT02]   Nelson S.H. Chu and Chiew-Lan Tai. An efficient brush model for
           physically-based 3D painting. In *Proceedings of Pacific Graphics
           (PG '02)*, Beijing, China: IEEE Computer Society, pages 413–
           421, 2002.

[HH90]   Pat Hanrahan and Paul Haeberli. Direct wysiwyg painting and
           texturing on 3D shapes. In *SIGGRAPH '90: Proceedings of the
           17th Annual Conference on Computer Graphics and Interactive
           Techniques*, Dallas, TX, USA: ACM Press, pages 215–223, 1990.

[HL94]   Siu-Chi Hsu and Irene H.H. Lee. Drawing and animation us-
           ing skeletal strokes. In *SIGGRAPH '94: Proceedings of the 21st
           Annual Conference on Computer Graphics and Interactive Tech-
           niques*, Orlando, FL, USA: ACM Press, pages 109–118, 1994.

[HLW93]   Siu-Chi Hsu, Irene H.H. Lee, and Neil E. Wiseman. Skeletal
           strokes. In *Proceedings of the 6th Annual ACM Symposium
           on User Interface Software and Technology*, Atlanta, GA, USA:
           ACM Press, pages 197–206, 1993.

[HOCS02]   Aaron Hertzmann, Nuria Oliver, Brian Curless, and Steven M.
           Seitz. Curve analogies. In *EGRW '02: Proceedings of the 13th
           Eurographics Workshop on Rendering*, Aire-la-Ville, Switzerland:
           Eurographics Association, pages 233–246, 2002.

[HSS02]   Nick Halper, Stefan Schlechtweg, and Thomas Strothotte. Cre-
           ating non-photorealistic images the designer's way. In *NPAR
           '02: Proceedings of the 2nd International Symposium on Non-*

photorealistic Animation and Rendering, Annecy, France: ACM Press, pages 97–104, 2002.

[Inc]   Adobe Systems Incorporated. Adobe photoshop (software).

[KMM+02]   Robert D. Kalnins, Lee Markosian, Barbara J. Meier, Michael A. Kowalski, Joseph C. Lee, Philip L. Davidson, Matthew Webb, John F. Hughes, and Adam Finkelstein. WYSIWYG NPR: drawing strokes directly on 3D models. In *SIGGRAPH '02: Proceedings of the 29th Annual Conference on Computer Graphics and Interactive Techniques*, San Antonio, TX, USA: ACM Press, pages 755–762, 2002.

[Lee99]   Jintae Lee. Simulating Oriental black-ink painting. *IEEE Computer Graphics and Applications*, 19(3):74–81, 1999.

[Pix00]   Pixologic. Z-brush, http://pixologic.com, 2000.

[SABS94]   Michael P. Salisbury, Sean E. Anderson, Ronen Barzel, and David H. Salesin. Interactive pen-and-ink illustration. In *SIGGRAPH '94: Proceedings of the 21st Annual Conference on Computer Graphics and Interactive Techniques*, Orlando, FL, USA: ACM Press, pages 101–108, 1994.

[Sma91]   David Small. Simulating watercolor by modeling diffusion, pigment, and paper fibers. In *Proc. of SPIE '91*, San Diego, CA, USA: SPIE Press, 1991.

[Smi01]   Alvy R. Smith. Digital paint systems: an anecdotal and historical overview. *IEEE Annals of the History of Computing*, 23(2):4–30, 2001.

[Str86]   Steve Strassmann. Hairy brushes. In *SIGGRAPH '86: Proceedings of the 13th Annual Conference on Computer Graphics and Interactive Techniques*, Dallas, TX, USA: ACM Press, pages 225–232, 1986.

[WI00]   Helena T.F. Wong and Horace H.S. Ip. Virtual brush: a model-based synthesis of Chinese calligraphy. *Computers and Graphics*, 24(1):99–113, 2000.

[XTLP02]   Songhua Xu, Min Tang, Francis C.M. Lau, and Yunhe Pan. A solid model-based virtual hairy brush. *Computer Graphics Forum (Proceedings of Eurographics '02)*, 21(3):299–308 & 625, 2002.

[ZST+99]   Qing Zhang, Youetsu Sato, Junya Takahashi, Kazunobu Muraoka, and Norishige Chiba. Simple cellular automaton-based simulation of ink behavior and its application to Suibokuga-like 3D rendering of trees. *Journal of Visualization and Computer Animation*, 10(1):27–37, 1999.

6

Pigment Component of an Advanced Virtual Hairy Paintbrush System

6.1 Overview

In this chapter we propose a novel generic pigment model suitable for digital painting in a wide range of genres including traditional Chinese painting and water-based painting. The model embodies a simulation of the pigment-water solution and its interaction with the brush and the paper at the level of pigment particles; such a level of detail is needed for achieving highly intricate effects by the artist. The simulation covers pigment diffusion and sorption processes at the paper surface, and aspects of pigment particle deposition on the paper. We follow rules and formulations from quantitative studies of adsorption and diffusion processes in surface chemistry and the textile industry. The result is a pigment model that spans a continuum from very wet to very dry brush stroke effects. We also propose a new pigment mixing method based on machine learning techniques to emulate pigment mixing in real life as well as to support the creation of new artificial pigments. To experiment with the proposed model, we embedded the model in a sophisticated digital brush system. The combined system exhibits interactive speed on a modest PC platform.

6.2 Introduction

A pigment model is a vitally important component of a digital painting system. Traditional pigment models are mostly built on fluid dynamics or its variations, which assume that pigment behavior is largely due to the autonomous flow of the *pigment-water solution*. One can simulate such a model based on the self-motion of water and pigment particles. Two representative pieces of work in this category are the watercolor model in [CAS+97] and the ink dispersion model in [CT05]. The former is based on the shallow water model and the latter on the modified lattice Boltzmann equation. Both consider the pigment-water solution's flow being subjected to external forces, resulting in very high-quality "wet brush" effects. For highly viscous pigment solutions the model proposed in [BWL04], which traces pigment advection through 3D incompressible Stokes equations, can produce highly impressive web brush effects. We find however that these existent models and other similar ones have only limited ability to emulate the "dry brush stroke" which is extremely important in both Western and Oriental painting. In this chapter we propose a new physically-based pigment model which tries to capture faithfully the behavior of the pigment-water solution over the continuum of a very wet to a very dry state of a brush.

6.2.1 Main Ideas

Our new pigment behavior model can support both dry and wet painting effects or anything in between. One should note that pigment behavior consists of much more than just the spontaneous flow of the solution. Our physically-based simulation deals also with the adsorption and desorption processes of the pigment-water solution as well as its diffusion process against the leaky brush hair and the paper fibers. For simplicity, in this chapter we do not differentiate between adsorption and desorption since one is the reverse process of the other, and refer to either of them as a sorption process. This deviates from traditional flow-based approaches [CAS+97, CT04, CT05] which focus mainly on the pigment-water solution's advection process. Our design makes use of relevant results in surface chemistry engineering [AG97, McC01] and the textile and petrochemical industries [McG74, Rut84]. According to surface chemistry, unlike liquids, solid phase solutions cannot easily expand their surface area to reduce free energy on the surface. Therefore, due to the high surface tension, solid phase materials have a strong adsorption or desorption tendency with any contacting external objects. So when the pigment-water solution touches the paper surface, adsorption takes place and for any flow that does happen the adsorption process is more significant than the flowing/advection process. The variation in adsorption ability across different areas of the paper caused by the non-uniform distribution of the paper fibers is an important contributor to the character of the resultant painting. In a nutshell, our approach is sorption and diffusion-based, which offers a closer resemblance to the true physical state of a real brush than traditional flow-based models over the continuum of wet to dry brush strokes.

To achieve greater realism, we carefully consider the coupling force and mutual influence between different materials both within the pigment-water solution and between the pigment-water solution and the paper fibers at various stages of the simulation.

To achieve fast execution, we try to take advantage of known analytic solutions applicable to our formulation. We are thus able to avoid much discrete numerical simulation. Unlike many others who model the paper as a number of layers, e.g. [BWL04], we classify all the particles in the pigment-water solution as being in either the mobile state or the immobile state—that is, only two layers (denoted by superscripts mo and im respectively). Thus depending on the relative concentrations of pigment particles in the fixed and mobile states respectively, a continuum from very wet to very dry layers can be concisely represented, as opposed to a fixed number of layers, during algorithm design time.

Fig. 6.1 gives a high-level view of the overall pigment behavior simulation procedure where, in step 1, transfer of the pigment-water solution occurs between the brush and the paper's contacting region during painting time, and between the brush and palette's contacting region during brush dipping time. Table 6.1 lists the major symbols used in the technical discussion part of this chapter.

---

proc *MainLoop*():
  for each time step **do**:

1. Transfer pigment-water solution between contacting brush and paper regions or palette region   (Sect. 6.4)
2. Diffuse pigment-water solution on the paper surface   (Sect. 6.5)
3. Diffuse pigment-water solution at the brush tip   (Sect. 6.6)
4. Simulate water evaporation   (Sect. 6.7)
5. Absorb pigment-water solution into paper fibers   (Sect. 6.8)
6. Render current painting simulation result   (Sect. 6.9)

  end for
end proc

Fig. 6.1. Steps of pigment behavior simulation

6.2.2 Pigment Model and the Brush

Going hand in hand with the pigment behavior simulation is the brush model. Strassmann [Str86] pioneered the research on the e-brush. A number of follow-up models were later proposed—e.g. Wong and Ip's model for Chinese callig-raphy writing [WI00], Baxter et al.'s model for oil painting [BSLM01], and Xu, et al.'s model [XLTP03] and Chu and Tai's model [CT04] for Oriental painting. Despite these efforts, the existent work offers only a loose coupling between the brush model and the pigment model. In both [BSLM01, Bax04] and [CT04]'s pigment models, the brush is used as a tool to deposit pigments onto the paper. Other models are also quite simplistic on this particular issue. We believe that the interaction between the pigment model and the brush is highly intricate, and the intricacies should be carefully considered in order to meet the demand for high expressiveness.

We adopt the brush model introduced in Chapter 5, which is physically-based. To recap, in that model the geometry representation for a brush tip bundle is created through the general sweeping operation in CAD by sweeping a variable ellipse along the trajectory of the brush. The brush dynamics are simulated through a two-staged process. In the first stage the skeleton of the brush tip bundle is deformed according to both the external forces exerted onto it and its collision with the canvas; in the second stage the brush surface deforms following the deformation of the skeleton. The split of

Table 6.1. Major symbols used in this chapter (ordered alphabetically)

(i)	the i-th pigment, the 0-th and 1-st pigments are reserved for pure water and glue respectively
(x, y)	a position on the paper
(r, θ, z)	a position on the brush tip bundle
t	time
$\rho_{r,\theta,z}^{\mathrm{bru},t}(i)$	the i-th pigment concentration in the brush
$\rho_{x,y}^{\mathrm{mo},t}(i)$	the concentration of the i-th pigment which is in diffusing state on the paper surface
$\rho_{x,y}^{\mathrm{im},t}(i)$	the concentration of the i-th pigment that has been deposited into the paper fiber
$\mathbf{v}_{x,y}^{t}$	the velocity of the brush
$\eta_{x,y}$	density of the paper grid
$P_{x,y}^{t}$	current brush pressure
$P_{\max,x,y}^{t}$	maximum brush pressure
T	temperature, which is always set to be 300K
κ_{d}	diffusion coefficient
κ_{a}	adsorption coefficient
κ_{l}	Langmuir coefficient
$\kappa_{\mathrm{o}}(i)$	opacity degree for the i-th pigment
$\kappa_{\mathrm{s},i}$	self-diffusion coefficient for the i-th pigment
$\kappa_{\mathrm{c},i,j}$	cross-diffusion coefficient between the i-th and j-th pigments
$\mathbf{C}(i)$	RGB vector of the i-th pigment's color
$\mathbf{H}(i)$	HSV vector of the i-th pigment's color
$\alpha_{x,y}^{\mathrm{mo},t}$	transparency degree of diffuse layer
$\alpha_{x,y}^{\mathrm{im},t}$	transparency degree of deposit layer
$\mathbf{C}_{x,y}^{\mathrm{water},t}$	RGB vector of water color
$\mathbf{C}_{x,y}^{\mathrm{paper},t}$	RGB vector of paper color
$\mathbf{C}_{x,y}^{\mathrm{app},t}$	RGB vector of appearance color
ξ	the number of pigments in reaction

the brush head is supported at the geometric model level and is caused by an estimated internal tension force distribution inside the brush tip bundle. This pressure term is very useful when integrating the brush model with our pigment model as our proposed pigment behavior simulation needs to carefully consider the pressure at the contact point between the brush and the paper. Furthermore, having explicitly the geometry of the split brush bundle (rather than some image-based shortcut) makes physically-based simulation of the pigment behaviors on a split brush head possible and not too tricky to implement.

6.2.3 Organization of the Chapter

Sect. 6.3 discusses related work. Sect. 6.4 explains the pigment-water solution transfer between the brush and the paper surface. Sects. 6.5 and 6.6 discuss pigment-water solution diffusion on the paper surface and at the brush tip respectively. Sect. 6.7 explains how evaporation is handled. Sect. 6.8 covers how the pigment-water solution is deposited into the paper fibers. The rendering process is presented in Sect. 6.9 which also presents a novel method for pigment mixing. We present the experiment results in Sect. 6.11. Sect. 6.12 concludes the chapter and points out some directions for future work.

6.3 Previous Work

6.3.1 Pigment Behavior Models

Pham [Pha91] was the first to generate brush strokes having different shading, scratchiness and spreading effects; it was done via a variable offset approximation of B-splines. Cockshott et al. [CPE92] suggested a "wet and sticky" model for simulating textured shiny paint using bump mapping and illumination models. Both methods are not physically-based—they produce various paintbrush effects without necessarily following the laws of physics. On the other hand, Guo and Kunii [GK91] proposed a diffuse paint behavior model based on analysis of the paper structure, which produces singularities in intensity for the diffuse ink painting process. Since then appearance centric and physically based methods represent two parallel threads in the development of paint brush effects by computer. Kunii et al. [LNH95, KNV01] suggested a phenomenological model for simulating the "initial zone–black border–gray zone" distribution of intensities in diffuse ink painting. Their simulation is based on highly simplified diffusion equations derived from observations of the real painting process. Such a simplification was needed because of the limited computing power available then. As a result, only blurry images can be generated which lack any flow pattern. What is interesting is that their method falls between purely physically-based and purely appearance centric methods, which is still a useful reference today when designing efficient and quality simulation models.

Benefitting from the abundance of computing power, recent research favored more physically-based simulation following first-principle physics laws. On this track, Small [Sma91] pioneered computer simulation of watercolor painting. Curtis et al. [CAS+97] then significantly advanced the watercolor simulation technique using a shallow-water-based model; their method relies on solving numerically shallow-water equations, which is too slow for interactive painting even with a powerful PC. Beside watercolor, Oriental ink-based painting simulation also attracted much research. Lee's [Lee01] was the first paper where an ink model was used together with a brush model [Lee97, Lee99] to mimic realistic black ink diffusion effects. Their extended algorithm can produce very impressive effects [GK03] and can also be used for calligraphy [Guo95]. Zhang et al. [ZST+99] proposed a simple cellular automaton-based model for capturing black ink painting behavior in Suibokuga painting, which they successfully applied to render painter-style 3D trees. Yu et al. [YLLC03] expanded this approach to support more Oriental painting styles using a local equilibrium model. Lin and Shih [LS04] simulated Chinese color ink painting based on phenomenological rules for the ink diffusion process which they obtained by observation. Their painting can be carried out on any simple device such as a tablet PC. Other than watercolor and Oriental ink painting, oil painting simulation is another active field. A representative work is that by Baxter et al. which produced impasto effects for oil or acrylic painting [BWL04]. Other types of painting were simulated include Rudolf et al.'s [RMN03] who studied the problem of wax crayon painting and obtained some very interesting results. But despite all that has been done in the field, support for the dry brush stroke effect yet remains very limited.

Along another line, Laerhoven et al. [LLR04, LR05] proposed a distributed paper model where the paper is divided into a grid of subpapers for concurrent evaluation through remote parallel processes. In their model a procedural texture creation technique based on the cellular texture basis function suggested in [Wor96] was employed to enhance the realism of painting. They also introduced textured tissues to remove pigments and water as a novel interactive device for the artist [BLR06]. In general we feel applying parallel computing techniques in first principal physically-based simulation for producing realistic paint effects is a promising area for more future work. On the other hand it is also interesting to notice that Xu et al. [XXK+06] proposed a single stroke appearance model for capturing stroke texture in Chinese paintings using a parametric approach.

6.3.2 Comparison with Chu & Tai's Work

Chu and Tai [CT05] proposed an ink dispersion model named Moxi for painting on absorbent paper based on modified Lattice Boltzmann Equations (LBE). The model can produce realistic wet Oriental paintings. However, LBE aren't really well suited for simulating dry brush effects or brush painting effects generated by a rich variation of pigment and water concentration, due to two of the method's inherent theoretical limits: 1) A principal limitation is "The LBE model was originally designed for situations where the simulated fluid fills the whole domain, with small local deviation in velocity and density (within 10 to 20 percent) from the mean. [CT05]" In Moxi the authors understood the assumption "with small local deviation in velocity and density (within 10 to 20 percent) from the mean". They realized violating such an assumption could lead to a negative density in certain positions and made modifications to the original LBE accordingly. However, they paid no attention to a characteristic of LBE for producing a motion field emphasizing too much in the mean behavior of the fluid, incurring a methodical basis to generate an average motion lacking variations, which on many occasions, aren't wanted by artists in their painting practices, in particular when they want to achieve brush painting effects demonstrating a strong contrast inside the stroke region. 2) Another important limitation is that the LBE model cannot be easily adopted to cope with free boundaries. A conventional situation would be to have a field fully permeated with fluid to start the simulation ("...the simulated fluid fills the whole domain..."). Under that circumstance, no effrot is needed to take care of the issue of free boundaries, which is often not the case in reality. And it is realized that "devising a single-phase free-boundary LBE model is, nevertheless, not straightforward. [CT05]" Unfortunately, when simulating dry brush painting we will constantly encounter the free boundary where the wet and dry sites meet. We suspect this may be a major reason why the results produced by Moxi don't contain dry brush effects.

To support dry brush painting, in a separate paper they published [CT04], where they use an intensity image from real dry-brush prints and a dynamic threshold to generate a dry map. Such a dry map directly controls the generation of dry brush stroke effects. Compared with Hsu and Lee's pure image based method [HL94], in which dry brush effects are produced by texture mapping deformed predefined 2D strokes, Chu and Tai's method is an important step forward on a physically-based approach for dry brush effects simulation. Nevertheless, the quasi-physically-based nature of their method brings them two sufferings that are common to non- or not-so-physically-based approaches: 1) the impossibility to support any arbitrary dry brush effect no matter how large the image library behind it is; 2) hence the dry brush stroke thus produced may be different from what the user intends, which leads to the unfaithful production of the brush stroke effects with respect to the authentic user input, and a potential danger of violating the user's original art creation intention.

Finally, because there are separate mechanisms for dry brush strokes and wet brush strokes, frequent switching between the two models is necessary during painting and the generation of some in-between effects becomes difficult.

6.4 Pigment Sorption between the Brush and the Paper Surface

When the brush touches the paper, transfer of the pigment-water solution takes place, the direction of which depends on the pigment concentration on either side, i.e. the brush surface in contact and the paper. This is a sorption process between the two media. We choose the Dubinin-Radushkevich isotherm equation [Mis69] to model the process because it considers the influence of pressure:

$$\Delta\rho = \rho e^{-(\frac{\kappa_G T}{\beta E_0} \ln \frac{P_{max}}{P})^2}, \tag{6.1}$$

where ρ is the pigment concentration in the source media; $\Delta\rho$ is the pigment concentration to be sorbed in the process; κ_G is the gas constant, i.e. 8.314 J/(mol · K); T is the temperature, which is set to 300K, a typical room temperature; β is the affinity coefficient characterizing the polarizability of the adsorbate; E_0 is the adsorption characteristic energy of the adsorbent, which is mainly affected by the pore density in the adsorbent and assumed to be proportional to the paper fiber density η; P_{max} is a pressure response coefficient for the pigment; and P is the local contacting pressure between the brush and the paper. $\ln(P_{max}/P)$ is a term reflecting the impact of brush pressure on the pigment-water solution sorption process. Note that the equation describes an equilibrium state. Because such a sorption process usually happens in a flash, for efficiency we adopt this equation but applied to it a simple scaling (to be explained at the end of this section), rather than to work out a series of intermediate results over some fine time steps.

Put Eq. (6.1) into the context of our simulation, we have:

$$
\begin{cases}
\Delta\rho_{x,y}^{mo,t}(i) = \gamma_{x,y}^t(i)\rho_{x,y}^{bru,t}(i)e^{-(\frac{\kappa_G T}{\beta(i)E_0}\ln\frac{P_{max}}{P_{x,y}^t})^2} & \text{if } \rho_{x,y}^{bru,t}(i) > \rho_{x,y}^{mo,t}(i); \\
\Delta\rho_{x,y}^{bru,t}(i) = \gamma_{x,y}^t(i)\rho_{x,y}^{mo,t}(i)e^{-(\frac{\kappa_G T}{\beta(i)E_0}\ln\frac{P_{max}}{P_{x,y}^t})^2} & \text{otherwise.}
\end{cases}
\tag{6.2}
$$

Here $P_{x,y}^t$ is the contacting pressure between the brush and the paper surface at the location of the paper site (x,y) at time t; $\rho_{x,y}^{mo,t}(i)$ is the concentration of the i-th pigment which is in mobile state at site (x,y) of the paper at time t and $\rho_{x,y}^{bru,t}(i)$ is the i-th pigment concentration on the brush surface which contacts the paper site (x,y) at time t. $\gamma_{x,y}^t(i)$ is a randomization term which is defined as:

$$
\begin{cases}
\text{Prob}[\gamma_{x,y}^t(i) = 1] = \min\{1, \kappa_{bru}|\rho_{x,y}^{bru,t}(i) - \rho_{x,y}^{mo,t}(i)|\eta_{x,y}\} \\
\text{Prob}[\gamma_{x,y}^t(i) = 0] = 1 - \min\{1, \kappa_{bru}|\rho_{x,y}^{bru,t}(i) - \rho_{x,y}^{mo,t}(i)|\eta_{x,y}\}
\end{cases},
\tag{6.3}
$$

in which $\eta_{x,y}$ is the local paper fiber density and κ_{bru} is a scaling coefficient to produce a suitable match between the magnitude of $|\rho_{x,y}^{bru,t}(i) - \rho_{x,y}^{mo,t}(i)|$ and $\eta_{x,y}$. The reason for introducing a randomization term in the above equation is that such an equation is used to describe the macro behavior of the sorption process; however, here we are doing per pixel location particle behavior simulation on a micro scale; thus adding some random deviation would make the simulation resemble more the real situation.

We also employ the following equation suggested in [Tie94] for the conservation of the pigment mass in the sorption process:

$$
|\mathbf{v}_{x,y}^{bru,t}|\Delta\rho_{x,y}^{bru,t}(i) + \eta_{x,y}\Delta\rho_{x,y}^{mo,t}(i) = 0,
\tag{6.4}
$$

where $\mathbf{v}_{x,y}^{bru,t}$ denotes the local velocity of the brush at time t; this is an input from the hosting e-brush system for the pigment model. Recall $\eta_{x,y}$ is the paper fiber density at the site (x,y).

To prevent oscillation during the simulated sorption process, we derive the limit on the amount of pigment transferable in the process:

$$
|\Delta\rho_{x,y}^{bru,t}(i)| + |\Delta\rho_{x,y}^{mo,t}(i)| = |\rho_{x,y}^{bru,t}(i) - \rho_{x,y}^{mo,t}(i)|.
\tag{6.5}
$$

Without loss of generality, we assume $\rho_{x,y}^{bru,t}(i) > \rho_{x,y}^{mo,t}(i)$. Solving the pair of Eqs. (6.4) and (6.5) gives the upper bound for $\Delta\rho_{x,y}^{mo,t}(i)$: $\frac{|\rho_{x,y}^{bru,t}(i) - \rho_{x,y}^{mo,t}(i)|}{\eta_{x,y}/|\mathbf{v}_{x,y}^{bru,t}| + 1}$. Incorporating this bound, we can modify Eq. (6.2) to be:

$$
\tilde{\Delta}\rho_{x,y}^{mo,t}(i) = \min\{\Delta\rho_{x,y}^{mo,t}(i), \frac{|\rho_{x,y}^{bru,t}(i) - \rho_{x,y}^{mo,t}(i)|}{\eta_{x,y}/|\mathbf{v}_{x,y}^{bru,t}| + 1}\}.
\tag{6.6}
$$

We also consider the mutual influence between multiple pigments in the sorption process, i.e.:

$$\widetilde{\Delta}\rho_{x,y}^{\text{mo},t}(i) = \kappa_{\text{mutual}}\widetilde{\Delta}\rho_{x,y}^{\text{mo},t}(i) + (1-\kappa_{\text{mutual}})\frac{\sum_{j=1,j\neq i}^{\xi}\widetilde{\Delta}\rho_{x,y}^{\text{mo},t}(j)}{\xi-1}. \qquad (6.7)$$

Here κ_{mutual} is a correlation coefficient depicting the mutual influence between the sorption of different pigments in the pigment-water solution, and ξ is the number of pigment species, including water and glue. Once $\widetilde{\Delta}\rho_{x,y}^{\text{mo},t}(i)$ is known, we can also update $\rho_{x,y}^{\text{bru},t+\Delta t}(i)$ with the relationship revealed by Eq. (6.4), i.e.:

$$\rho_{x,y}^{\text{bru},t+\Delta t}(i) = \rho_{x,y}^{\text{bru},t}(i) - \frac{\eta_{x,y}}{|\mathbf{v}_{x,y}^{\text{bru},t}|}\widetilde{\Delta}\rho_{x,y}^{\text{mo},t}(i).$$

For the case of $\rho_{x,y}^{\text{bru},t}(i) < \rho_{x,y}^{\text{mo},t}(i)$, a similar treatment is applied. The only difference is that we derive $\widetilde{\Delta}\rho_{x,y}^{\text{bru},t}(i)$, $\widetilde{\Delta}\rho_{x,y}^{\text{bru},t}(i)$ instead of $\widetilde{\Delta}\rho_{x,y}^{\text{mo},t}(i)$, $\widetilde{\Delta}\rho_{x,y}^{\text{mo},t}(i)$ through a variant of Eqs. (6.6) and (6.7).

Finally, we apply a simplifying treatment to scale the amount of sorbed concentration $\widetilde{\Delta}\rho$ to account for the sorption time. We model the sorption speed, $v_{\text{sorption}}(t)$, as an exponentially decreasing variable, which is true of most natural sorption processes; i.e. $v_{\text{sorption}}(t) = \kappa_v e^{-t}$ where κ_v is a sorption speed parameter. We also denote the period of time needed to reach the equilibrium state as χ. That is, it is assumed $\int_{t=0}^{\chi} v_{\text{sorption}}(t)\,\mathrm{d}t = \widetilde{\Delta}\rho$, from which we can get the relationship $\widetilde{\Delta}\rho(t) = \min\{\frac{1-e^{-t}}{1-e^{-\chi}},1\}\widetilde{\Delta}\rho$. Since our simulation time step is Δt, substituting the corresponding variables into the equation, we have $\rho_{x,y}^{\text{mo},t+\Delta t}(i) = \rho_{x,y}^{\text{mo},t}(i) + \widetilde{\Delta}\rho_{x,y}^{\text{mo},t}(i)$ where $\widetilde{\Delta}\rho_{x,y}^{\text{mo},t}(i) = \min\{\frac{1-e^{-\Delta t}}{1-e^{-\chi}},1\}\widetilde{\Delta}\rho_{x,y}^{\text{mo},t}(i)$.

6.5 Pigment Diffusion on the Paper Surface

To simulate pigment behavior on the surface of a porous paper, we assume a diffusion process. We choose the following advection diffusion equation [SW04] since it considers pigment advection in the midst of diffusion, and is thus capable of supporting both dry and wet brushing.

$$\frac{\partial\rho}{\partial t} = \kappa_{\text{d}}\nabla^2\rho - \mathbf{v}\cdot\nabla\rho, \qquad (6.8)$$

where ρ is the pigment concentration in the adsorbate solution, κ_{d} is the diffusion coefficient, and $\mathbf{v}$ is the external advection field in which the diffusion takes place.

Inspired by Kallmes and Corte's pioneering work on modeling the paper as a random fiber network [KC60, Ran82], we carefully treat the underlying non-uniform paper fiber structure and introduce anisotropy in the diffusion process. Eq. (6.8) is thus extended to be:

$$\begin{cases} \frac{\partial \rho}{\partial t} = \kappa_{d,x,y}^{x} \frac{\partial^2 \rho}{\partial x^2} + \kappa_{d,x,y}^{y} \frac{\partial^2 \rho}{\partial y^2} - \mathbf{v} \cdot \nabla \rho & (6.9.1), \\ \kappa_{d,x,y}^{x} = \sum_{i=1}^{\text{nfiber}(x,y)} \left(\kappa_{d,i} \cos(\varphi_{x,y,i}) \right) & (6.9.2), \\ \kappa_{d,x,y}^{y} = \sum_{i=1}^{\text{nfiber}(x,y)} \left(\kappa_{d,i} \sin(\varphi_{x,y,i}) \right) & (6.9.3), \end{cases} \qquad (6.9)$$

where $\kappa_{d,x,y}^{x}$ and $\kappa_{d,x,y}^{y}$ are the x and y dimensional diffusion coefficients respectively at paper position (x,y); $\varphi_{x,y,i}$ is the i-th principal direction of the local paper fiber at site (x,y), which is initialized at the beginning of our simulation through the method suggested in [GK91, Lee01], and $\kappa_{d,i}$ is the associated diffusion coefficient for the direction. At each paper site (x,y), there may be multiple principal diffusion angles, which are determined by the number of fibers passing through the paper site, $\text{nfiber}(x,y)$.

For high fidelity, we employ variable diffusion coefficients in our simulation. In addition to the influence from the underlying fiber structure on the diffusion coefficient, as is done via Eqs. (6.9.2) and (6.9.3), for $i \geqslant 2$, the i-th pigment's diffusion coefficient $\kappa_{d,i,x,y}^{t}$ at paper site (x,y) also depends on the concentration of water, $\rho_{x,y}^{\text{mo},t}(0)$, the concentration of glue, $\rho_{x,y}^{\text{mo},t}(1)$, as well as the local paper fiber density $\eta_{x,y}$. The media of diffusion described here is initialized according to the micro-structures of a real scanned paper at the beginning of the simulation. Thus, we refine Eqs. (6.9.2) and (6.9.3) to be:

$$\begin{cases} \Delta\kappa_{d,i,x,y}^{t} = \kappa_{d,\text{water}} \frac{\rho_{x,y}^{\text{mo},t}(0)}{\rho_{x,y}^{\text{mo},t}(i)} - \kappa_{d,\text{glue}} \frac{\rho_{x,y}^{\text{mo},t}(1)}{\rho_{x,y}^{\text{mo},t}(i)} + \kappa_{d,\text{den}}\eta_{x,y} \\ \kappa_{d,i,x,y}^{x} = \Delta\kappa_{d,i,x,y}^{t} + \sum_{i=1}^{\text{nfiber}(x,y)} \left(\kappa_{d,i} \cos(\varphi_{x,y,i}) \right) \\ \kappa_{d,i,x,y}^{y} = \Delta\kappa_{d,i,x,y}^{t} + \sum_{i=1}^{\text{nfiber}(x,y)} \left(\kappa_{d,i} \sin(\varphi_{x,y,i}) \right) \end{cases} \qquad (6.10)$$

where $\kappa_{d,\text{water}}$, $\kappa_{d,\text{glue}}$ and $\kappa_{d,\text{den}}$ are the diffusion influence coefficients of water, glue and fiber density respectively.

We also notice in the diffusion process that multiple pigments compete with one another, which is the so-called "cross diffusion phenomenon" in surface chemistry. The Lotla-Volterra competition model [LMP06] is a standard mathematical treatment for the cross diffusion process with two participating diffusing substances in a 1D domain. In our problem, however, the paper is modeled as a 2D plane. We extend their model to the 2D domain with multiple competing pigments:

$$\frac{\partial \rho(i)}{\partial t} = \kappa_{s,i}\nabla^2 \rho(i) + \sum_{j \neq i}^{\xi} \kappa_{c,i,j}\nabla^2 \rho(j) \ (i = 0, \cdots, n), \qquad (6.11)$$

where $\rho(i)$ is the concentration of the i-th pigment, $\kappa_{s,i} \geqslant 0$ is the self-diffusivity of the i-th pigment, $\kappa_{c,i,j}$ is the cross-diffusivity between the i-th and the j-th pigment species, and n is the number of pigment species participating in the process. In our design the 0-th pigment is water and the 1-st pigment is glue.

In our context ρ actually refers to $\rho_{x,y}^{\text{mo},t}(i)$. Combining the advection diffusion Eq. (6.8) with the above extended cross-diffusion Eq. (6.11) gives the final form of the equation to be used in our simulation:

$$\frac{\partial \rho_{x,y}^{\mathrm{mo},t}(i)}{\partial t} = \kappa_{\mathrm{d},i,x,y} \nabla^2 \rho_{x,y}^{\mathrm{mo},t}(i) + \sum_{j \neq i}^{\xi} \kappa_{\mathrm{c},i,j} \nabla^2 \rho_{x,y}^{\mathrm{mo},t}(j),$$
$$- \mathbf{v}_{x,y}^t \cdot \nabla \rho_{x,y}^{\mathrm{mo},t}(i) \qquad (i = 0, \cdots, n) \tag{6.12}$$

where $\kappa_{\mathrm{d},i,x,y}$ is the diffusion coefficient at paper position (x,y) for the i-th pigment, $\mathbf{v}_{x,y}^t$ denotes the velocity field imposed by the external conditions, which here is estimated to be half of the velocity of the brush movement, as suggested by [BWL04]. Notice that since $\kappa_{\mathrm{s},i}$ and $\kappa_{\mathrm{d},i,x,y}$ are acting on the term $\nabla^2 \rho$ in Eq. (6.8) and Eq. (6.11) respectively, for simplicity we absorb $\kappa_{\mathrm{s},i}$ into $\kappa_{\mathrm{d},i,x,y}$ during the above combined operation. Once $\frac{\partial \rho_{x,y}^{\mathrm{mo},t}(i)}{\partial t}$ is known, $\rho_{x,y}^{\mathrm{mo},t+\Delta t}(i)$ can be trivially updated as:

$$\rho_{x,y}^{\mathrm{mo},t+\Delta t}(i) = \rho_{x,y}^{\mathrm{mo},t}(i) + \frac{\partial \rho_{x,y}^{\mathrm{mo},t}(i)}{\partial t} \Delta t.$$

6.6 Pigment Diffusion at the Brush Tip

Pigment diffusion at the brush tip includes the diffusion both inside the brush tip's volume and on its surface. When an exchange of pigment between the brush and the paper as described in Sect. 6.4 happens, the new pigment concentration needs to be propagated to other parts of the brush tip. This is most necessary when the local brush tip runs out of pigment and needs the supply from its surroundings during dry painting, and similarly when the brush is dipped into the ink bottle or pigment palette. Simulation of pigment diffusion inside the brush tip volume is discussed in a later part of this section; simulation of pigment diffusion on the brush surface is given the same treatment as explained in Sect. 6.5 except that 1) we first flatten the brush surface to a 2D plane before the simulation; and 2) the advection term in Eq. (6.12) is omitted as we assume there is no advection on the brush surface because of the strong surface tension force.

The classical Fick's second law of diffusion [Fic55] in terms of the cylindrical coordinates r, θ, z can be expressed as:

$$\frac{\partial \rho_{r,\theta,z}}{\partial t} = \frac{1}{r} \left(\frac{\partial}{\partial r} (r\kappa_{\mathrm{d}} \frac{\partial \rho_{r,\theta,z}}{\partial r}) + \frac{\partial}{\partial \theta} (\frac{\kappa_{\mathrm{d}}}{r} \frac{\partial \rho_{r,\theta,z}}{\partial \theta}) + \frac{\partial}{\partial z} (r\kappa_{\mathrm{d}} \frac{\partial \rho_{r,\theta,z}}{\partial z}) \right), \tag{6.13}$$

where $\rho_{r,\theta,z}$ is the pigment concentration in position (r, θ, z) of the brush tip and κ_{d} is the diffusion coefficient. The reason for expressing the diffusion equation in the cylindrical coordinate system is two-fold: 1) for certain types of diffusion for a cylinder or a sphere, people have derived analytic solutions [Cra75], which can be used to improve the simulation efficiency and accuracy; 2) in the brush model we adopt [XLTP03], hair bundles are represented as generalized cylinders, and so diffusion inside a cylinder is the closest form of a sample problem to our simulation task, which has an analytic solution.

In the case where the diffusion takes place in a cylinder of radius R with the diffusion conditions being $\rho(r) = f(r)$, $0 < r < R$, $t = 0$; $\rho(r) = \rho_0$, $r = R$, $t \geqslant 0$, its analytic solution can be found in [Cra75], as follows:

$$\rho(r) = \rho_0 \{1 - \frac{2}{R}\sum_{n=1}^{\infty} \frac{1}{\alpha_n} \frac{J_0(r\alpha_n)}{J_1(R\alpha_n)} e^{-\kappa_d \alpha_n^2 t}\} + \frac{2}{R^2}\sum_{n=1}^{\infty} e^{-\kappa_d \alpha_n^2 t} \frac{J_0(r\alpha_n)}{J_1^2(R\alpha_n)} \int_0^R r f(r) J_0(r\alpha_n) dr, \qquad (6.14)$$

where $J_0(x)$ is the Bessel function of the first kind of order zero; $J_1(x)$ is the Bessel function of the first order; the α_n's are the positive roots of $J_0(R\alpha_n) = 0$; $f(r)$ is the initial distribution, and ρ_0 is a constant diffusion source. For greater efficiency we pre-compute a range of α_n's and store them in a table.

Similar to Eq. (6.10) when we simulate pigment diffusion on the paper surface we also adopt a variable diffusion coefficient $\kappa_{d,i,r,\theta,z}^t$:

$$\kappa_{d,i,r,\theta,z}^t = \kappa_{d,i}' + \kappa_{d,\,\text{water}} \frac{\rho_{x,y}^{\text{mo},t}(0)}{\rho_{x,y}^{\text{mo},t}(i)} - \kappa_{d,\,\text{glue}} \frac{\rho_{x,y}^{\text{mo},t}(1)}{\rho_{x,y}^{\text{mo},t}(i)} + \kappa_{d,\,\text{den}}\eta_{r,\theta,z}, \qquad (6.15)$$

where $\kappa_{d,i}'$ is the intrinsic diffusion coefficient of the i-th pigment, and $\eta_{r,\theta,z}$ is the hair density at position (r,θ,z) inside the brush tip volume, the value of which is provided by the e-brush model [XLTP03]. The higher the density is, the more hair strands are concentrated at that location, which intensifies the diffusion. The remaining parameters have the same meanings as in Eq. (6.10).

Note that the three boundary conditions in the above sample problem appear differently in our problem: 1) the shape of a brush cluster in our model is a generalized cylinder, not a standard cylinder having constant radius R; 2) during the diffusion process, the external concentration does not necessarily remain at a constant level of ρ_0; 3) the initial distribution could be different for points with the same r coordinate. To account for these differences we modify the solution form of Eq. (6.14) by performing several interpolation and random sampling operations:

$$
\begin{cases}
\rho_{r,\theta,z}^{\text{bru},t+\Delta t}(i) = \dfrac{\sum_{(\tilde{r},\tilde{\theta},\tilde{z})\in ball(r,\theta,z)} \left(\rho_{\tilde{r},\tilde{\theta},\tilde{z}}^{\text{bru},t+\Delta t}(i)\omega(\tilde{r},\tilde{\theta},\tilde{z}) \right)}{\sum_{(\tilde{r},\tilde{\theta},\tilde{z})\in ball(r,\theta,z)} \omega(\tilde{r},\tilde{\theta},\tilde{z})}. & (6.16.1) \\[4mm]
\tilde{\rho}_{r,\theta,z}^{\text{bru},t+\Delta t}(i) = \dfrac{\sum_{y=0}^{7} \left(\rho_{R(z),\frac{\pi}{4}y+\phi,z}^{\text{bru},t}(i) A(r,\theta,z)\omega(r,\theta,\frac{\pi}{4}y+\phi,z) \right)}{\sum_{y=0}^{7} \omega(r,\theta,\frac{\pi}{4}y+\phi,z)}. & (6.16.2) \\[4mm]
A(r,\theta,z) = \left(1 - \dfrac{2}{R(z)}\sum_{n=1}^{\infty} \dfrac{1}{\alpha_n} \dfrac{J_0(r\alpha_n)}{J_1(R(z)\alpha_n)} e^{-\kappa_{d,i,r,\theta,z}^t \alpha_n^2 t}\right) + \\ \quad \dfrac{2}{R^2(z)}\sum_{n=1}^{\infty} e^{-\kappa_{d,i,r,\theta,z}^t \alpha_n^2 t} \dfrac{J_0(r\alpha_n)}{J_1^2(R(z)\alpha_n)} \int_0^{R(z)} r\rho_{r,\theta,z}^{\text{bru},t}(i) J_0(r\alpha_n) dr. & (6.16.3)
\end{cases}
$$
$$\qquad (6.16)$$

Here $ball(r,\theta,z)$ is the set of points inside the brush tip volume, which are within a certain distance of (r,θ,z); ϕ is a randomly generated phase angle; $R(z)$ is the radius of the generalized cylinder at the height of z; $\omega(r,\theta,m,z)$ is a weight inversely proportional to the Cartesian distance between the points (r,θ,z) and $(R(z),m,z)$; $\rho_{r,\theta,z}^{\text{bru},t}(i)$ is the initial concentration of the i-th pigment at site (r,θ,z) before the current step of diffusion.

To understand why Eq. (6.16) can be used to adapt the above three differences from the standard problem, we note that Eq. (6.16.3) gives the rate of $\rho(r)/\rho_0$, which takes the same form as Eq. (6.14), except that Eq. (6.16.3) additionally considers the varying diffusion coefficient κ, the varying radius $R(z)$ at different heights z of the clustered brush hair, as well as the difference in density between different positions in the cluster. These modifications are for the first and the third differences listed above. Based on Eq. (6.16.3), Eq. (6.16.2) performs a random sampling followed by scaling to account for the different external pigment density ρ_0, the second difference above. Finally, Eq. (6.16.1) computes a weighted average to simulate the correlation between adjacent points in the brush volume, which accounts for the second and third differences above.

6.7 Evaporation

We consider evaporation at the brush tip and on the paper surface. For simplicity and efficiency concerns, we only deal with the water (the 0-th pigment) evaporation process.

6.7.1 At the Brush Tip Bundle

We adopt the diffusion-based evaporation equation suggested in [Cra75] which considers both evaporation and the propagation of the evaporation results to the surroundings:

$$-\kappa_e \frac{\partial \rho_{r,\theta,z}^{bru,t}(0)}{\partial r} = \epsilon_{bru}\big(\rho_{equi}(0) - \rho_{r,\theta,z}^{bru,t}(0)\big), \qquad (6.17)$$

where $\rho_{equi}(0)$ is the current water concentration in the atmosphere, i.e. the equilibrium vapor pressure; and $\rho_{r,\theta,z}^{bru,t}(0)$ is the actual water concentration; κ_e is an evaporation coefficient; ϵ_{bru} is a user adjustable scaling constant. Fortunately, [New31] gives the analytic solution for Eq. (6.17), which is:

$$\frac{\rho_{r,\theta,z}^{bru,t+\Delta t}(0) - \rho_{r,\theta,z}^{bru,t}(0)}{\rho_{equi}(0) - \rho_{r,\theta,z}^{bru,t}(0)} = 1 - \sum_{n=1}^{\infty} \frac{2LJ_0(r\beta_n/\epsilon_{bru})}{(\beta_n^2 + L^2)J_0(\beta_n)} e^{-\beta_n^2 \kappa_e t/\epsilon_{bru}^2}, \qquad (6.18)$$

where β_n's are the roots of $\beta J_1(\beta) - LJ_0(\beta) = 0$ and $L = \epsilon_{bru}/\kappa_e$. Again, for speed, we store the pre-computed β_n's for a range of equations in the above form in a table.

6.7.2 On the Paper Surface

We employ a slightly different diffusion-based evaporation Eq. (6.19) to handle evaporation on the paper surface since pigment concentrations at different depths of the paper differ insignificantly; we ignore these differences in our simulation.

$$-\kappa_e \frac{\partial \rho_{x,y}^{mo,t}(0)}{\partial t} = \epsilon_{paper}\big(\rho_{equi}(0) - \rho_{x,y}^{mo,t}(0)\big), \qquad (6.19)$$

where ϵ_{paper} is a user adjustable scaling constant. Note that as mentioned earlier, unlike in [BWL04] where the paper is modeled as a number of layers, we only classify all the particles in the pigment-water solution as either in a mobile state or in an immobile state. According to this equation, at the end of each time step we update $\rho_{x,y}^{mo,t}(0)$ numerically.

6.8 Pigment Deposition on the Paper Fibers

During the process of pigment diffusion, pigment particles whose velocity is relatively low tend to be captured by and thus fixed to those paper fibers having a high surface free energy [Mas96]. In chemical engineering this is the phenomenon of a typical adsorption process [Rut84, Suz90]. Similar to the process described by the Dubinin-Radushkevich isotherm equation, see Eq. (6.1), the intermediate adsorption process progresses towards the equilibrium state rather rapidly [Tie94]. Thus we model the above rapid adsorption process via the Langmuir isotherm equation [Lan08], an equation to describe the equilibrium state of a system:

$$\Delta\rho(i) = \frac{\kappa_{1,i}\,\rho(i)}{1+\sum_{j=1}^{\xi}\kappa_{1,j}\,\rho(j)}, \tag{6.20}$$

where ξ is the number of participating species of adsorbates; $\rho(i)$ and $\Delta\rho(i)$ are the concentration of the i-th adsorbate in the solution phase and that of the adsorbed adsorbate in the adsorbent phase respectively; $\kappa_{1,i}$ is the Langmuir constant for the i-th adsorbate. As pointed out in [Yan03], $\kappa_{1,i}$ can be estimated as:

$$\kappa_{1,i} \triangleq \frac{\kappa_{\text{behavior},i}\kappa_{\text{behavior}}^{\text{paper}}}{2\pi\rho(i)T\sqrt{\eta_{x,y}}}e^{\kappa_t/T},$$

where κ_t is a thermodynamics coefficient, $\eta_{x,y}$ is the local density of the paper fiber, and $\kappa_{\text{behavior}}^{\text{paper}}$, $\kappa_{\text{behavior},i}$ are the adsorption behavior coefficients of the paper and the i-th pigment respectively. $\kappa_{\text{behavior}}^{\text{paper}}$ is determined by the smoothness of the paper surface, the size and distribution of the micro-scale pores formed by neighboring paper fibers; $\kappa_{\text{behavior},i}$ is affected by the adsorption ability of the i-th pigment, e.g. its material polarity. Since the factor $\frac{1}{2\pi T}e^{\kappa_t/T}$ remains constant, we absorb the term into $\kappa_{\text{behavior}}^{\text{paper}}$, giving the simplified form of

$$\kappa_{1,i} \triangleq \frac{\kappa_{\text{behavior},i}\kappa_{\text{behavior}}^{\text{paper}}}{\rho(i)\sqrt{\eta_{x,y}}}.$$

Because the deposition process is caused by the random walk of diffusing substance particles [Cra75, Rut84], we further modulate $\kappa_{1,i}$ with a random walk coefficient κ_{ranwk}, which is a random number from a user adjustable random distribution.

Similar to the treatment where we employ the Dubinin-Radushkevich equation in Sect. 6.4, we perform the same simplifying scaling conversion to derive the intermediate results of the sorption process. Substituting the corresponding variables in our context into Eq. (6.20), we have the final form of the equation for our simulation:

$$\Delta\rho_{x,y}^{\text{im},t}(i) = \min\left(\frac{1-e^{\Delta t}}{1-e^{-\chi}}, 1\right)\frac{\frac{\kappa_{\text{ranwk}}\kappa_{\text{behavior},i}\kappa_{\text{behavior}}^{\text{paper}}}{\rho_{x,y}^{\text{im},t}(i)\sqrt{\eta_{x,y}}}\rho_{x,y}^{\text{mo},t}(i)}{1+\sum_{j=1}^{\xi}\left(\frac{\kappa_{\text{ranwk}}\kappa_{\text{behavior},j}\kappa_{\text{behavior}}^{\text{paper}}}{\rho_{x,y}^{\text{im},t}(j)\sqrt{\eta_{x,y}}}\rho_{x,y}^{\text{mo},t}(j)\right)}. \tag{6.21}$$

where $\rho_{x,y}^{\text{im},t}(i)$ is the concentration of the portion of the i-th pigment in an immobile state at paper site (x,y) at time t; and χ is the time span to arrive at the equilibrium state.

To ensure the conservation of pigment mass during the deposition process, we additionally employ a mass transfer conservation formula [Tie94]:

$$|\mathbf{v}_{x,y}^t|\Delta\rho_{x,y}^{\text{mo},t}(i) + \eta_{x,y}\Delta\rho_{x,y}^{\text{im},t}(i) = 0, \tag{6.22}$$

according to which we can update $\rho_{x,y}^{\text{mo},t+\Delta t}(i)$ as

$$\rho_{x,y}^{\text{mo},t+\Delta t}(i) = \rho_{x,y}^{\text{mo},t}(i) - (\eta_{x,y}/|\mathbf{v}_{x,y}^t|)\Delta\rho_{x,y}^{\text{im},t}(i).$$

6.9 Rendering the Simulation Results

The result of the simulation is a collection of pigment concentrations: $\rho_{x,y}^{\text{im},t}(i)$ and $\rho_{x,y}^{\text{mo},t}(i)$ $(i = 1, \cdots, \xi)$ for each paper site (x,y). To render the painting, we need to solve two problems: 1) to derive the overall appearance of the mobile layer and that of the fixture (immobile) layer, each containing a number of pigment constituents; 2) to superimpose these two layers on top of the background paper layer. To address the first problem and to achieve high fidelity we propose a new machine learning approach for pigment mixing, which will be detailed shortly; the second problem is solved via the Kubelka-Munk model (KM model) [Kub48] with inspiration from [CAS+97].

6.9.1 Pigment Mixing with High Fidelity

Among the popular models for pigment mixing, such as average mixing, additive or subtractive mixing, and the KM model, the KM model is the most superior from an accuracy standpoint, as suggested by Haase and Meyer [HM92]. However, even with the KM model, simulation of pigment mixing behavior still fails to agree completely with real behavior. Baxter et al. reported in [BWL04] that using 101 samples, each corresponding to a wavelength, pigment mixing through the KM model still deviated markedly from reality. We propose a novel kernel method-assisted neural network approach for pigment mixing.

6.9.1.1 Acquisition of training samples

In the preprocessing stage, we collect a number of pigment mixing samples for training our pigment mixing prediction network. We rely on three ways to collect training samples: one through physical measurement and the other two based on interactive user inputs. In the physical measurement method we use the desktop reflective spectrophotometer X-RiteColor® Digital Swatchbook® [X-R06] to measure the reflectance of pigments. We measure the reflectance of both pure pigments before mixing and that of the resultant pigment mixture for the training samples. For each measurement we put the sample against a background material whose reflectance is known. We measure the overall reflectance of the two superimposing layers. According to the layer composition Eq.(6.23), we have two unknowns, namely R and T of the pigment. Thus two measurements are enough to solve R and T. For robustness we carry out five measurements for five different background materials and use a least squares approach to determine the optimal R and T. According to the KM model, once R is known, we can compute K/S through a function of R, i.e. $K/S = (1 - R)^2/(2R)$ [Kub48]. We then assume a value for S so that K is also known.

Obtaining a comprehensive set of pigment mixing samples and the pigments' relative concentrations is not easy practically. These samples are important for our neural network in order to do pigment mixing predication. Instead of turning to expensive physi-chemical equipment for the needed measurements, we suggest a handy computational approach, which is based on the KM model and the K, S, R values we estimated above.

One technical detail that is important for reproducing our experiment results is how to determine the relative pigment concentration when mixing multiple pigments. In our current experiments we only study the case of mixing two pigments. The relative concentration data are also needed for introducing the kernel functions into our neural network to boost the learning capability: 1) For the first kernel function, ψ_1, which is based on the KM model, the relative pigment concentration is useful to compute the overall pigment mixture's K and S values; 2) for the second and third kernel functions, ψ_2 and ψ_3, which essentially predict pigment mixing through additive composition, the relative concentrations are useful to determine the interpolation weights. To collect training samples, given the constituent pigments' relative concentrations, one could paint a number of overlapping stroke pairs, where each stroke is painted using one pigment. Even though it is feasible to paint a single stroke with a constant concentration throughout, it is difficult to paint both overlapping strokes in more or less the same concentration. This makes the procedure impractical. To overcome the problem, we utilize the K,S values of each pigment, which are acquired according to the methods introduced in Sect. 6.9.1.1. According to the KM model, given the R, G, B values of a pigment, its associated K, S values, and the thickness of the pigment layer d, there exist the following relationships:

$$b = \sqrt{(K/S)(K/S + 2)}, \qquad R = [1 + K/S + b\coth(bSd)]^{-1},$$

where R is the reflectance of the pigment, which can be estimated according to the R, G, B values for a natural white incoming light. Notice there is one free variable, d, and six constraining equations above as for each of the R, G, B light, it is associated with certain K, S, R values. We find the optimal value for d so that these equations are best satisfied in the least squared sense. For each of the mixing pigments, we estimate their relative concentration to be the ratio between their layer thicknesses.

To support customizing new pigments by the user, we provide two inter-active method for the user to specify the reflectance of a pure pigment species and the reflectance after it is mixed with another pigment. This straightfor-ward method is to allow the user to directly give the wavelength-dependent R and T values of the pigment, and then the system for following the same rou-tine above to determine K and S. Since reflectance is somehow non-intuitive for normal users, our system also allows the user to interactively specify the K and S coefficients using the method suggested in [CAS+97]. With K and S known, the reflectance, R, of the pigment or pigment mixture and its transmittance, T, can both be analytically computed [CAS+97].

6.9.1.2 Kernel functions

Kernel methods are popular in machine learning because they can increase the learnability of many models [CS02]. To enhance the learning ability of our pigment mixing prediction network, we employ three kernel functions: ψ_1, which is based on the KM model, and ψ_2 and ψ_3, which are based on average mixing.

With the KM model and the K and S coefficients known for each pigment constituent, the overall pigment mixture's coefficients, K_{mix} and S_{mix}, are computed as the weighted average of each pigment component's K and S coefficients using the pigment's relative concentration as the weight. With K_{mix} and S_{mix}, the overall reflectance R_{mix} and transmittance T_{mix} of the layer can be computed [Kub48, CAS+97]. R_{mix} and T_{mix} will be used as the input to our neural network and also for superimposing the layers.

For the kernel function of average mixing, the overall appearance of a pigment mixture can be simply derived through weighted average, i.e.:

$$\mathbf{C}^{\mathrm{mix},t}_{x,y} = \frac{\sum_{i=1}^{\xi} \rho^t_{x,y}(i)\mathbf{C}_{x,y}(i)}{\sum_{i=1}^{\xi} \rho^t_{x,y}(i)}.$$

Here $\mathbf{C}_{x,y}(i)$ is determined according to the input reflectance of the i-th pigment whose acquisition has been discussed in Sect. 6.9.1.1.

We also conduct interpolation in the HSV color space since it captures some non-linear relationship between colors and could give us a very different prediction of pigment mixing than operations in a linear space; the prediction could serve as a good clue for our neural network. We use $\mathbf{H}(\cdot)$ to denote the transformation from the RGB space to the HSV space and $\mathbf{H}^{-1}(\cdot)$ for the inverse transformation. Thus, our interpolation can be expressed as:

$$\mathbf{C}^{\mathrm{mix},t}_{x,y} = \mathbf{H}^{-1}\Big(\frac{\sum_{i=1}^{\xi} \rho^t_{x,y}(i)\mathbf{H}\big(\mathbf{C}_{x,y}(i)\big)}{\sum_{i=1}^{\xi} \rho^t_{x,y}(i)}\Big).$$

In this work we always use a particular yellow-white light source, which is widely used in Oriental art exhibitions and many museums. Under this condition we perform the above pigment mixing in the color space, and given the predicted color after pigment mixing, $\mathbf{C}^{\mathrm{mix},t}_{x,y}$, we can inversely compute the reflectance R_{mix} of the overall pigment mixture. Unfortunately we do not have a handy way to estimate T_{mix} for these two average mixing methods. As can be seen in Fig. 6.2, only the first kernel function gives an intermediate estimated T value to help the learning process of the neural network.

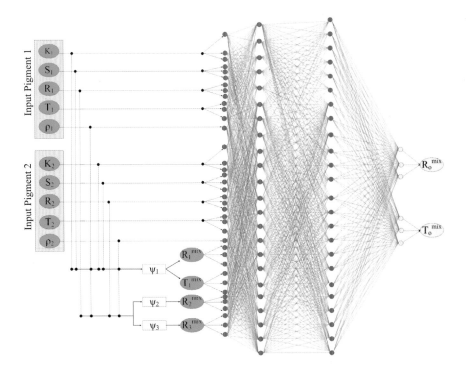

Fig. 6.2. Pigment mixing prediction neural network

6.9.1.3 Neural network for pigment mixing prediction

Our neural network takes as input the concentrations of the two pigment components to be mixed, ρ_1, ρ_2, their absorption and scattering coefficients, K_1, K_2, S_1, S_2, as well as their reflectances and transmittances R_1, R_2, T_1, T_2, whose estimations have been discussed in Sect. 6.9.1.2. Strictly speaking, these quantities are all wavelength-dependent. For simplicity we only consider three typical wavelengths—those of pure red, green and blue light. Thus each of $K_1, K_2, S_1, S_2, R_1, R_2, T_1, T_2$ is a vector carrying three scalar components. For each pair of pigments to be mixed, we designate a dedicated neural network for pigment mixing prediction. This is because some pigments made from different chemical compounds may carry the same color yet behave differently during pigment mixing. This also enables the user to freely customize a pigment which may not be present in the physical world. We feed the outputs of the three kernel functions, ψ_1, ψ_2, ψ_3, as the additional inputs to the neural network. The output of the neural network is the reflectance of the pigment mixture $R_o^{\text{mix}}, T_o^{\text{mix}}$. In the prediction network, we introduce two hidden layers with full connections to all the intermediate, input and output nodes.

The schema of our neural network approach for pigment mixing prediction is shown in Fig. 6.2. We use the resilient back propagation technique [Hay01] to train our multi-layer neural network at the preprocessing stage. Each neuron in the network takes a linear function as its associated transfer function. The performance function used when training the network is the mean square error measure. The total sample space contains 1,377 two-component pigment mixture instances over every pair of the 18 kinds of pure pigments, and each pair has three different concentrations. To prevent overtraining the learning network, we employ the early stopping technique [HK06]. In each run of the early stopping, we randomly pick 90% of the samples for the training set, and the remaining 10% go to the validation set. We then make the neural network go through 350,000 iterations for training, which takes about 4.5 hours to complete on a desktop computer (Pentium IV with 3.0 GHz CPU). During each run, the neural network converges very rapidly in the first 50,000 iterations. For now we use a fixed learning rate throughout the learning process. We expect, when employing a new mechanism that supports an adaptive learning rate, the total number of learning iterations could be significantly reduced. Finishing the whole 10 runs of the early stopping training process takes about two days.

Our neural network based approach can capture the possible chemical reactions, the mutual influences between pigments and other factors not considered in the KM model or the average mixing method. This approach also supports users in creating novel pigments. The assistance from kernel functions largely improves the learning capability of our pigment mixing prediction network and at the same time ensures the robustness of our learning method—in the worst case where the training data are very sparse or ill posed, our approach can still perform at least as well as the KM model or the average mixing.

6.9.2 Superimposing the Layers

Following the approach in [CAS+97], we derive the overall reflectance R_{over} and transmittance T_{over} of two merged adjacent layers according to the layers' reflectances R_1, R_2 and transmittances T_1, T_2. By the KM model we have:

$$\begin{cases} R_{over} = R_1 + \frac{T_1^2 R_2}{1-R_1 R_2} \\ T_{over} = \frac{T_1 T_2}{1-R_1 R_2} \end{cases}. \tag{6.23}$$

The reflectance and transmittance of the background paper, R_{bg}, T_{bg}, are interactively input. By default, $T_{bg} = 0$. For the mobile and fixture layers of the pigment mixture, their R_{mix}, T_{mix} are in the output from the above neural network. Since Eq. (6.23) can only be used to merge two layers at a time, we first merge the mobile layer with the fixture layer and then the result with the background paper layer. The final R after merging all the three layers is used to render the pixel.

6.10 Hardware-Accelerated Implementation

As mentioned in Sect. 6.2.1, during our algorithm design, we try to utilize standard problem instances with analytic solutions as much as possible so as to cut down on the amount of discrete numerical computations needed. In addition, we also speed up the equation solving through tabulation in the preprocessing stage. There is one outstanding equation, however, Eq. (6.12), which does not have an analytic solution and cannot be efficiently solved. Inspired by recent work in using GPUs to do general purpose computations, in particular [HBSL03, KW03], we speed up the numerical process to resolve the equation through a hardware-accelerated implementation. The idea is first to approximate the second order partial derivatives, including the Laplacian operator, through finite differences, and then represent each of the pigment concentrations, $\rho(i)$, and the velocity field, $\mathbf{v}$, using a separate texture map. After this we can numerically solve the differential equation by manipulating the texture maps using the parallel computing power of the GPU.

6.11 Experiment Results

We implemented our method using Microsoft Visual C++ 6.0 and with the support of Microsoft Direct3D V9.0 on a PC with a Pentium IV 3.0 GHz processor, 1 GB main memory and an NVidia GeForce 6600 GT graphics card. The paintbrush system came from our e-brush prototype system [XTLP02, XLTP03, XTLP04] as discussed in the previous two chapters. Table 6.2 reports the timing statistics of our implemented pigment model which has been integrated in the e-brush prototype system. Figs. 6.3—6.10 show some stroke effects produced by our new pigment model. Fig. 6.11 gives some pigment mixing results using our proposed boosted neural network approach. Fig. 6.12 shows one full scale painting generated using our system. More results are available on our project website. We also employ GPU hardware to

Table 6.2. Timing statistics. The column "Size" is the number of pixels in the painted stroke; "Pigment #" is the number of pigment species in each of the stroke painting experiments; "Pigment FPS", "Mix & Render FPS", and "Brush FPS" are the numbers of frames per second when running in isolation the pigment behavior simulation module, the pigment mixing and rendering module, as well as the brush simulation module, respectively. "Overall FPS" is the FPS of the overall prototype system when all the modules are running together

No.	Size	Pigment #	Pigment FPS	Mix & Render FPS	Brush FPS	Overall FPS
1	4198	3	62.25	32.25	32.25	16.12
2	13140	3	32.25	15.87	32.25	8.00
3	4463	4	31.25	21.27	32.25	10.75
4	13325	4	21.27	10.63	32.25	5.84
5	4663	5	21.27	12.82	32.25	8.00
6	13310	5	12.65	9.17	32.25	4.58

perform general purpose computations to accelerate the equation solving process [HBSL03, KW03], particularly when evaluating the Eq. (6.12). This is done in a way similar to that suggested in [PF05] (Part IV: General-purpose computation on GPUs: A Primer, Sect. 31.5, pp. 505–508).

Fig. 6.3. Some wet strokes (left), and a quick sketch of some flowers using mostly wet strokes (right)

Fig. 6.4. Dry strokes

Fig. 6.5. Some strokes with mixed wet and dry effects

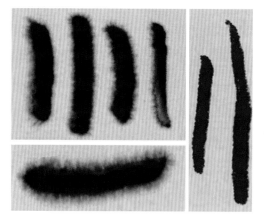

Fig. 6.6. Feathering effects: strong feathering (left) and weak feathering (right). To show the interplay between the feathering effects and the background paper texture, we superimpose our results on top of a section of a scanned real paper. A close view of a stroke with strong feathering is displayed at the bottom left

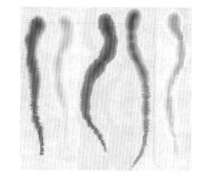

Fig. 6.7. Modest feathering effects with wet color strokes

Fig. 6.8. From dry strokes to semi-dry, semi-wet strokes

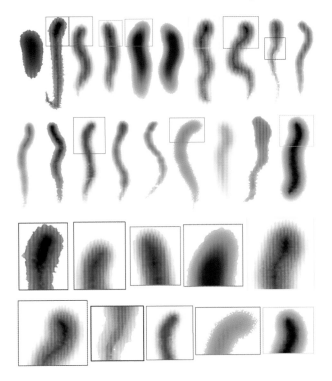

Fig. 6.9. Different wet strokes in colors

Fig. 6.10. Some stroke overlapping simulation results

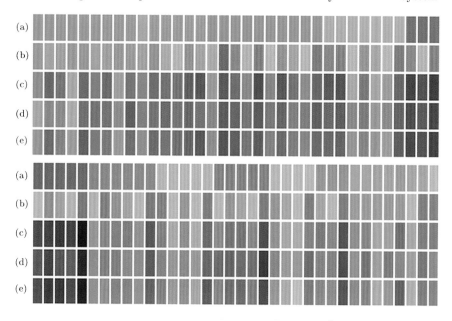

Fig. 6.11. Pigment mixing using our neural network. Row (a) and row (b) are the two source pigments before mixing. Row (c) is the pigment mixing results sampled from real world experiment. Row (d) is the prediction of the pigment mixing behavior using our proposed neural network, but without employing the kernel functions. Row (e) is the prediction using our proposed neural network with the kernel functions

Fig. 6.12. A simple painting with wet and dry strokes

6.12 Conclusion and Future Work

In this chapter, we introduce a novel pigment model based on careful treatment of many minute physical factors, which can achieve the best attainable effects for Oriental and water-based painting. Experiment results have verified the success of the design and its implementation. Future work includes further acceleration of our current algorithm, providing a more friendly graphical user interface, and extending our algorithm to other forms of painting such as oil painting and wax painting.

References

[AG97]   Arthur W. Adamson and Alice P. Gast. *Physical Chemistry of Surfaces*. Wiley-Interscience, August 1997.

[Bax04]   William Baxter. *Physically-based Modeling Techniques for Interactrive Digital Painting*. PhD Thesis, University of North Carolina at Chapel Hill, 2004.

[BLR06]   Koen Beets, Tom Van Laerhoven, and Frank Van Reeth. Introducing artistic tools in an interactive paint system. In *Proc. of WSCG*, Plzen, Czech Republic: Union Agency-Science Press, 2006.

[BSLM01]   Bill Baxter, Vincent Scheib, Ming C. Lin, and Dinesh Manocha. DAB: Interactive haptic painting with 3D virtual brushes. In *SIGGRAPH '01: Proceedings of the 28th Annual Conference on Computer Graphics and Interactive Techniques*, Los Angeles, CA, USA: ACM Press, pages 461–468, 2001.

[BWL04]   William Baxter, Jeremy Wendt, and Ming C. Lin. Impasto: a realistic, interactive model for paint. In *NPAR '04: Proceedings of the 3rd International Symposium on Non-photorealistic Animation and Rendering*, Annecy, France: ACM Press, pages 45–148, 2004.

[CAS+97]   Cassidy J. Curtis, Sean E. Anderson, Joshua E. Seims, Kurt W. Fleischer, and David H. Salesin. Computer-generated watercolor. In *SIGGRAPH '97: Proceedings of the 24th Annual Conference on Computer Graphics and Interactive Techniques*, pages 421–430, Los Angeles, CA, USA: ACM Press/Addison-Wesley Publishing Co., 1997.

[CPE92]   Tunde Cockshott, John Patterson, and David England. Modelling the texture of paint. *Computer Graphics Forum*, 11(3):217–226, 1992.

[Cra75]   John Crank. *The Mathematics of Diffusion*. Oxford, UK: Clarendon Press, 1975.

[CS02]   Nello Cristianini and Bernhard Scholkopf. Support vector machines and kernel methods: the new generation of learning machines. *AI Magazine*, 23(3):31–41, 2002.

[CT04]   Nelson S.H. Chu and Chiew-Lan Tai. Real-time painting with an expressive virtual Chinese brush. *IEEE Computer Graphics and Applicationss*, 24(5):76–85, 2004.

[CT05]   Nelson S.H. Chu and Chiew-Lan Tai. Moxi: real-time ink dispersion in absorbent paper. *ACM Transactions on Graphics*, 24 (3):504–511, 2005.

[Fic55]   A. Fick. *Ann. Physik* (Leipzig), 94:59, 1855.

[GK91]   Qinglian Guo and Tosiyasu L. Kunii. Modeling the diffuse painting of Sumie. *IFIP Modeling in Computer Graphics*, Tokyo, Japan: Springer-Verlag, pages 329–338, 1991.

[GK03]   Qinglian Guo and Tosiyasu L. Kunii. "Nijimi" rendering algorithm for creating quality black ink paintings. In *Proceedings* of Computer Graphics International (CGI), Tokyo, Japan: IEEE Computer Society, pages 152–159, 2003.

[Guo95] Qinglian Guo. Generating realistic calligraphy words. *IEICE Transactions on Fundametals of Electronics Communications and Computer Sciences*, E78A(11):1556–1558, 1995.

[Hay01] Simon Haykin. *Neural Networks: A Comprehensive Foundation.* Prentice Hall, 2nd edition, 2001.

[HBSL03] Mark J. Harris, William V. Baxter, Thorsten Scheuermann, and Anselmo Lastra. Simulation of cloud dynamics on graphics hardware. In *HWWS '03: Proceedings of the ACM SIGGRAPH/EUROGRAPHICS Conference on Graphics Hardware*, Aire-la-Ville, Switzerland: Eurographics Association, pages 92–101, 2003.

[HK06] Jiawei Han and Micheline Kamber. *Data Mining: Concepts and Techniques.* Elsevier, 2nd edition, 2006.

[HL94] Siu-Chi Hsu and Irene H. H. Lee. Drawing and animation using skeletal strokes. In *SIGGRAPH '94: Proceedings of the 21st Annual Conference on Computer Graphics and Interactive Techniques*, Orlando, FL, USA: ACM Press, pages 109–118, 1994.

[HM92] Chet S. Haase and Gary W. Meyer. Modeling pigmented materials for realistic image synthesis. *ACM Transactions on Graphics*, 11(4):305–335, 1992.

[KC60] O. Kallmes and H. Corte. The structure of paper, I. the statistical geometry of an ideal two dimensional fiber network. *Tappi Journal*, 43(9):737–752, 1960.

[KNV01] Tosiyasu L. Kunii, Gleb V. Nosovskij, and Vladimir L. Vecherlinin. Two-dimensional diffusion model for diffuse ink painting. *International Journal of Shape Modeling*, 7(1):45–58, 2001.

[Kub48] P. Kubelka. New contributions to the optics of intensely light-scattering material, part I. *Journal of the Optical Society of America*, 38:448–457, 1948.

[KW03] Jens Kruger and Rudiger Westermann. Linear algebra operators for GPU implementation of numerical algorithms. *ACM Transactions on Graphics*, 22(3):908–916, 2003.

[Lan08] I. Langmuir. The adsorption of gases on plane surfaces of glass, mica and platinum. *J. Amer. Chem. Soc.*, 40:1361–1403, 1908.

[Lee97] Jintae Lee. Physically-based modeling of brush painting. *Computer Networks and ISDN Systems*, 29(14):1571–1576, 1997.

[Lee99] Jintae Lee. Simulating Oriental black-ink painting. *IEEE Computer Graphics and Applications*, 19(3):74–81, 1999.

[Lee01] Jintae Lee. Diffusion rendering of black ink paintings using new paper and ink models. *Computers and Graphics*, 25(2):295–308, 2001.

[LLR04] Tom Van Laerhoven, Jori Liesenborgs, and Frank Van Reeth. Real-time watercolor painting on a distributed paper model. In *CGI'04: Proc. of Computer Graphics International*, Crete, Greece: IEEE Computer Society, pages 640–643, 2004.

[LMP06] Yuan Lou, Salome Martinez, and Peter Polacik. Loops and branches of coexistence states in a Lotka-Volterra competition model. *Journal of Differential Equations*, 230(2):720–742, 2006.

[LNH95] Tosiyasu L. Kunii, Gleb V. Nosovskij, and Takafumi Hayashi. A diffusion model for computer animation of diffuse ink painting. In *Proceedings of Computer Animation*, Geneva, Switzerland: IEEE Computer Society, pages 98–102, 1995.

[LR05] Tom Van Laerhoven and Frank Van Reeth. Real-time simulation of thin paint media. In *SIGGRAPH2005 sketch*, Los Angeles, CA, USA: ACM Press, 2005.

[LS04] Wei-Jin Lin and Zhen-Chung Shih. Computer-generated Chinese painting with physically-based ink and color diffusion. In *CGW'04: Proc. of Cracow Grid Workshop*, Cracow, Poland: IOS Press, 2004.

[Mas96] Richard I. Masel. *Principles of Adsorption and Reaction on Solid Surfaces*. Wiley-Interscience, 1996.

[McC01] Elaine M. McCash. *Surface Chemistry*. Oxford University Press, 2001.

[McG74] R. McGregor. *Diffusion and Sorption in Fibres and Films: an Introduction with Particular Reference to Dyes*, London,UK; New York, NY, USA: Academic Press, volume 1, 1974.

[Mis69] D. N. Misra. *Adsorption on Heterogeneous Surfaces: A Dubinin-Radushkevich Equation*. Surface Science, 1969.

[New31] A. B. Newman. *Trans. Am. Inst. Chem. Engrs.*, 27:203–220, 1931.

[PF05] Matt Pharr and Randima Fernando. *GPU Gems 2: Programming Techniques for High-performance Graphics and General-purpose Computation*. nVIDIA, 2005.

[Pha91] Binh Pham. Expressive brush strokes. *CVGIP: Graph. Models Image Process.*, 53(1):1–6, 1991.

[Ran82] H. F. Rance. *Handbook of Paper Science: Science and Technology of Papermaking, Paper Properties and Paper Usage*, Amsterdam: Elsevier, volume 2, 1982.

[RMN03] Dave Rudolf, David Mould, and Eric Neufeld. Simulating wax crayons. In *Proc. of Pacific Graphics*, Alberta, Canada: IEEE Computer Society, pages 164–173, 2003.

[Rut84] Douglas M. Ruthven. *Principles of Adsorption and Adsorption Processes*. John Wiley & Sons, Inc., 1984.

[Sma91] David Small. Simulating watercolor by modeling diffusion, pigment, and paper fibers. In *Proc. of SPIE '91*, San Diego, CA, USA: SPIE Press, 1991.

[Str86] Steve Strassmann. Hairy brushes. In *SIGGRAPH '86: Proceedings of the 13th Annual Conference on Computer Graphics and Interactive Techniques*, Dallas, TX, USA: ACM Press, pages 225–232, 1986.

[Suz90] Motoyuki Suzuki. *Adsorption Engineering*. Elsevier, 1990.

[SW04] Shriram Santhanagopalanm and Ralph E. White. Series solution to the transient convective diffusion equation for a rotating disk electrode. *Journal of the Electrochemical Society*, 151(8):550–553, 2004.

[Tie94]   Chi Tien. *Adsorption Calculations and Modeling*. Butterworth-Heinemann, 1994.

[WI00]   Helena T.F. Wong and Horace H.S. Ip. Virtual brush: a model-based synthesis of Chinese calligraphy. *Computers and Graphics*, 24(1):99–113, 2000.

[Wor96]   Steven Worley. A cellular texture basis function. In *Proc. of SIGGRAPH*, New Orleans, LA, USA: ACM Press, pages 291–294, 1996.

[X-R06]   X-Rite Incorporated, http://www.xrite.com/, 2006.

[XLTP03]   Songhua Xu, Francis C. M. Lau, Feng Tang, and Yunhe Pan. Advanced design for a realistic virtual brush. Computer Graphics Forum. *In Proceedings of Eurographics '03*, 22(3):533–542, 2003.

[XTLP02]   Songhua Xu, Min Tang, Francis C.M. Lau, and Yunhe Pan. A solid model based virtual hairy brush. Computer Graphics Forum. *In Proceedings of Eurographics '02*, 21(3):299–308 & 625, 2002.

[XTLP04]   Songhua Xu, Min Tang, Francis C.M. Lau, and Yunhe Pan. Virtual hairy brush for painterly rendering. *Graphical Models*, 66(5):263–302, 2004.

[XXK+06]   Songhua Xu, Yingqing Xu, Sing-Bing Kang, David H. Salesin, Yunhe Pan, and Heung-Yeung Shum. Animating Chinese paintings through stroke-based decomposition. *ACM Transactions on Graphics*, 25(2):239–267, 2006.

[Yan03]   Ralph T. Yang. *Adsorbents: Fundamentals and Applications*. Wiley-Interscience, 2003.

[YLLC03]   Young-Jung Yu, Do-Hoon Lee, Young-Bock Lee, and Hwan-Gue Cho. Interactive rendering technique for realistic oriental painting. *Journal of WSCG*, 11:538–545, 2003.

[ZST+99]   Qing Zhang, Youetsu Sato, Junya Takahashi, Kazunobu Muraoka, and Norishige Chiba. Simple cellular automaton-based simulation of ink behavior and its application to Suibokuga-like 3D rendering of trees. *Journal of Visualization and Computer Animation*, 10(1):27–37, 1999.

Rendering Component of an Advanced Virtual Hairy Paintbrush System

7.1 Motivation

In this chapter we introduce a new method for fast and high-quality rendering of hair and its associated data structure support for hair modeling. The method is capable of rendering sophisticated hair models in real time with high quality, both of which are key properties for the satisfactory running of a virtual hairy brush-based digital painting system. Why is hair rendering and modeling relevant and important for such a system? In the following, we try to answer this question from two major angles.

7.1.1 Necessity and Importance of Brush Hair Rendering

7.1.1.1 A friendly and familiar user interface

We believe the more realistic a virtual paintbrush would appear on the computer screen, the more comfortable and interested an end user would feel when operating it. Thus it is crucial that we provide a user friendly interface that includes a faithful rendition of a virtual paintbrush, especially in view of the aim of ultimately replacing the real physical paintbrush. We can better appreciate this point if we take a broader view looking at the effect that a user interface could have on the deployment of a computing system or machine. Why is it necessary to have such a visual effect? On the one hand such a system will encounter the least amount of natural resistance from users when they migrate from their usual, brick-and-mortar painting environment to a digital emulation. On the other hand the attractive interface itself would be the best salesman for the system, who can also provide a tour of the latent but powerful functionalities behind the scene available via the interface.

7.1.1.2 Accurate visual feedback

We envision that a most realistic rendering of a virtual paintbrush can provide a reliable visual feedback to the user on the current state of the paintbrush head to enable him to mentally predicate what the probable ink mark will be from his manipulation. This feedback must be absolutely accurate in order not to mislead or confuse the artist who is so used to a real brush. The need becomes even greater when the brush head is heavily split or deformed, resulting in very sophisticated geometries. Any substitute for a real looking head, e.g. a polygonal model with a very rough approximation, could easily become a bottleneck to any serious digital painting pursuit. Like all virtual reality systems, our virtual paintbrush system is also subject to the bucketing principle—the water level in the bucket will be determined by the weakest link in a chain. The visual display of the brush in action is this short piece.

7.1.2 Performance Requirements

Meeting the performance requirements for brush hair rendering is very challenging: it needs to be done both realistically and in real time. The two are intimately related and should work together to strike a good balance. Real-timeness probably should be given the priority because any slight delay in the visual display of the brush would mean a sluggish, non-real brush, and no serious artist can put up with that. Once we have the real-time requirement settled, we can then push the realistic looking part to the limit, or to any extent what is still distinguishable by the human eye. To achieve real-time response, a naive brutal force approach can fail miserably—a typical brush head bundle consists of hundreds if not thousands of individual hair strands. Without a careful design and optimization strategy, the rendering component alone will consume all the CPU resources. To us the very clear objective is to have a real-time responsive rendering component that can deliver realistic rendition of the latest geometry of the brush head throughout the painting process with the least amount of CPU and other system resources.

7.1.3 Brush Hair versus Human Hair

Brush hair shares many commonalities with human hair. In terms of material composition both are similar and tend to deform and split easily. The modeling of human hair needs to deal with external forces such as that against the human body (e.g. shoulder) and from wind or air flows. Similarly for the brush, the pressure from the artist against the canvas needs to be properly and accurately treated. For the paintbrush, the shape of brush hair matters a lot since that will determine the corresponding ink mark on canvas. Indeed, we can think of more similarities than we can think of differences. Hence the studies and results reported in this chapter can be readily applied to the modeling of a virtual paintbrush. Interestingly, there is an abundance of previous research efforts on human hair rendering, thus forming an important area in computer graphics studies, whereas projects on brush hair rendering are rare. It will be worthwhile in the future to apply human hair rendering results to the optimal display of a virtual brush, in real-time and with high realism. Both the human hair results and the brush results should be of good potential reference value to both the non-photorealistic rendering community and the digital painting community.

7.2 Overview

To achieve high speed and quality, the method makes use of an offline-generated database of reusable intermediate rendering results. The database covers a range of sample geometries under different viewing and lighting conditions. This database lookup step replaces what would otherwise be a time-consuming process of rendering the basic appearance of a hair bundle on the fly. This special database is a discretization of a new appearance modeling function called a Semantics-Aware Texture Function (SATF), where semantics refer to the particular distribution of hair in the section of hair bundle being rendered. We model the hair on four levels, and use an efficient disk-like structure to represent hair distributions inside a hair cluster. Since the intermediate database carries opacity information, the method can use an efficient self-shadow algorithm to enhance the realism during the online phase. We give experiment results to show that our method can indeed produce high quality rendering results in real time for reasonably complex hair samples.

7.3 Introduction

To design fast algorithms for high quality hair rendering, especially using inexpensive hardware, is a grand challenge. Of the latest hair rendering algorithms, the majority are either designed for high quality rendering with non-interactive response or for fast/interactive rendering but with much lowered quality.

The difficulties of hair rendering are due to the following:

(1) There are on average tens of thousands of hair strands on a typical human head. The sum of processing is a huge computational burden.

(2) Hair can be in many styles, sometimes completely chaotic, and a single hair strand could represent a complex geometry.

(3) Real hair strands are semi-transparent and have a tiny volume, which calls for an extremely careful and delicate treatment.

(4) Intricate interactions exist between hair strands, including self-shadowing, inter-reflection and other subtle lighting effects, which are not easy to simulate efficiently.

7.3.1 Ideas and Contributions

Our main idea is to split the task into an offline and an online phase. Most of the time-consuming rendering steps are completed in the offline phase which generates re-usable intermediate computation results in a specialized database. During the online phase, appearance maps are synthesized from records in the database selected according to index terms provided to the appearance modeling function. After that, lightweight hair lighting calculations and fast self-shadow generation are applied to generate the final results.

The hair is represented internally as a generalized disk structure. This structure makes easy the generation of a density function to represent succinctly a cluster of hair strands in a statistic sense, which is used as the main "semantic" information for indexing the database.

More specifically, for the database we compute a simplified reflectance representation of hair clusters as a function of hair density and the viewing and lighting directions. This precomputation step only considers appearance changes due to changes in the lighting and viewing angles along the lateral directions of the hair. The database is indexed based on hair density distribution and these two azimuthal angles. During the online phase, this simplified precomputed representation containing reflectance and alpha values from the database is used to compute the reflectance and opacity maps. The remaining steps take into account self-shadowing and shading of each layer of a hair cluster, using approximations to compute the final shading. Combining the offline and the online steps, we have a real-time algorithm for rendering hair in high quality.

7.3.2 Organization of the Chapter

The remainder of this chapter is organized as follows. Sect. 7.4 surveys the most relevant work. Sect. 7.5 describes our hierarchical hair modeling approach and its associated data structure support. Sect. 7.6 discusses the representation of our semantics-aware texture function in a hair rendering intermediate result database. Sect. 7.7 discusses how to construct our rendering database in the offline phase. Sect. 7.8 explains the online phase of our rendering algorithm. Sect. 7.9 presents our experiment results. Sect. 7.10 concludes this chapter and points out directions for future work.

7.4 Related Work

7.4.1 Hair Rendering for Quality

Most of hair rendering work aimed at the visual quality of the output with little or no concern for the algorithm's running time. Perhaps the earliest work on hair and fuzzy objects in computer graphics was the particle system by Reeves [Ree83], in which rendering was done by projecting each particle onto a frame buffer separately. Perlin and Hoffert [PH89] introduced hypertextures for furry objects modeling. Blinn [Bli82] introduced the use of volume density for rendering. Kajiya and Von Herzen [KH84] applied volume densities to rendering complex objects. Kajiya and Kay [KK89] proposed a 3D texture primitive, called "texels", which extends Blinn's volume density method by including a distributed lighting model in the volume density field. They successfully used texels to realistically model and render the appearance of hair with complex geometries.

In Goldman's probabilistic algorithm for faked fur rendering [Gol97], emphasis was placed on rendering the visual characteristics of fur while the fine details of the fur geometry were invisible in the output. In Yang, et al.'s work [YXYW00], ray tracing was employed to compute the appearance of hair cluster boundaries, followed by volume rendering along the tracing rays to capture the hair density distribution. Recently Marschner et al. [MJC$^+$03] measured and simulated the scattering effect from individual hair, which exhibited visual effects not predicted by Kajiya-Kay's model [KK89]. However, executing these ray tracing based algorithms by software will be too slow for interactive applications: the method described in [YXYW00] took 24 minutes to render a single hair braid image and the algorithm presented in [MJC$^+$03] took 8 minutes to render a single frame of human hair, both on their machines a few years ago.

7.4.2 Hair Rendering for Speed

Along another direction of hair rendering research, attention is focused on bringing up fast algorithms at the possible cost of compromising the rendering quality. Existent real-time/interactive hair rendering algorithms often cannot produce satisfyingly realistic hair appearance in order to meet strict response time constraints. Lengyel et al. [LPFH01] developed a real-time algorithm to render a furry object through a series of concentric, semi-transparent textured shells applied to hair volume samples. Koster et al. [KHS04] developed a real-time rendering algorithm taking into account the hair's anisotropic reflection and self-shadowing. Scheuermann [Sch04] proposed a real-time human hair rendering algorithm whose lighting model was essentially a mixture of Kajiya-Kay's model and Marschner et al.'s model discussed above. Both Koster et al.'s and Scheuermann's methods employed a polygonal hair model and used textures to represent hair strands. However, due to the consideration of rendering efficiency, they both always used the same, fixed texture, ignoring the change of hair density in the hair model and the variation of lighting conditions in the lateral direction of a hair strand. Such a problem of always using a fixed texture source is addressed by our newly proposed algorithm in this chapter. Our method dynamically generates semantics aware texture maps, which can represent more faithfully the target object's appearance.

For a complete survey on hair simulation before 2002, one can refer to [MTHK02]. There is also a more recent survey dedicated to hair modeling, rendering and animation [WBK$^+$07]. Despite much wonderful work that has been so far, we are still short of a practically feasible algorithm which can render a hair model in both high speed (i.e. with real-time or quasi-real-time response) and high quality.

7.4.3 Image-Based Rendering

Our newly proposed offline/online rendering algorithm is also related to Image-Based Rendering (IBR) approaches. But unlike these approaches, whose rendering capability comes exclusively from information entailed in the underlying images, geometry models of the rendering targets are used in our lightweight online rendering phase to augment the rendering quality initially achieved through pure texture mapping. Second, for IBR approaches, if a high rendering quality is to be reached, images need to be sampled not too sparsely, which could easily result in a very large image database. In comparison, our rendering algorithm produces a rendering database of modest size by storing 1D records rather than 2D images in the database; these 1D records will then be used to dynamically generate the images needed for texture mapping according to semantics-related features of rendering targets. Our strategy to control the size of the database so that it can comfortably fit in the memory is key for fast rendering. In fact so far there has been little work done on using IBR for animated scenes. Our work can also be viewed as an initial attempt in this direction, since the texture maps needed in the online phase of our algorithm are dynamically generated according to the current rendering sceneries.

7.4.4 Appearance Modeling

Our hair appearance modeling and rendering work also belongs to one of the most fundamental problems in computer graphics—object appearance modeling in particular, surface reflectance modeling, which is critical to the accurate rendering of surface geometry. Surface appearance is subject to viewing and lighting conditions as well as the scale at which it is observed. On a coarse scale, where local surface variations are sub-pixel and the local intensity is uniform, appearance is characterized by BRDFs (Bidirectional Reflectance Distribution Functions) [NRH+77]. BRDFs assume surface reflectance is not affected by surface geometry details and thus only include viewing and illumination directions at their appearance modeling functions. On a fine scale, where surface variations give rise to local intensity variations, appearance can be characterized by BTFs (Bidirectional Texture Functions) [DvGNK99]. A BTF can be interpreted as a mapping from a 4D space of lighting and viewing directions to a space of 2D texture images. BTFs refine BRDF's practice by accounting for effects caused by geometry details through including surface positions in their appearance modeling functions. A BTF dataset is a collection of images indexed by both the viewing direction and the lighting direction.

Conventional BTF is a 6D function in which 4 parameters are for viewing and lighting directions and the remaining two parameters form a pair (x, y) to locate a specific image position for texture retrieval. Hence, one BTF can only be used to describe the reflectance field of a homogeneous material or that of a particular instance of a non-homogeneous material and cannot at the same time faithfully represent reflectance fields of all the instances of a non-homogeneous material, whose texture can vary significantly over time or spatially, e.g. cloud, smoke, hair, skin.

In this chapter, we propose yet another appearance modeling function which uses also an offline-constructed database to render complex hair efficiently and in high quality. In comparison with traditional BRDFs and BTFs, our proposed SATF (Semantics-Aware Texture Function) uses a semantics characteristic term to compute the corresponding texture best correlated with the local semantics. This offers the possibility to use one single SATF to capture a class of objects of the same non-homogeneous material and can also be used for dynamically changing objects, i.e. animating hair. For simplicity, our newly suggested SATF can be understood as a kind of parameterized BTFs wherein the parameters hold physical meanings.

7.5 Hair Modeling and Representation

Our work focuses on the rendering of hair, and less on the modeling. But the two cannot be easily separated, as it is obvious that the hair model affects directly the quality and efficiency of the rendering results.

7.5.1 Modeling Hair as Virtual Material

In our SATF approach we introduce an appearance modeling function which is semantics-aware. By "semantics-aware" we mean the function is supposed to reflect the differences in visual appearance caused by changes in the semantics of the rendering target. The specific rendering target in our design is a section (on a normal plane) of a hair cluster (see Figs. 7.1(a) and (b)), and its semantic property is represented by a vector measuring the hair density distribution within the section. That is, our SATF includes a hair density distribution feature vector, in addition to the lighting and viewing directions (see Fig. 7.1(c)). With the hair density vector, we implicitly model the aggregate appearance of a hair cluster as a kind of *virtual aggregate material* which has a variable texture over the surface of an object.

7.5.2 Four-level Hierarchy of Hair Modeling

To model the hair and capture its appearance with high fidelity, we adopt a four-level hierarchy. The four levels are the entire hair volume, the hair macro-cluster level, the hair cluster level and the hair density level (hair strand level) respectively, as listed in Table 7.1. In this hierarchy, a hair cluster (the third level) serves as our modeling primitive, which helps cut down the hair modeling cost as suffered by strand-based hair modeling approaches. Similar to the approach in [XLTP03], macro-clusters (the second level) are used to eliminate as much redundancy in hair modeling and simulation as possible; a macro-cluster groups together hair clusters whose geometries are similar but their physical positions may not be adjacent. In a hair macro-cluster, geometries of all the hair clusters can be trivially derived from each other via simple transformations. This is a reasonable strategy as there are usually only a limited number of sharply distinctive geometries among hair clusters in a hair volume. Hair macro-clusters thus make up the entire hair volume (the first level) at the top of the hierarchy. At the very bottom we keep track of the distribution of hair strands inside a hair cluster in the form of a hair density field or an explicit representation of each hair strand's

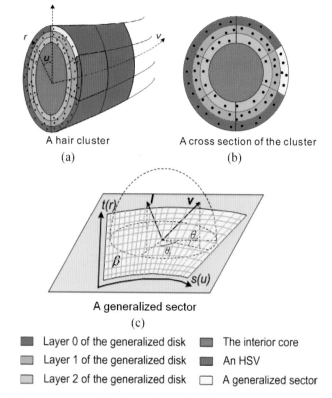

A hair cluster
(a)

A cross section of the cluster
(b)

A generalized sector
(c)

■ Layer 0 of the generalized disk   ■ The interior core
▨ Layer 1 of the generalized disk   ▦ An HSV
▢ Layer 2 of the generalized disk   ▫ A generalized sector

Fig. 7.1. A hair cluster modeled as a layered solid object with an interior core and multiple layers of volumetric shells

Table 7.1. Four-level hierarchy of our hair modeling method

No.	Level Name	Representing object
1st	Entire hair volume	Whole hair volume
2nd	Hair macro-cluster	Geometrically similar clusters
3rd	Hair cluster	Clustered hair strands
4th	Hair strand	Individual hair strands

position as used in many strand-based approaches. The hair density field can be obtained from density-based hair modeling tools, e.g. [XY01], or density-based hair dynamics simulations, e.g. [BCN03].

7.5.3 Generalized Disk Structure for Representing Hair Clusters

To support the four-level hierarchy we propose a *generalized disk structure* to represent a hair cluster's envelope shape as well as the distribution of its constituent hair strands. It is called "generalized" because, unlike its analogy the real hard disk, which is cylindric, the envelope of a hair cluster is a generalized cylinder.

We generate generalized cylinders through the general sweeping operation in CAD by sweeping a 2D variable contour curve along a 3D spline curve. Similarly to the concept of hair macro in Xu et al.'s work on the realistic virtual brush [XLTP03], we sweep an ellipse along a 3D curve to generate a generalized cylinder. During sweeping we make sure that the ellipse always lies on the normal plane with respect to the 3D curve. The shape of the moving ellipse can be varied during sweeping. We denote the sweeping trajectory as $T(t)(0 \leqslant t \leqslant 1)$, which is a B-spline in 3D space, and the ellipse $E(t_0)$ lying on the normal plane of $T(t)|_{t=t_0}$ as:

$$E(t_0) \triangleq \{(x,y)|x = A(t_0)v\cos\left(\theta(t_0) + u\right), y = B(t_0)v\sin\left(\theta(t_0) + u\right), \\ v \in [0,1], u \in [0,2\pi]\}, \tag{7.1}$$

where $A(t_0)$ and $B(t_0)$ are half of the lengths of the major and minor axes of the ellipse $E(t_0)$ respectively, and $\theta(t_0)$ is the corresponding self-twisting phase of the ellipse $E(t_0)$. Here $A(t)$, $B(t)$ and $\theta(t)$ $(0 \leqslant t \leqslant 1)$ are three one-dimensional B-splines. The geometry modeling parameters needed for constructing the hair cluster H can therefore be compactly stated as:

$$H \triangleq Modeling\Big(T(t), A(t), B(t), \theta(t)\Big) \ (0 \leqslant t \leqslant 1). \tag{7.2}$$

To represent the hair density field, we divide the hair cluster into two components: a heterogeneous volumetric shell part with mesostructures and a homogeneous transparent interior core (see Fig. 7.1). The appearance of the cluster is principally determined by hair distributions in the volumetric shells. For a hair cluster there are multiple layered shell surfaces, each of which is logically further divided uniformly into several *Hair Shell Volumes* (HSV). The division is done by connecting the neighboring points obtained by sampling the parametric equation of the generalized cylinder uniformly in the parametric domain $\{t, v, u\}$, where t $(0 \leqslant t \leqslant 1)$ is the relative arc length along the sweeping trajectory, with v $(0 \leqslant v \leqslant 1)$ and u $(0 \leqslant u < 2\pi)$ being two parameters on the radius and phase of the sampling position as defined in Eq. (7.1). Thus, each of the samples is in terms of (t, v, u), and the set of all the sampling points $\mathbf{S} \triangleq \{(t_i, v_j, u_k)\}$ is collected by:

$$\mathbf{S} \triangleq \{i/s_t|i = 0, 1, \cdots, s_t\} \times \{j/s_v|j = 0, 1, \cdots, s_v\} \\ \times \{2\pi k/s_u|k = 0, 1, \cdots, s_u - 1\} \tag{7.3}$$

where $1/s_t$, $1/s_v$ and $2\pi/s_u$ are the sampling step sizes for the three parameters respectively. In the rendering algorithm, we consider the density field within every HSV separately.

As illustrated in Fig. 7.1(b), the structure of a cross section of our hair cluster model looks very much like that of a hard disk, hence the name "generalized disk structure". As shown in Fig. 7.1, each plate (cross section) of the structure is made up of an interior core and some exterior shells. Every cross section is divided into several "generalized tracks", each of which is further organized as multiple "generalized sectors". Notice that each HSV has two boundary generalized sectors.

7.5.4 Hair Density Field for Sector

Hair strand distribution within a hair cluster is captured as a density field. The density field can be directly obtained from either a density-based hair modeling tool, e.g. the V-HairStudio [XY01], or density-based dynamic hair simulations, e.g. [BCN03]. In case the hair model to be rendered is not given in the form of hair density distribution, we need to first establish the density field for a generalized sector. This is usually the case when only hair strand positions are given. We assume the cross section of a hair strand is always circular and the hair's density due to the existence of a single hair strand follows a Gaussian distribution. The overall density distribution can thus be safely defined as the sum of all these Gaussian distributions due to individual hair strands. In the following we use ρ to denote hair density.

More precisely, when establishing the micro-density field for a generalized sector, β, we use a grid map with a 2D parametric coordinate system $\{s, t\}$ (see Fig. 7.1.(c)). This grid map is similar to the base density map used in [YXYW00]. We first consider the case where the hair strand level is in the form of explicit representation of hair strand positions. Suppose there are n hair strands passing through β, and the centers of these hair strands are $\mathbf{c}_i$ ($i = 0, \cdots, n - 1$). We assume the cross section of a hair strand is always circular and the hair's micro-density g due to the existence of a single hair strand follows the Gaussian distribution, i.e.:

$$g(s, t, \mathbf{c}_i) \triangleq \frac{1}{\sigma\sqrt{2\pi}} e^{-|\mathbf{c}_i - (s,t)|^2/(2\sigma^2)}$$

where $|\mathbf{c}_i - (s, t)|$ is the distance from the position (s, t) on β to $\mathbf{c}_i$. And the overall micro-density at a point (s, t) is the sum of all these Gaussian distributions due to individual hair strands, i.e.:

$$\rho(s, t) \triangleq \sum_{i=0}^{n-1} g(s, t, \mathbf{c}_i).$$

We store values of this micro-density field discretely at each grid point in the grid map for ease of processing later on. Now we consider the case where the hair strand level is in the form of a hair density distribution. In that case we generate the hair strands according to the given hair density distribution in β and denote their center positions as $\mathbf{c}_i$ ($i = 0, \cdots, n - 1$). The rest of the processing is the same as above. In the following we do not distinguish between hair micro-density and hair density and use the same notation ρ to denote them.

7.6 HRIR-DB and Semantics-Aware Texture Function

7.6.1 SATF and Our Offline/Online Two-phased Rendering Algorithm

With the above modeling strategy, the aggregate appearance of the virtual material is indexed by a semantics term in the SATF. By abstracting out such an appearance property, meaning the challenge of hair rendering, dealing with the hair's complex geometric details in tiny volumes and their possible dynamic deformations is reduced to applying an image-based rendering method over a geometry with a much smoother and simplified surface. Texture mapping then suffices, wherein the map is generated through the SATF in response to the underlying object semantics. This is where an offline phase can be introduced.

To approach the possibility of real-time rendering of hair, we try to shift as much computation as possible to an offline pre-processing phase. Past good results are worth remembering and should be made available for future re-use. Our strategy is to execute as much of the time-consuming rendering tasks offline as possible to produce a collection of re-usable partial rendering results that are stored in a special database. These partial results are referred to as Hair Rendering Intermediate Results (HRIRs), and the database Hair Rendering Intermediate Result DataBase (HRIR-DB). The HRIR-DB in fact serves as the range of our newly-proposed appearance modeling function—Semantics-Aware Texture Function (SATF)—which accepts as parameters the key distinguishing features of the rendering target. In our present context, the rendering target is a hair cluster, and its semantics are represented compactly by a hair density distribution. Intuitively, our SATF is a database lookup based on the input parameters of the hair density distribution of the rendering target and the viewing and lighting directions. Thus, mathematically, SATF defines the following mapping relationship:

$$\mathrm{SATF}(\beta, \mathrm{v}, \mathrm{l}) = \mathrm{HRIR}\big(\boldsymbol{\rho}_{\mathrm{feature}}(\beta), \theta_{\mathrm{v}}(\beta), \theta_{\mathrm{l}}(\beta)\big), \tag{7.4}$$

where $\theta_{\mathrm{v}}(\beta)$ and $\theta_{\mathrm{l}}(\beta)$ are the viewing and lighting directions respectively and $\boldsymbol{\rho}_{\mathrm{feature}}(\beta)$ is a hair density distribution feature vector. The subscript "feature" in the notation of $\boldsymbol{\rho}_{\mathrm{feature}}(\beta)$ indicates only selected features related to density distribution are used in the process, resulting in a much reduced number of dimensions for the database records.

The HRIR-DB is similar to a BTF database in that both of them contain image samples produced under different viewing and lighting settings. The important difference is that our method includes additionally an appearance-related parameter based on the density distribution of the generalized sector $(\boldsymbol{\rho}_{\mathrm{feature}}(\beta))$. Therefore a record in the database is the salient appearance map of the rendering object, and not merely a texture map for a certain fixed geometric pattern.

Once HRIR-DB is set up at the online rendering phase, the appearance of hair strands inside a hair cluster can be visualized by texture mapping a series of alpha/reflectance maps of the cluster, which are dynamically constructed based on reflectance and opacity information provided by the HRIR-DB and according to the hair density distribution inside the cluster. After that, light-weight hair lighting calculations are performed on the fly to arrive at the final rendered results. By this collaboration between the online and the offline phases, our algorithm achieves both efficiency and high quality of output.

7.6.2 Minimizing the Size of HRIR-DB

To guarantee that our rendering algorithm will be fast and responsive, it is crucial also to control the size of the HRIR-DB so that it can be loaded completely into memory. This is a non-trivial goal. In existing BTF approaches they store 2D images sampled under different viewing and lighting directions, both being 2D vectors in spherical coordinates, which could easily result in the database having too huge a size for the memory. To overcome this size problem, we observe that as an HSV is only used to stand for a small part of hair volume, the lateral directions of the hair strands in an HSV are mostly consistent. Therefore, variations of viewing and lighting conditions along the lengthwise direction of the hair would only affect the global lengthwise rendering result. By taking advantage of this locality of hair distribution, we only attempt to model via the HRIR-DB different rendering effects brought about by the changes of the illumination conditions along the lateral direction of hair. Illumination conditions along the lengthwise direction of hair would only affect the global lengthwise rendering result, which can be efficiently calculated online. To be more specific, an HRIR represents the appearance of a generalized sector, β, which is a boundary cross section of an HSV with a certain density field defined inside. An HRIR represents the appearance of a generalized sector, β, under a certain viewing direction θ_v and lighting direction θ_l. We denote such an HRIR as $HRIR(\beta, \theta_v, \theta_l)$. $\theta_v(\beta)$ and $\theta_l(\beta)$ are respectively the 1D viewing and lighting direction in the current rendering, which are the azimuth angles on the plane that β lies on and obtained through projecting the 3D viewing and lighting directions onto the plane (see Fig. 7.1.(c)). By such restriction on the scope of hair appearances to be captured, the spectrum of samples the HRIR-DB is supposed to cover is greatly reduced. Each $HRIR(\beta, \theta_v, \theta_l)$ carries two kinds of information: reflectance values and opacity (alpha) values, represented as two 1D arrays: (*re-array*, *α-array*), which are offline partial results to be used in the online phase of the rendering (Sect. 7.7).

To compute $HRIR(\beta, \theta_v, \theta_l)$, we use a *planar ray tracing* procedure (Sect. 7.7.1). The difference between "planar ray tracing" and traditional ray tracing is that for the former, the viewing and lighting directions are both confined to the plane on which the planar rendering target, β, lies. Confining the rendering result $HRIR(\beta, \theta_v, \theta_l)$ to the 1D domain means that our HRIR-DB needs only to carry 1D signals of *re-array*s and *α-array*s and rely on a texture map synthesis algorithm to reconstruct the smooth-looking reflectance maps (*re-maps*) and alpha maps (*α-maps*) on the fly. Compared with storing a 2D reflectance map and an alpha map for a small volume of the hair shell, our 1D HRIR record format for a cross section of an HSV contributes significantly to miniaturization of the HRIR-DB. This downsizing is very important and effective.

With all these space-saving techniques, we effectively control the size of the HRIR-DB, making it feasible to load the HRIR-DB entirely into the main memory for carrying out the fast online rendering process.

7.7 Constructing the Database of Hair Rendering Intermediate Results

To construct the HRIR-DB, we first obtain a collection of samples of generalized sectors, $\{\beta_i\}$, by initializing control parameters of a generalized sector β using random values. For each of these generalized sector samples, two major tasks are performed for establishing the HRIR-DB: 1) to compute the HRIRs for β under a number of typical viewing and lighting directions (Sect. 7.7.1); these directions are all confined to the plane on which β lies; 2) to compute the hair density distribution feature vector $\boldsymbol{\rho}_{\text{feature}}(\beta)$ for β, which is used as an index when storing these HRIRs arising from β in the database. The top part of Fig. 7.2 summarizes the overall process of the HRIR-DB establishment.

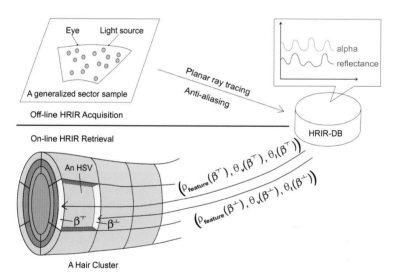

Fig. 7.2. HRIR-DB: In the offline rendering phase, generalized sectors of different density distributions are ray-traced in various viewing and lighting directions to generate *HRIRs* for establishing the HRIR-DB; in the online rendering phase, *HRIRs* are retrieved according to the index vector

7.7.1 Deriving an HRIR Record

We introduce a "planar ray tracing" procedure to compute HRIR for the given input generalized sector β with the viewing direction v and lighting direction l. The difference between "planar ray tracing" and those normal ray tracing procedures is that both the viewing and lighting directions are confined to the plane that the rendering target β lies on; and the rendering result HRIR, namely the hair appearance for β, is a 1D signal rather than a 2D image. We modify the ray tracing procedure for a volume as suggested in [YXYW00] into a planar version and carry out the procedure on β. After tracing all the rays and recording all the accumulated reflectance and opacity in their corresponding locations, we obtain an array of reflectance and an array of alpha values, which are denoted as *re-array* and *α-array* respectively. These two arrays constitute one single Hair Rendering Intermediate Result (HRIR) record.

More formally, when tracing a ray R_j, we denote the k-th grid point in the grid map (through which the hair density field is discretely recorded (Sect. 7.5.4)) met by R_j as $\eta_{j,k}$. We compute $\eta_{j,k}$'s opacity $\alpha(\eta_{j,k})$ as a value proportional to the local hair density $\rho(\eta_{j,k})$, and $\eta_{j,k}$'s reflectance $re(\eta_{j,k})$ using the Phong illumination model with the normal direction of hair strand surface approximated as the gradient of the local hair micro-density, i.e. $\mathbf{n}(\eta_{j,k}) \approx \nabla\rho(\eta_{j,k})$. During our planar ray tracing, after hitting R_j with $\eta_{j,k}$, we update R_j's accumulated reflectance $\widehat{re}(R_j)$ and its accumulated opacity $\widehat{\alpha}(R_j)$ by Eq. (7.5).

$$\begin{cases} \widehat{re}(R_j) = \widehat{re}(R_j) + \alpha(\eta_{j,k}) \times re(\eta_{j,k}) \times \left(1 - \widehat{\alpha}(R_j)\right) \\ \widehat{\alpha}(R_j) = \widehat{\alpha}(R_j) + \alpha(\eta_{j,k}) \times \left(1 - \widehat{\alpha}(R_j)\right) \end{cases}. \tag{7.5}$$

We also apply a visibility test with the accumulated opacity of a ray such that our algorithm stops tracing R_j when either the ray's accumulated opacity $\widehat{\alpha}(R_j)$ becomes very close to 1, or it has penetrated the rendering target, i.e. β. After tracing all the rays, we record all the penetrating rays' accumulated reflectances $\widehat{re}(R_j)$'s and opacities $\widehat{\alpha}(R_j)$'s at their corresponding pixel locations to establish a 1D array of reflectance values and another 1D array of alpha values. They form the HRIR.

Since it is normal for a hair strand to cover only a fraction of a pixel, severe aliasing artifacts may arise. To overcome this, the above computed HRIR will be smoothed using a 1D Gaussian kernel. The distribution feature parameter needed by the Gaussian kernel is set according to the distribution feature used when establishing the hair density field (Sect. 7.5.4). In our experiment we empirically find that a ratio of 1.5 times between them would lead to visually most satisfying results.

7.7.2 Indexing an HRIR Record

As outlined in Eq. (7.4), the complete index term for storing SATF$(\beta, \mathrm{v}, \mathrm{l})$ in the HRIR-DB is $\left(\rho_{\text{feature}}(\beta), \theta_{\mathrm{v}}(\beta), \theta_{\mathrm{l}}(\beta)\right)$. The schema is illustrated in the bottom part of Fig. 7.2. The feature vector $\rho_{\text{feature}}(\beta)$ consists of three terms in our design, i.e. $\rho_{\text{feature}}(\beta) \triangleq \left(\overline{\rho}_{st}(\beta), \overline{\rho}_{s}(\beta), \overline{\rho}_{t}(\beta)\right)$ where $\overline{\rho}_{st}(\beta)$, $\overline{\rho}_{s}(\beta)$, $\overline{\rho}_{t}(\beta)$ are β's average hair density, s-dimensional and t-dimensional projected average hair density respectively. The average hair density of β, $\overline{\rho}_{st}(\beta)$, can be trivially computed since the hair density distribution within β is either initially given or derived in the preprocessing step (Sect. 7.5.4). To compute $\overline{\rho}_{s}(\beta)$ and $\overline{\rho}_{t}(\beta)$, assume $\{s, t\}$ is the 2D parametric coordinate system defined over β. We first derive the density distribution histogram curves versus the s and t axes and then compute the average values of the derived histogram curves to be $\overline{\rho}_{s}(\beta)$ and $\overline{\rho}_{t}(\beta)$ respectively.

More mathematically, to derive the vector $\boldsymbol{\rho}_{\text{feature}}(\beta)$, recall $\{s,t\}$ is the 2D parametric coordinate system defined over β (Sect. 7.5.3). $\overline{\rho}_{st}(\beta)$, $\overline{\rho}_s(\beta)$ and $\overline{\rho}_t(\beta)$ are computed through Eq. (7.6).

$$
\begin{cases}
\overline{\rho}_{st}(\beta) \triangleq \dfrac{\int_{s_{\min}}^{s_{\max}} \int_{t_{\min}(s)}^{t_{\max}(s)} \rho(s,t)dtds}{\int_{s_{\min}}^{s_{\max}} \int_{t_{\min}(s)}^{t_{\max}(s)} dtds} & (7.6.1) \\[4mm]
\overline{\rho}_s(\beta) \triangleq \dfrac{1}{\int_{s_{\min}}^{s_{\max}} ds} \int_{s_{\min}}^{s_{\max}} \dfrac{\int_{t_{\min}(s)}^{t_{\max}(s)} \rho(s,t)dt}{\int_{t_{\min}(s)}^{t_{\max}(s)} dt} ds & (7.6.2) \\[4mm]
\overline{\rho}_t(\beta) \triangleq \dfrac{1}{\int_{t_{\min}}^{t_{\max}} dt} \int_{t_{\min}}^{t_{\max}} \dfrac{\int_{s_{\min}(t)}^{s_{\max}(t)} \rho(s,t)ds}{\int_{s_{\min}(t)}^{s_{\max}(t)} ds} dt & (7.6.3)
\end{cases}
\qquad (7.6)
$$

Here $\rho(s,t)$ is the local hair density around the spacial location (s,t) inside β.

Eq. (7.6.1) is approximated as:

$$
\overline{\rho}_{st}(\beta) \approx \widetilde{\rho}_{st}(\beta) \triangleq \sum_i \rho(s_i, t_i)/\sum_i,
$$

where $\{(s_i, t_i)\}$ is a set of randomly chosen spacial locations within β and $\rho(s_i, t_i)$ is the local density around the location (s_i, t_i). In our experiment, the cardinality of $\{(s_i, t_i)\}$ is set to be 10. Following the same practice, we also derive the randomized version of Eq. (7.6.2) as:

$$
\overline{\rho}_s(\beta) \approx \widetilde{\rho}_s(\beta) \triangleq \left(\sum_i \frac{\sum_{j(i)} \rho(s_i, t_{j(i)})}{\sum_{j(i)}} \right) / \sum_i,
$$

where $\{s_i\}$ is a set of randomly chosen s coordinates within β and $\{(s_i, t_{j(i)})\}$ is a set of locations within β, whose s coordinate is an element, s_i, of the set $\{s_i\}$ and whose t coordinate enumerates several randomly chosen values $t_{j(i)}$ for s_i. Similarly, we can derive the randomized version of Eq. (7.6.3) as:

$$
\overline{\rho}_t(\beta) \approx \widetilde{\rho}_t(\beta) \triangleq \left(\sum_j \frac{\sum_{i(j)} \rho(s_{i(j)}, t_j)}{\sum_{i(j)}} \right) / \sum_j.
$$

Now we can approximate $\boldsymbol{\rho}_{\text{feature}}(\beta)$ using $(\widetilde{\rho}_{st}(\beta), \widetilde{\rho}_s(\beta), \widetilde{\rho}_t(\beta))$.

7.8 Fast and High Quality Online Hair Rendering

7.8.1 Main Steps of Online Hair Rendering

As mentioned in Sect. 7.5 that hair clusters are rendering primitives in our algorithm. Given a hair cluster with a certain hair density field, we can render its appearance under arbitrary viewing and illumination directions efficiently and realistically with the support of the offline acquired HRIR-DB. Recall in Sect. 7.5.3 that a hair cluster consists of a transparent interior core and an exterior ring volume, the latter of which is divided into multiple layers.

By tessellating the outer surface of each of these layers, we obtain the layer's associated mesh. In the following we use $P_{(u,v),k}$ to denote the point on the mesh for the k-th layer of the hair cluster, whose coordinates in the parameterized texture space of the mesh is (u, v) (see Fig. 7.1). By definition, $P_{(u,v),k}$ and $P_{(u,v),k+1}$ have the same texture coordinates in their respective meshes.

The main steps of our online hair rendering are as follows, which are illustrated in Fig. 7.3. For each layer of the mesh, we use the local hair density distribution and the current viewing and lighting directions as input of the SATF to construct a *re-map* and an *α-map* (Sect. 7.8.2). For each point on a layer we compute a lighting term for it, with the anisotropy of hair appearance taken into account (Sect. 7.8.3). And then we simulate the self-shadowing effect by utilizing the computed *α-maps* and organize the resultant shadow values as a shadow map (*s-map*) (Sect. 7.8.4). Finally we derive the shading for each layer by modulating all the lighting terms belonging to the layer using corresponding reflectance values and shadow values recorded at the layer's *re-map* and *s-map* respectively. The final overall shading for the hair cluster can be generated by blending together individual shadings of the layers according to their *α-maps* (Sect. 7.8.5). We also make use of hardware acceleration (Sect. 7.8.6).

7.8.2 SATF and *re-* and *α-map* Construction

The first step of our online rendering is to construct the *re-maps* and *α-maps* for each layer in the hair cluster via the SATF. We realize this by first constructing local *re-maps* and *α-maps* for each HSV separately, and then patching up all these maps associated with the different HSVs in the same layer. There are two sub-tasks when constructing a local *re-map* and a local *α-map* for a given HSV: 1) to compute the parameters for the HSV's two boundary generalized sectors to retrieve the best matched HRIR(s) from the HRIR-DB; and 2) according to the extracted HRIR(s), to construct the *re-map* and the *α-map* for the HSV.

7.8.2.1 Calculating SATF parameters for HSV

Each HSV is associated with two boundary generalized sectors, one at the top, $\beta^{\top}$, and one at the bottom, $\beta^{\perp}$ (see Fig. 7.2). For each of them, say β, we calculate a hair density distribution feature vector $\boldsymbol{\rho}_{\text{feature}}(\beta)$ (see Sect. 7.7.2). The SATF parameters for β are completed by putting together the current viewing and lighting directions w.r.t. β, namely $Params(\beta) = \left(\boldsymbol{\rho}_{\text{feature}}(\beta), \theta_{\text{v}}(\beta), \theta_{\text{l}}(\beta)\right)$.

With both $Params(\beta^{\top})$ and $Params(\beta^{\perp})$ calculated as described in the above, we check whether the rendering context of the HSV—hair density distribution inside the HSV as well as the lighting and viewing directions across the HSV—is relatively uniform or not. It is considered uniform if Eq. (7.7) holds:

$$||Params(\beta^{\top}) - Params(\beta^{\perp})|| < \kappa^{\text{threshold}}. \tag{7.7}$$

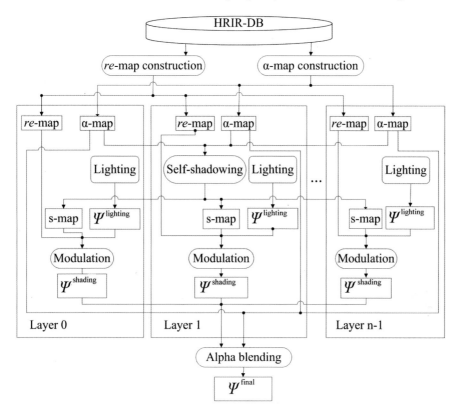

(a) The online rendering procedure

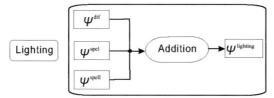

(b) The online lighting sub-procedure

Fig. 7.3. Our online phase rendering algorithm: (a) Main steps. For each layer of the generalized disk, first a *re-map* and an *α-map* are constructed procedurally with the help of HRIR-DB and according to the hair density distribution within the layer as well as the current viewing and illumination directions. And then an *s-map* is computed by our fast self-shadowing algorithm. Having prepared all the rendering maps, our algorithm performs shading for each layer of the mesh. For each pixel in a certain layer of the mesh, lighting is simulated. The resultant lighting term is modulated by the reflectance values sampled from the *re-map* and the light transmittance sampled from the *s-map* to calculate the RGB value of the pixel. Finally, all the layers of meshes are blended together according to the *α-maps* to generate the final rendering image. (b) The sub-procedure of the online lighting step, which computes a diffuse term, a primary and a secondary specular term. An example showing intermediate results generated at various steps of our online phase rendering algorithm is given at Fig. 7.4

(a) *re-map*   (b) *α-map*   (c) *s-map*   (d) Ψ^{dif} (e) Ψ^{speI}

(f) Ψ^{speII} (g) Ψ^{lighting} (h) Ψ^{shading} (i) Ψ^{final}

Fig. 7.4. An example showing intermediate results generated at various steps of our online phase rendering algorithm

7.8.2.2 Constructing *re-map* and *α-map* for HSV

If the rendering context across the HSV is considered uniform, we simply use $Params_{\mathrm{ave}} \triangleq (Params(\beta^{\top}) + Params(\beta^{\perp}))/2$ to retrieve the best matched HRIR record, $\mathrm{HRIR}(Params_{\mathrm{ave}})$, from the HRIR-DB. Recall that an HRIR carries two 1D arrays: a *re-array* and an *α-array* (Sect. 7.6 and Sect. 7.7.1). In this situation we can construct the local *re-map* and *α-map* for the HSV by simply sweeping the *re-array* and *α-array* along the lengthwise direction of the HSV.

If by Eq. (7.7) the rendering condition across the HSV is non-uniform, we would fetch two HRIR records, $\mathrm{HRIR}_1 = \mathrm{SATF}\big(Index(\beta^{\top})\big)$ and $\mathrm{HRIR}_2 = \mathrm{SATF}\big(Index(\beta^{\perp})\big)$. The local *re-map* and *α-map* for the HSV can then be generated by interpolating between HRIR_1 and HRIR_2. Assume $\mathrm{HRIR}_1 \triangleq \{c_{1,1}, c_{1,2}, \cdots, c_{1,n}\}$ and $\mathrm{HRIR}_2 \triangleq \{c_{2,1}, c_{2,2}, \cdots, c_{2,n}\}$, where $c_{i,j}$ is either the j-th reflectance value or the j-th alpha value carried in HRIR_i ($i = 1, 2; 0 < j \leqslant n$). Then the intermediate value can be derived through a linear interpolation:

$$\lambda(i, \gamma) = c_{1,i} \times (1 - \gamma) + c_{2,i} \times \gamma, \tag{7.8}$$

where γ is the interpolation parameter which indicates the relative position of the intermediate value between HRIR_1 and HRIR_2. This simple linear interpolation might not appear to be good enough to generate a smooth looking texture transition. Our experiment results, however, show that this simple method can indeed yield visually satisfying results. This could be due to the following two reasons: 1) local hair lighting conditions and density distributions change continuously, and so the difference in reflectance and alpha values between two adjacent HRIRs is limited; 2) as long as the surface of a hair cluster is not too severely undersampled, the sufficient number of sample points would reduce the texture difference between corresponding sample points in the two HRIRs.

We construct *re-maps* and α-*maps* for all the layers in the generalized disk, which are to be used for deriving shading for these meshes on the fly (Sect. 7.8.5). In the following, we use $re_{(u,v),k}$ and $\alpha_{(u,v),k}$ to denote the reflectance and opacity of $P_{(u,v),k}$ recorded in the reflectance map and alpha map of the k-th layer, namely re-map_k and α-map_k, respectively.

7.8.3 Online Hair Lighting

Similar to the practice in [Sch04], our hair rendering pays special attention to the anisotropic characteristics of hair appearance.

For each $P_{(u,v),k}$, we evaluate a diffusion term $\Psi^{\mathrm{dif}}_{(u,v),k}$, a primary specular term $\Psi^{\mathrm{speI}}_{(u,v),k}$, and a secondary specular term $\Psi^{\mathrm{speII}}_{(u,v),k}$. That is, in our system the online hair lighting term $\Psi^{\mathrm{lighting}}_{(u,v),k}$ for $P_{(u,v),k}$ is the overall effect of the above three terms:

$$\Psi^{\mathrm{lighting}}_{(u,v),k} \triangleq \Psi^{\mathrm{dif}}_{(u,v),k} + \Psi^{\mathrm{speI}}_{(u,v),k} + \Psi^{\mathrm{speII}}_{(u,v),k}. \tag{7.9}$$

Like [KK89], we compute the diffusion terms of the lighting model as:

$$\Psi^{\mathrm{dif}}_{(u,v),k} \triangleq \kappa^{\mathrm{dif}} \sin(\mathbf{t}_{(u,v),k}, \mathbf{l}_{(u,v),k}) \phi^{\mathrm{dif}}, \tag{7.10}$$

where κ^{dif} is the diffusion coefficient; $\mathbf{t}_{(u,v),k}$ and $\mathbf{l}_{(u,v),k}$ are the tangent direction and the lighting direction at the point $P_{(u,v),k}$ respectively; $\phi^{\mathrm{dif}} = (\phi^{\mathrm{dif}}.r,\ \phi^{\mathrm{dif}}.g,\ \phi^{\mathrm{dif}}.b)^{\mathrm{T}}$ is the diffusion color of the hair in the form of RGB values. Notice: the operator $\sin(\mathbf{X}, \mathbf{Y})$ here calculates the sine value of the angle spanned by the two vectors $\mathbf{X}$ and $\mathbf{Y}$.

Following Marschner et al.'s work [MJC+03], we simulate two highlight regions at our online hair lighting stage: one is the primary region which is shifted towards the tip part of the hair and the other is a secondary region which is shifted towards the root part of the hair. To evaluate the specular term for the primary highlight we employ Eq. (7.11), which is a modified version of [KK89]'s specular equation.

$$\begin{cases} \Psi^{\mathrm{speI}}_{(u,v),k} \triangleq \kappa^{\mathrm{speI}}\Big((\tilde{\mathbf{t}}_{(u,v),k} \cdot \mathbf{l}_{(u,v),k})(\tilde{\mathbf{t}}_{(u,v),k} \cdot \mathbf{v}_{(u,v),k}) + \\ \qquad \sin(\tilde{\mathbf{t}}_{(u,v),k}, \mathbf{l}_{(u,v),k})\sin(\tilde{\mathbf{t}}_{(u,v),k}, \mathbf{v}_{(u,v),k})\Big)^{\kappa^{\mathrm{h}}} \phi^{\mathrm{speI}} \\ \tilde{\mathbf{t}}_{(u,v),k} \triangleq \dfrac{\mathbf{t}_{(u,v),k} + s_{(u,v),k} \times \mathbf{n}_{(u,v),k}}{\|\mathbf{t}_{(u,v),k} + s_{(u,v),k} \times \mathbf{n}_{(u,v),k}\|} \end{cases} \tag{7.11}$$

Here κ^{speI} is the primary specular coefficient. κ^{h} is the specular Phong exponent specifying the sharpness of the highlight. $\mathbf{l}_{(u,v),k}$ and $\mathbf{v}_{(u,v),k}$ are the lighting and viewing vectors at $P_{(u,v),k}$ respectively. $\phi^{\mathrm{speI}} = (\phi^{\mathrm{speI}}.r,\ \phi^{\mathrm{speI}}.g,$

$\phi^{\text{speI}}.b)^{\text{T}}$ is the primary specular color of the hair, which is same as the color of the light source because the primary highlight is mainly due to the light reflected off the hair surface. $\tilde{\mathbf{t}}_{(u,v),k}$ is the perturbed version of $\mathbf{t}_{(u,v),k}$, which is introduced here to shift the primary highlight region towards the tip of the hair by adding a small portion of the normal vector of the cluster surface, $\mathbf{n}_{(u,v),k}$, onto the true hair tangent direction, $\mathbf{t}_{(u,v),k}$. Such a primary highlight region shift process is controlled by a positive parameter $s_{(u,v),k}$.

The secondary specular term is computed through a very similar equation, as follows:

$$
\begin{cases}
\boldsymbol{\Psi}^{\text{speII}}_{(u,v),k} \triangleq \kappa^{\text{speII}}\big((\tilde{\mathbf{t}}_{(u,v),k} \cdot \mathbf{l}_{(u,v),k})(\tilde{\mathbf{t}}_{(u,v),k} \cdot \mathbf{v}_{(u,v),k}) + \\
\qquad \sin(\tilde{\mathbf{t}}_{(u,v),k}, \mathbf{l}_{(u,v),k}) \sin(\tilde{\mathbf{t}}_{(u,v),k}, \mathbf{v}_{(u,v),k})\big)^{\kappa^h} \phi^{\text{speII}} \\
\tilde{\mathbf{t}}_{(u,v),k} \triangleq \frac{\mathbf{t}_{(u,v),k} - s_{(u,v),k} \times \mathbf{n}_{(u,v),k}}{||\mathbf{t}_{(u,v),k} - s_{(u,v),k} \times \mathbf{n}_{(u,v),k}||}
\end{cases} \quad . \quad (7.12)
$$

Here $\phi^{\text{speII}} = (\phi^{\text{speII}}.r, \phi^{\text{speII}}.g, \phi^{\text{speII}}.b)^{\text{T}}$ is the secondary specular color of the hair, which is the same as the color of the hair because the secondary highlight is mainly caused by the light transmitted into the hair strands and its reflection. κ^{speII} is the secondary specular coefficient. This time $\tilde{\mathbf{t}}_{(u,v),k}$ serves as a perturbed version of the hair's tangent direction to shift the secondary highlight region towards the root of the hair by deducting a small portion of the normal vector of cluster surface, $\mathbf{n}_{(u,v),k}$, from the true hair tangent direction, $\mathbf{t}_{(u,v),k}$. Such a highlight region shift process is also controlled by a positive parameter $s_{(u,v),k}$.

7.8.4 Online Hair Self-shadowing

During online hair rendering we compute two kinds of hair self-shadows: local shadows within a hair cluster and global shadows among multiple hair clusters. To simulate global shadows among hair clusters we employ the shadow volume technique [Cro77]. In the following we explain how we simulate local shadows within a hair cluster.

For local shadows within a hair cluster, complicated interactions between light rays and hair volume need to be considered. Kajiya and Hersen [KK89] first applied ray tracing to compute self-shadows during hair rendering. Later researchers proposed methods based on shadow maps [LV00, KN01, AL04]; the same idea was recently exploited by [MKBR04, KHS04] to achieve fast rendering with hair self-shadowing utilizing the power of the GPU.

Inspired by shadow map techniques, we use shadow maps (s-$maps$) to record results of simulated self-shadowing effects, one for each layer. In s-map_k, the s-map for the k-th layer, we store transmittance of light $\tau_{(u,v),k}$ at point $P_{(u,v),k}$, which approximates the portion of external light penetrating the hair volume to reach $P_{(u,v),k}$. To calculate $\tau_{(u,v),k}$ precisely, all the points that are passed through by the same light ray as $P_{(u,v),k}$ need to be identified, which is computationally expensive. Current shadow map-based approaches, e.g. "opacity shadow map" [KN01], avoid this expense through a separate pass to render the scene from the light's point of view to prepare the shadow maps. This separate pass, however, is in any case a non-zero computation load, which is still undesirable for a fast rendering algorithm. Our method completely does away with this additional separate pass by taking advantage of the property of our layered generalized disk structure for hair clusters: self-shadows are always cast from the outer layers onto the inner layers. Since human eyes are not highly sensitive to the accuracy of shadowing, we introduce a simple and fast method to simulate the shadowing effect which gets darker as we move from the outer layers to the inner layers. Therefore, in our method, $\tau_{(u,v),k}$ is estimated as:

$$\tau_{(u,v),k} \triangleq e^{-\sum_{m\in\chi(k)} \kappa^{\text{shadow}} \times \alpha_{(u,v),m}} \approx 1 - \kappa^{\text{shadow}} \times \sum_{m\in\chi(k)} \alpha_{(u,v),m}, \quad (7.13)$$

where $\chi(k) \triangleq \{m \mid \text{layer } L_m \text{ covers layer } L_k$, namely L_m is an outer layer w.r.t. $L_k\}$. In the above equation, κ^{shadow} is a self-shadow intensity parameter controlling the darkness of self-shadowing, and $\alpha_{(u,v),m}$ is the light attenuation of $P_{(u,v),m}$ as recorded at $\alpha\text{-}map_m$.

Compared with recent shadow map approaches, our shadow map generation method is very fast because it has a computationally trivial shadow map preparation process in which we only need to sample $\alpha\text{-}maps$ to read out alpha values with the same texture coordinates. Although our method is not theoretically exact, in practice it can achieve visually satisfying results, as can be seen in the examples shown in Figs. 7.5 and 7.6; this is due to the fact that by design the HSVs in our generalized disk structure are not very large, and hence the hair layers are not very thick.

7.8.5 Deriving Shading through Integrating All the Rendering Effects Together

By integrating all the rendering effects obtained in the previous steps, we derive the shading for each layer. For $P_{(u,v),k}$, its overall shading result, $\Psi^{\text{shading}}_{(u,v),k}$, in terms of RGB value is the product of its lighting term, $\Psi^{\text{lighting}}_{(u,v),k}$, its reflectance term, $re_{(u,v),k}$, as recorded in $re\text{-}map_k$, and the light transmittance term, $\tau_{(u,v),k}$, as recorded in $s\text{-}map_k$:

$$\Psi^{\text{shading}}_{(u,v),k} \triangleq \Psi^{\text{lighting}}_{(u,v),k} \times re_{(u,v),k} \times \tau_{(u,v),k}. \quad (7.14)$$

With $\Psi^{\text{shading}}_{(u,v),k}$, the RGBA value for $P_{(u,v),k}$ can be extracted as: ($\Psi^{\text{shading}}_{(u,v),k}.r$, $\Psi^{\text{shading}}_{(u,v),k}.g$, $\Psi^{\text{shading}}_{(u,v),k}.b$, $\alpha_{(u,v),k}$). Once the shading results for all the layers are calculated, we can derive the final hair rendering image Ψ^{final} by blending the shading results of all the layers through a standard alpha blending process:

$$\Psi^{\text{final}}_{(u,v)} \triangleq \Psi^{bk}_{(u,v)} \times \prod_{k=0}^{n-1}\left(1-\alpha_{(u,v),k}\right)+ \\ \sum_{k=0}^{n-1}\left(\Psi^{\text{shading}}_{(u,v),k} \times \alpha_{(u,v),k} \times \prod_{j=k+1}^{n-1}\left(1-\alpha_{(u,v),j}\right)\right). \quad (7.15)$$

Here $\Psi^{\text{final}}_{(u,v)} = (\Psi^{\text{final}}_{(u,v)}.r \ \Psi^{\text{final}}_{(u,v)}.g \ \Psi^{\text{final}}_{(u,v)}.b)^{\text{T}}$ is the RGB value in the final hair rendering image that is in correspondence with the eye ray $R_{(u,v)}$.

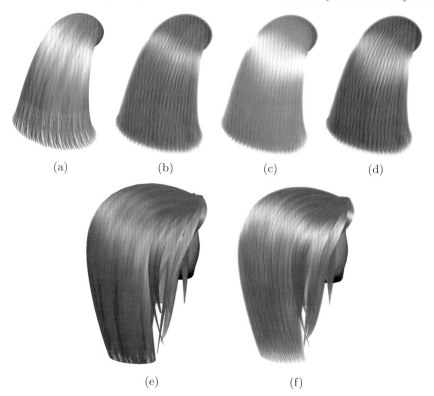

Fig. 7.5. Comparison of rendering results: (a) rendering result produced by Scheuermann's algorithm; (b) result produced by our algorithm with secondary highlight effect disabled; (c) result produced by our algorithm with self-shadowing effect disabled; (d) result produced by our algorithm with all the effects enabled. A comparison between rendering results of a human hair model is shown at (e) and (f). (e) rendering result produced by Scheuermann's algorithm; (f) result of human hair by our algorithm

$$\mathbf{\Psi}^{bk}_{(u,v)} = (\mathbf{\Psi}^{bk}_{(u,v)}.r \ \mathbf{\Psi}^{bk}_{(u,v)}.g \ \mathbf{\Psi}^{bk}_{(u,v)}.b)^{\mathrm{T}}$$ is the RGB value of the penetrating light from the interior core on $R_{(u,v)}$, which is taken from the background color.

7.8.6 Hardware Acceleration

Our algorithm is carefully constructed and implemented to take advantage of the computing power offered by current programmable graphics cards. For each layer, the constructed *re-map* and *α-map* are organized as two channels in a texture map to be passed simultaneously to the graphics card. To efficiently eliminate texture aliasing when an object is at a distance, we enable hardware MIP-mapping. The highest resolution MIP-map image is the original texture map initially passed to the graphics card, as mentioned above. Each successively lower resolution MIP-map image is computed by averaging every four neighboring pixels in its immediately preceding higher resolution

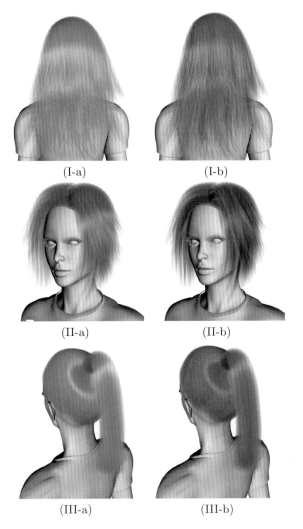

(I-a)   (I-b)

(II-a)   (II-b)

(III-a)   (III-b)

Fig. 7.6. The effect of self-shadowing: results without self-shadowing (a) vs. results with self-shadowing (b)

version. For the online phase of our rendering algorithm, except for constructing the *re-* and *α-map*s and the above MIP-map source image preparation process, all the other computing tasks are executed by the GPU. More exactly, inside the GPU the vertex shader passes down all the necessary data including viewing and lighting directions, surface normals, hair tangent directions, as well as texture coordinates to the pixel shader. The pixel shader is responsible for computing the *s-map*s, performing lighting calculation, modulating all the lighting terms against the light transmittance terms stored in the *s-map*s, and the reflectance terms stored in the *re-map*s. The derivation of the final shading result is implemented using the alpha blending functionality provided by the graphics card when we render the layers of meshes from inside out.

7.9 Experiment Results

We implemented our algorithm using Microsoft Visual C++ 6.0 and Microsoft Direct3D V9.0 on a PC with an Intel Core 2 Duo 2.4GHz CPU, 1G main memory and a graphics card having an NVIDIA GeForce 7950GT processor. In our implementation we take advantage of the graphics card's computing power by executing most of the online rendering tasks through pixel shaders and vertex shaders.

In the offline phase we generate the HRIR-DB by sampling uniformly over the viewing and lighting directions at an interval of 1 degree, and sampling 128 randomly generated hair density distributions inside an HSV under the given viewing and lighting directions. This results in an HRIR-DB containing around $180 \times 180 \times 128 = 4,147,200$ HRIR records and having a total size of about 500MB. The offline stage took 2 hours to complete.

We show the rendering results of six hair clusters with different geometries and density distributions in Fig. 7.7, and twelve hair models on a human head

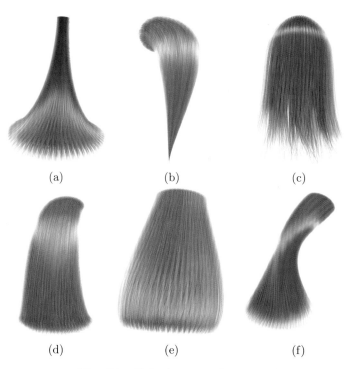

(a)   (b)   (c)

(d)   (e)   (f)

Fig. 7.7. Hair cluster rendering results

in Fig. 7.8. A partial sequence of hair animation results are shown in Fig. 7.9.

We also render several hair styles in multiple views in Fig. 7.10 and Fig. 7.11. Fig. 7.12 illustrates the performance statistics of all these examples and the time needed to fulfill various stages of our online phase of the rendering algorithm, which include estimating the hair density distribution parameter for the SATF (index calculation); computing the SATF, i.e. HRIR-DB lookup, and the re/α-map construction (map construction); texture mapping the constructed re/α-$maps$ onto the generalized disk structure; online hair lighting; and online hair shadowing. For the hair animation results (Fig. 7.9), the statistics reported are for the average performance. Table 7.2 reports these detailed data. The performance is clearly of real-time quality when rendering a single hair cluster and of interactive quality when rendering a human hair model.

Table 7.2. Statistics of hair rendering experiments shown in Fig. 7.7 to Fig. 7.11, including the total number of hair clusters (Cluster#), layers (Layer#), hair strands (Strand#) and HSVs (HSV#) in the hair model as well as rendered image resolution and the overall Frames Per Second (FPS) rate achieved by our rendering algorithm

No.	Experiment	Cluster#	Layer#	Strand#	HSV#	Resolution	FPS
1	Fig. 7.7.(a)	1	12	2,208	12,672	280×745	71
2	Fig. 7.7.(b)	1	15	2,812	15,840	500×600	49
3	Fig. 7.7.(c)	1	10	3,680	41,600	695×956	34
4	Fig. 7.7.(d)	1	15	2,895	15,840	366×600	54
5	Fig. 7.7.(e)	1	10	1,850	10,560	400×600	77
6	Fig. 7.7.(f)	1	15	2,760	15,840	400×600	47
7	Fig. 7.8.(a)	12	60	19,680	61,440	600×680	26
8	Fig. 7.8.(b)	4	36	12,024	74,880	783×837	22
9	Fig. 7.8.(c)	6	55	13,695	58,080	841×903	31
10	Fig. 7.8.(d)	6	42	21,252	87,360	735×796	19
11	Fig. 7.8.(e)	2	40	18,680	83,200	574×593	22
12	Fig. 7.8.(f)	2	20	8,120	83,200	823×893	21
13	Fig. 7.8.(g)	7	70	11,760	73,920	530×818	22
14	Fig. 7.8.(h)	6	54	18,684	112,320	659×792	16
15	Fig. 7.8.(i)	5	34	12,706	70,176	680×680	20
16	Fig. 7.8.(j)	2	34	15,817	140,352	696×705	13
17	Fig. 7.8.(k)	1	20	9,022	82,560	676×685	22
18	Fig. 7.8.(l)	8	52	19,432	108,160	680×680	15
19	Fig. 7.9	40	80	21,440	42,240	700×700	21
20	Fig. 7.10.(I)	6	60	9,120	63,360	728×721	30
21	Fig. 7.10.(II)	4	60	20,340	126,720	673×664	14
22	Fig. 7.10.(III)	2	28	23,044	115,584	636×636	14
23	Fig. 7.11.(I)	5	50	9,050	52,800	556×653	26
24	Fig. 7.11.(II)	7	49	10,965	51,744	590×614	29
25	Fig. 7.11.(III)	55	224	32,841	64,608	680×680	11
26	Fig. 7.11.(IV)	52	130	30,064	70,680	680×680	9

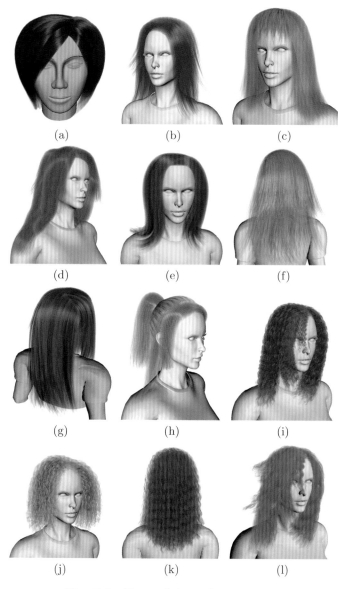

(a)   (b)   (c)

(d)   (e)   (f)

(g)   (h)   (i)

(j)   (k)   (l)

Fig. 7.8. Human hair rendering results

From these performance statistics, we can see that the number of clusters and the number of HSVs are two principal factors affecting the overall FPS. Interestingly, Fig. 7.10(III) and Fig. 7.11(III) have similar FPSs. However, Fig. 7.11(III) has 27 times more clusters than Fig. 7.10(III), but yet the number of HSVs of Fig. 7.11(III) is half that of Fig. 7.10(III). These two factors in fact cancel out and result in a similar overall FPS. We can also draw the conclusion from this phenomenon that the performance of our algorithm is more sensitive to the number of HSVs than the number of clusters. This sug-

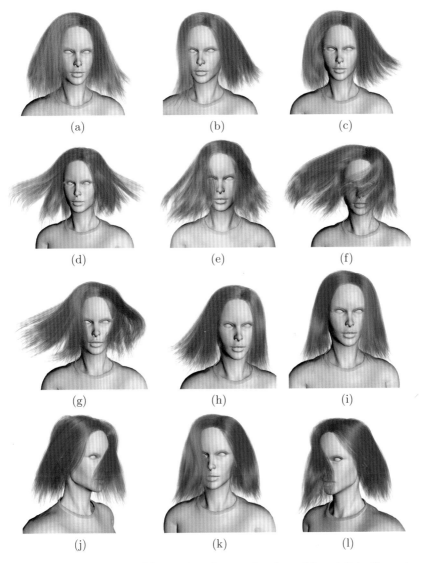

Fig. 7.9. Two sequences of hair animation results. (a to h) and (i to l) are two sequences of hair animation, which happened to have similar timing performance. The minimal and maximal FPSs of rendering either animation are 19 and 23 respectively. The average FPS is 21. More average performance statistics are reported in Table 7.2

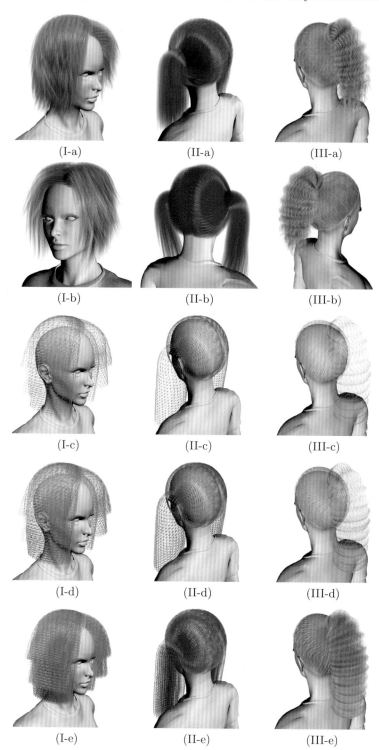

(I-a)   (II-a)   (III-a)

(I-b)   (II-b)   (III-b)

(I-c)   (II-c)   (III-c)

(I-d)   (II-d)   (III-d)

(I-e)   (II-e)   (III-e)

Fig. 7.10. Three hair models rendered in different views (a), (b) together with their underlying generalized disk structure's outmost layer (c), their two outmost layers (d) and all the layers (e)

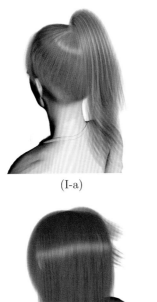
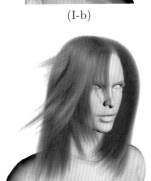

(I-a)   (I-b)

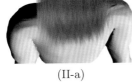
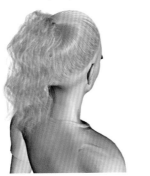
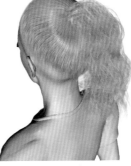

(II-a)   (II-b)

(III-a)   (III-b)

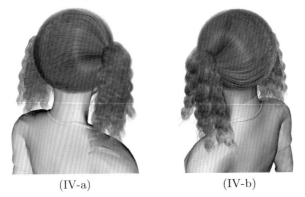

(IV-a)   (IV-b)

Fig. 7.11. Four more hair models rendered in different views

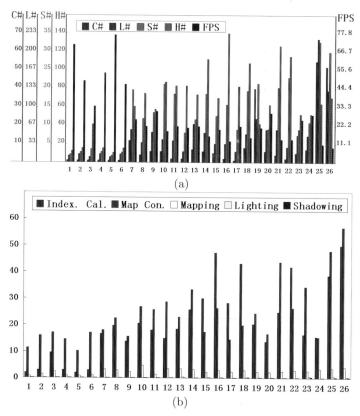

Fig. 7.12. Performance statistics. The numbers on the *x*-axis reflect the hair model numbers in the leftmost column of Table 7.2. In (a), the performance statistics include number of clusters (C#), number of layers (L#), number of hair strands (S#) (in K, i.e. in 1,000), number of HSVs (H#) (in K) and the overall FPS for each hair model. In (b), each table entry presents the computation time in milliseconds consumed by each step

gests future research to adaptively optimize the number of HSVs according to the screen resolution and the sophistication of the models.

Our approach in achieving high quality hair rendering effects can be seen as similar to that of Kajiya-Kay for hair modeling and rendering via volume densities [KK89]. We add three features: (I) varying visual effects to reflect changes in hair distributions as well as the viewing and lighting directions; (II) shifted secondary highlight effect as proposed by Marschner, et al. [MJC+03]; and (III) self-shadowing effect. We compare the rendering results produced by our algorithm with those using Scheuermann's algorithm [Sch04]. We choose Scheuermann's for comparison because among all the existent work, his algorithm is the closest to ours in that his algorithm is also based on Kajiya-Kay's; also both our own and Scheuermann's algorithms are designed for the purpose of efficient hair rendering. But Scheuermann's algorithm has incorporated only the effect (II) above. Fig. 7.5 shows the com-

Table 7.3. The computation time in milliseconds consumed by each step of the online phase of our rendering algorithm for the examples reported in Fig. 7.2, i.e. index calculation (Index Cal.), map construction (Map Con.), texture mapping, online lighting, shadowing

No.	Experiment	Index Cal.	Map Con.	Mapping	Lighting	Shadowing
1	Fig. 7.7.(a)	1.9/13.8%	11.3/79.9%	0.7/5.2%	0.1/0.6%	0.1/0.5%
2	Fig. 7.7.(b)	2.9/14.1%	15.9/77.8%	1.4/6.9%	0.1/0.7%	0.1/0.5%
3	Fig. 7.7.(c)	9.5/32.4%	17.1/58.3%	2.4/8.0%	0.2/0.7%	0.2/0.6%
4	Fig. 7.7.(d)	3.0/16.2%	14.5/78.1%	0.9/5.0%	0.1/0.4%	0.1/0.3%
5	Fig. 7.7.(e)	1.9/15.0%	10.2/78.2%	0.8/5.8%	0.1/0.5%	0.1/0.5%
6	Fig. 7.7.(f)	2.9/13.4%	17.1/80.6%	1.1/5.1%	0.1/0.5%	0.1/0.4%
7	Fig. 7.8.(a)	16.7/43.5%	18.1/47.0%	3.2/8.3%	0.2/0.6%	0.2/0.6%
8	Fig. 7.8.(b)	19.7/43.3%	22.5/49.6%	2.9/6.4%	0.2/0.4%	0.1/0.3%
9	Fig. 7.8.(c)	13.9/43.0%	15.7/48.6%	2.4/7.4%	0.2/0.5%	0.2/0.5%
10	Fig. 7.8.(d)	20.6/39.1%	26.9/51.2%	4.7/9.0%	0.2/0.4%	0.2/0.3%
11	Fig. 7.8.(e)	18.1/39.9%	25.7/56.6%	1.4/3.1%	0.1/0.2%	0.1/0.2%
12	Fig. 7.8.(f)	15.0/31.6%	28.7/60.2%	3.5/7.3%	0.2/0.5%	0.2/0.4%
13	Fig. 7.8.(g)	18.5/40.7%	22.9/50.3%	3.5/7.7%	0.4/0.8%	0.2/0.5%
14	Fig. 7.8.(h)	25.7/41.1%	33.3/53.3%	3.2/5.1%	0.2/0.3%	0.1/0.2%
15	Fig. 7.8.(i)	30.0/59.9%	17.4/34.8%	2.2/4.3%	0.3/0.6%	0.2/0.4%
16	Fig. 7.8.(j)	47.2/61.3%	26.3/34.2%	2.9/3.8%	0.3/0.4%	0.2/0.3%
17	Fig. 7.8.(k)	28.2/62.0%	14.5/31.9%	2.4/5.3%	0.2/0.4%	0.2/0.4%
18	Fig. 7.8.(l)	43.1/64.7%	19.9/29.8%	3.0/4.5%	0.3/0.5%	0.3/0.5%
19	Fig. 7.9	20.3/42.6%	24.3/51.1%	2.4/5.1%	0.3/0.7%	0.2/0.5%
20	Fig. 7.10.(I)	13.7/41.0%	16.7/50.1%	2.2/7.2%	0.3/1.0%	0.2/0.7%
21	Fig. 7.10.(II)	24.8/34.7%	43.7/61.2%	2.5/3.5%	0.2/0.3%	0.2/0.3%
22	Fig. 7.10.(III)	41.9/58.6%	26.3/36.8%	3.0/4.2%	0.2/0.2%	0.1/0.2%
23	Fig. 7.11.(I)	16.4/42.7%	34.3/48.0%	2.7/6.9%	0.5/1.3%	0.4/1.1%
24	Fig. 7.11.(II)	15.6/45.1%	15.4/44.6%	3.3/9.5%	0.1/0.4%	0.1/0.4%
25	Fig. 7.11.(III)	38.6/42.5%	47.8/52.6%	3.7/4.1%	0.5/0.5%	0.3/0.3%
26	Fig. 7.11.(IV)	49.8/44.8%	56.6/50.9%	4.0/3.6%	0.4/0.4%	0.3/0.3%

parative results where (a) is Scheuermann's result and (d) is our result. In comparison (a) looks flat and lacks the sense of stereo because his algorithm does not simulate the effects (I) and (III) in the above. The Fig. 7.5((b) and (c)) also shows how the effects (II) and (III) would enhance the realism of the rendered result. Fig. 7.5. (e) and (f) compares the two algorithms with a complete hair model.

Due to space limitations, more experiment results are put on our website, together with our prototype system implementing the algorithm and the files of hair styles used in our rendering experiments.

7.10 Conclusion and Future Work

7.10.1 Conclusion

In this chapter we propose a new method for hair rendering which can achieve both interactive speed and high quality on ordinary hardware. The following five aspects of our work contribute to this feasibility. 1) Resting on the assumption that retrieving a data record from a suitably constructed database can be many times faster than computing the same on the fly, the method employs an offline/online two-phase strategy. This strategy reduces a major, time-consuming step of the rendering process to a quick and simple database lookup, leaving only a few remaining lightweight tasks to the online phase. 2) The online phase features the new texture function SATF which interacts with the static database to return an image for a given set of dynamically computed parameters. The rendering target is a hair cluster, and its semantics are represented compactly by a hair density distribution. This representation turns hair strands in a neighborhood into a kind of virtual aggregate material with the appearance of a texture. This design can increase the appearance modeling ability of the method and greatly simplify the geometry details that need to be considered during hair rendering. 3) Like BRDF and BTF approaches, we represent our SATF for the target virtual aggregate material via a database. The establishment of the database is the major task of the offline part of the design. Special attention is needed when making design decisions on the contents to be captured by the database, data representation, and the choice of the database's index structure. These efforts effectively reduce the size of the resultant database and contribute significantly to the fast lookup mechanism. 4) The modeling of the hair (as virtual aggregate material) is via a four-level modeling hierarchy which captures the highly complex geometry of the entire hair volume as well as the detailed hair strand distribution inside. We also introduce a specific data structure called "generalized disk" as a rather handy medium for representation. 5) By utilizing intermediate results obtained during the online phase of the above rendering algorithm, our method uses a shadow map based, fast self-shadow generation algorithm to further enhance the rendering realism.

As an immediate next step we will integrate the efficient and high-quality hair rendering algorithm proposed in this chapter into our virtual hairy brush based digital painting platform to provide more realistic visual feedback of the paintbrush for the end users during their electronic painting experiences.

7.10.2 Discussion and Future Work

Our proposed rendering algorithm is based on a database of precomputed intermediate results, which can achieve interactive rates in hair rendering without lowering the image quality. The mapping from input parameters to the precomputed hair rendering intermediate results forms our Semantics-Aware Texture Function (SATF), which is a form of parameterized BTF. The dimensionality involved in the mapping is reduced by making some simplification assumptions concerning visual aspects. These intermediate results are then used to compute for each hair strand a *re-map* and an *α-map*. These maps are further used to compute images including different lighting effects, which are then combined to form a single final rendering result. For a volumetric model of a generalized cylinder, the rendering treats hair strand meshes like shells, projecting them from the inner-most ring to the outer-most one.

Compared with conventional appearance modeling approaches such as BRDF and BTF, which only model the light transmission under certain viewing and lighting conditions for fixed material or a fixed geometry pattern, our new approach can be interpreted as a way to model the aggregate appearance of the target as a special kind of virtual "material appearance property". By such an aggregate virtual material appearance property, the challenge of rendering the highly sophisticated geometry of the target object can be reduced to applying an image-based rendering over a much smoother and simplified surface geometry, followed by some computationally inexpensive online lighting and shadowing procedures.

Our offline/online rendering algorithm is also related to Image-Based Rendering (IBR) [MB95, LH96, GGSC96]. But unlike IBR, whose rendering capability derives mainly from the information captured in the image database, by including appearance-related semantics features in the modeling function and the extension of a lightweight and effective online rendering phase, our rendering algorithm can perform much more comprehensively in terms of its support for dynamically changing rendering scenes. In fact, our work can be viewed as a special image-based rendering algorithm capable of responding to dynamic changes in the target.

In our design of the online/offline two-phase rendering algorithm, to capture the reflectance we split the computation task into two parts: in the offline process we only consider appearance changes arising due to lighting and viewing changes along the lateral directions of the hair; in the online phase we focus on reproducing appearance changes due to lighting conditions along the lengthwise direction of the hair. The split is based on the following regarding the effects caused by lighting conditions. To capture the effects caused by different lighting conditions in the lateral direction, we need to take into account the delicate hair geometry and its tiny volume, distribution and positions, which is the most time consuming part of the rendering work. In comparison, the effects caused by different lengthwise direction lighting conditions are much easier to compute, which only needs to be operated at the level of hair cluster geometry. The split leads to much time saving in the online phase. A secondary benefit is that this can narrow the spectrum of HRIR samples that the HRIR-DB is supposed to capture, giving rise to a database that is more compact in size.

Currently most of the hair we rendered are of straight styles. To support curly hair rendering we will need to introduce additional semantics in our current hair appearance modeling function. Developing a better user interface for creating and customizing curly hair styles is a highly practical goal.

There are limitations to our approach: 1) Since we employ clustering in the hair modeling hierarchy and assume the hair strands in one cluster are roughly aligned to the sweeping trajectory of the cluster during rendering, we cannot handle highly chaotic hair styles at the moment. 2) Backlighting is not simulated because we assume lights do not come from behind when we apply ray-tracing to render the generalized sector samples and when we simulate self-shadowing.

The following are some possible directions for further work. First, for hair volumes whose density distribution is extremely non-uniform, their density following our current formulation of the density terms may not be reliable enough to identify the best matched HRIR records in the HRIR-DB. So the issue is to investigate what might be a better compact set of expressive and reliable features.   Second, one could refine the current algorithm to adaptively divide the whole hair volume into HSVs according to the density distribution. For an HSV in which the density distribution varies greatly, we can subdivide it into smaller HSVs until the density distribution in each HSV becomes relatively uniform; on the other hand, for adjacent HSVs whose density features are nearly identical, we can merge them into one larger HSV. This adaptive division/merging may help improve both the efficiency and realism of the algorithm significantly.   Third, following [FKIS02], it might be meaningful to use machine learning techniques to "compress" the HRIR-DB so that memory space will only be used to store representative records. Finally, right now our SATF for hair uses synthetic (as opposed to real) data, but theoretically our new appearance modeling approach should be applicable to real, camera-captured images. Capturing appearance measurement data and extending our algorithm to handling dynamically changing real non-homogeneous materials, e.g. fire and hair in motion, should be extremely challenging.

The research work presented in this chapter is an initial attempt to build semantics features directly into the appearance modeling function. These features are density-related in the case of hair, and because of that we believe the same methodology can be applied to the modeling and rendering of other objects such as smoke, cloud, grass, fire and the like. Our success in designing the fast offline/online hybrid algorithm has to do with the capturing of appearance-related semantics. For hair as well as grass, cloud, smoke, etc., their appearance under certain viewing and lighting conditions is mostly determined by their density distribution. Thus we can categorize density distribution features for these targets as semantics-related information and build them into the appearance model. An offline/online algorithm can then be designed, just like what has been done in this chapter.

Table 7.4. Symbols and abbreviations used in this chapter

Symbol	Definition	Description
SATF	Sect. 7.2	Semantics-Aware Texture Function
(s,t)	Sect. 7.5.4	Position in a generalized sector
(u,v)	Sect. 7.8.1	The position of a certain point on a certain layer of mesh, defined in texture space
$\alpha_{(u,v),k}$	Sect. 7.8.2.2	The alpha value of a point at (u,v) on the k-th layer of the mesh
$\alpha(\eta_{j,k})$	Sect. 7.7.1	Opacity of $\eta_{j,k}$, proportional to $\eta_{j,k}$'s local density
α-$array$	Sect. 7.6	Alpha array of HRIR
α-map	Sect. 7.8.1	Alpha map
α-map_k	Sect. 7.8.2.2	The α-map for the k-th mesh
$\widehat{\alpha}(R_j)$	Sect. 7.7.1	Accumulated opacity along a certain tracing ray R_j
β	Sect. 7.5.4	A generalized sector
$\beta^{\top}, \beta^{\perp}$	Sect. 7.8.2.1	Upper and bottom boundary βs of an HSV
$\{\beta_j\}$	Sect. 7.7	A collection of samples of generalized sectors
$\eta_{j,k}$	Sect. 7.7.1	The k-th point in the grid map met by R_j
$\theta_l(\beta), \theta_v(\beta)$	Sect. 7.6	1D lighting and viewing directions w.r.t. β
κ^{shadow}	Sect. 7.8.4	Local self-shadow darkness coefficient. Typical value: 0.4
$\kappa^{\text{threshold}}$	Sect. 7.8.2.1	Uniform hair density distribution tolerance threshold. Typical value: $\lVert (0, \frac{\pi}{180}, \frac{\pi}{180}) \rVert$
$\rho(\eta_{j,k})$	Sect. 7.7.1	$\eta_{j,k}$'s local density
$\rho(s,t)$	Sect. 7.5.4	Local density in the hair micro-density field at (s,t)
$\overline{\rho}_s(\beta), \overline{\rho}_t(\beta)$	Sect. 7.7.2	s- and t-dimensional projected average densities of β
$\overline{\rho}_{st}(\beta)$	Sect. 7.7.2	Average density of β
$\rho_{\text{feature}}(\beta)$	Sect. 7.6	Hair density distribution feature of β
σ	Sect. 7.5.4	Gaussian distribution parameter. Typical value: 0.5
$\tau_{(u,v),k}$	Sect. 7.8.4	Transmittance of light to (u,v) on the k-th layer of the mesh
$\chi(k)$	Sect. 7.8.4	The set of layers covering the k-th layer
$\Psi^{\text{lighting}}_{(u,v),k}$	Sect. 7.8.3	The lighting term of (u,v) on the k-th layer of the mesh
$\Psi^{\text{dif}}_{(u,v),k}$	Sect. 7.8.3	Diffuse term of (u,v) on the k-th layer of the mesh
$\Psi^{\text{speI}}_{(u,v),k}, \Psi^{\text{speII}}_{(u,v),k}$	Sect. 7.8.3	Primary and secondary specular terms of a point at (u,v) on the k-th layer of the mesh
$\Psi^{\text{shading}}_{(u,v),k}$	Sect. 7.8.5	Shading term of (u,v) on the k-th layer of the mesh
Ψ^{final}	Sect. 7.8.5	The final rendering result of a hair cluster

To be continued

$\mathbf{c}_i$	Sect. 7.5.4	A hair center in a generalized sector
$g(s, t, \mathbf{c}_i)$	Sect. 7.5.4	Gaussian distribution function. $g(s, t, \mathbf{c}_i) \triangleq \frac{1}{\sigma\sqrt{2\pi}} e^{-|\mathbf{c}_i - (s,t)|^2/(2\sigma^2)}$
HRIR	Sect. 7.6	Hair Rendering Intermediate Result
HRIR-DB	Sect. 7.6	Hair Rendering Intermediate Result DataBase
HSV	Sect. 7.5.3	Hair Sector Volume
$\mathbf{n}(\eta_{j,k})$	Sect. 7.7.1	Normal direction used in Phong illumination model while ray-tracing. $\mathbf{n}(\eta_{j,k}) \approx \nabla\rho(\eta_{j,k})$
$P_{(u,v),k}$	Sect. 7.8.1	A point at the position of (u, v) on the k-th layer of the mesh
$Params(\beta)$	Sect. 7.8.2.1	The index of β
$Params_{\text{ave}}$	Sect. 7.8.2.2	The average of the index of two boundary generalized sectors, i.e. $Param_{\text{ave}} \triangleq (Param(\beta^\top) + Param(\beta^\perp))/2$
$re_{(u,v),k}$	Sect. 7.8.2.2	The reflectance value of a point at (u, v) on the k-th layer of the mesh
$re(\eta_{j,k})$	Sect. 7.7.1	Reflectance value of $\eta_{j,k}$, computed with Phong model
re-$array$	Sect. 7.6	Reflectance array of HRIR
re-map_k	Sect. 7.8.2.2	The reflectance map for the k-th mesh
$\widehat{re}(R_j)$	Sect. 7.7.1	Accumulated reflectance along a certain tracing ray R_j
s-map	Sect. 7.8.1	Shadow map

References

[AL04] Timo Aila and Samuli Laine. Alias-free shadow maps. In *Proceedings of Eurographics Symposium on Rendering*, Norrkoping, Sweden: Eurographics Association, pages 161–166, 2004.

[BCN03] Yosuke Bando, Bing-Yu Chen, and Tomoyuki Nishita. Animating hair with loosely connected particles. *Computer Graphics Forum*, 22(3):411–418, 2003.

[Bli82] James F. Blinn. Light reflection functions for simulation of clouds and dusty surfaces. In *Proceedings of ACM SIGGRAPH Conference*, New York, NY, USA: ACM Press, pages 21–29, 1982.

[Cro77] Franklin C. Crow. Shadow algorithms for computer graphics. In *Proceedings of ACM SIGGRAPH Conference*, San Jose, CA, USA: ACM Press, pages 242–248, 1977.

[DvGNK99] Kristin J. Dana, Bram van Ginneken, Shree K. Nayar, and Jan J. Koenderink. Reflectance and texture of real-world surfaces. *ACM Transactions on Graphics*, 18(1):1–34, 1999.

[FKIS02] Ryo Furukawa, Hiroshi Kawasaki, Katsushi Ikeuchi, and Masao Sakauchi. Appearance-based object modeling using texture database: acquisition, compression and rendering. In *EGRW '02: Proceedings of the 13th Eurographics Workshop on Rendering*, Aire-la-Ville, Switzerland: Eurographics Association, pages 257–266, 2002.

[GGSC96] Steven J. Gortler, Radek Grzeszczuk, Richard Szeliski, and Michael F. Cohen. The lumigraph. In *SIGGRAPH '96: Proceedings of the 23rd Annual Conference on Computer Graphics and Interactive Techniques*, New Orleans, LA, USA: ACM Press, pages 43–54, 1996.

[Gol97] Dan B. Goldman. Fake fur rendering. In *SIGGRAPH '97: Proceedings of the 24th Annual Conference on Computer Graphics and Interactive Techniques*, Los Angeles, CA, USA: ACM Press/Addison-Wesley Publishing Co., pages 127–134, 1997.

[KH84] James T. Kajiya and Brian P. Von Herzen. Ray tracing volume densities. *Proceedings of ACM SIGGRAPH Conference*, New York, NY, USA: ACM Press, pages 165–174, 1984.

[KHS04] Martin Koster, Jorg Haber, and Hans-Peter Seidel. Real-time rendering of human hair using programmable graphics hardware. In CGI'04: *Proceedings of Computer Graphics International*, Grete, Greece: ACM Press, pages 248–256, 2004.

[KK89] James T. Kajiya and Timothy L. Kay. Rendering fur with three-dimensional textures. *Computer Graphics (SIGGRAPH)*, 23(3):271–280, 1989.

[KN01] Tae-Yong Kim and Ulrich Neumann. Opacity shadow maps. In *Proceedings of the 12th Eurographics Workshop on Rendering*, London, UK, pages 177–182, 2001.

[LH96] Marc Levoy and Pat Hanrahan. Light field rendering. In *SIG-GRAPH '96: Proceedings of the 23rd Annual Conference on Computer Graphics and Interactive Techniques*, New Orleans, LA, USA: ACM Press, pages 31–42, 1996.

[LPFH01] Jerome Lengyel, Emil Praun, Adam Finkelstein, and Hugues Hoppe. Real-time fur over arbitrary surfaces. In *I3D '01: Proceedings of the 2001 Symposium on Interactive 3D Graphics*, Triangle Park, NC, USA: ACM Press, pages 227–232, 2001.

[LV00] Tom Lokovic and Eric Veach. Deep shadow maps. In *SIG-GRAPH '00: Proceedings of the 27th Annual Conference on Computer Graphics and Interactive Techniques*, New Orleans, LA, USA: ACM Press/Addison-Wesley Publishing Co., pages 385–392, 2000.

[MB95] Leonard McMillan and Gary Bishop. Plenoptic modeling: an image-based rendering system. In *SIGGRAPH '95: Proceedings of the 22nd Annual Conference on Computer Graphics and Interactive Techniques*, Los Angeles, CA, USA: ACM Press, pages 39–46, 1995.

[MJC+03] Stephen R. Marschner, Henrik W. Jensen, Mike Cammarano, Steve Worley, and Pat Hanrahan. Light scattering from human hair fibers. In *SIGGRAPH '03: ACM SIGGRAPH 2003 Papers*, San Diego, CA, USA: ACM Press, pages 780–791, 2003.

[MKBR04] Tom Mertens, Jan Kautz, Philippe Bekaert, and Frank Van Reeth. A self-shadow algorithm for dynamic hair using density clustering. In *Proceedings of Eurographics Symposium on Rendering*, Norrkoping, Sweden: Eurographics Association, 2004.

[MTHK02] Nadia Magnenat-Thalmann, Sunil Hadap, and Prem Kalra. State of the art in hair simulation. *International Workshop on Human Modeling and Animation*. Seoul, Korea: Korea Computer Graphics Society, pages 3–9, 2002.

[NRH+77] F.E. Nicodemus, J.C. Richmond, J.J. Hsia, I.W. Ginsberg, and T. Limperis. Geometric considerations and nomenclature for reflectance. *Monograph 161, National Bureau of Standards (US)*, 1977.

[PH89] Kenneth Perlin and Eric Hoffert. Hypertexture. In *SIGGRAPH '89: Proceedings of the 16th Annual Conference on Computer Graphics and Interactive Techniques*, Boston, MA, USA: ACM Press, pages 253–262, 1989.

[Ree83] William T. Reeves. Particle systems—a technique for modeling a class of fuzzy objects. *ACM Transactions on Graphics*, 2(2):91–108, 1983.

[Sch04] Thorsten Scheuermann. Practical real-time hair rendering and shading. In *SIGGRAPH '04: ACM SIGGRAPH 2004 Sketches*, Los Angeles, CA, USA: ACM Press, page 147, 2004.

[WBK+07] Kelly Ward, Florence Bertails, Tae-Yong Kim, Stephen R. Marschner, Marie-Paule Cani, and Ming C. Lin. A survey on hair modeling: styling, simulation, and rendering. *IEEE Trans-*

actions on Visualization and Computer Graphics, 13(2):213–234, 2007.

[XLTP03] Songhua Xu, Francis C. M. Lau, Feng Tang, and Yunhe Pan. Advanced design for a realistic virtual brush. *Computer Graphics Forum (Proceedings of Eurographics '03)*, 22(3):533–542, 2003.

[XY01] Zhan Xu and Xuedong Yang. V-hairstudio: an interactive tool for hair design. *IEEE Computer Graphics and Applications*, 21(3):36–43, 2001.

[YXYW00] Xudong Yang, Zhan Xu, Jun Yang, and Tao Wang. The cluster hair model. *Graphical Models*, 62(2):85–103, 2000.

Part IV

Automatic Generation of Artistic Chinese Calligraphy

This part consists of three chapters, Chapter 8—Chapter10, sharing one common target which is the generation of artistic Chinese calligraphy automatically through machine intelligence.

Chapter 8 introduces our own computing principles for generating artistic Chinese calligraphy automatically. It discusses an algorithmic framework simulating the human learning process of calligraphy skills which range from copying existing calligraphy to synthesizing new calligraphic styles based on learned examples. The chapter goes on to explain the way to enforce aesthetic constraints for controlling the visual quality of the automatically generated calligraphic artwork. This chapter aims at providing a high-level abstract view of, and a quick introduction to, a computing system design for achieving the automatic artistic generation goal. Accompanying the framework are some overall pictures and case examples on the behavior of the underlying algorithmic components. We defer the discussion of the algorithmic details and the mathematics behind this till Chapter 9. A set of experiments using the prototype system are presented to give the readers a concrete impression of the quality achievable by the automatic calligraphy generation system. At the end of the chapter we suggest some interesting applications arising from the automatic calligraphy generation system we have developed, including practical and commercial ones outside the computer art domain.

Chapter 9 offers two perspectives on a better understanding of the automatic artistic Chinese calligraphy generation work introduced in Chapter 8: from a system engineering point of view and from an artificial intelligence research point of view, respectively. For the first perspective we focus on how to re-implement the prototype system we have at hand and reproduce the experiment results shown in Chapter 8. Intensive algorithm constructs and mathematical models employed in the low level of our algorithmic framework supporting the system's functioning are revealed and discussed. They provide the reference materials for anyone needing to overcome potential problems that will be encountered in trying to build an automatic Chinese calligraphy generation system similar to ours. For the second perspective we review and discuss the design philosophy behind our attempt to explore the topic of automatic calligraphy generation—the synthesis reasoning model and its support for carrying out analogous reasoning for the purpose of simulating creative thinking in an imaginary thinking domain, especially when human beings are performing shape related tasks. This answers the basic question of what makes us think it is possible and technically feasible to develop a computing system that is capable of generating artistic Chinese calligraphy automatically. Is it by pure luck or some random process, or are there any general models, rules or mechanisms which we have followed? We present the synthesis reasoning model and its related knowledge representation and reasoning mechanisms for simulating analogous reasoning in the imaginary thinking domain as a fundamental theory. This theory explains the algorithm design work we studied in the first part of the chapter, offering a view from the angle of artificial intelligence research to understand the steps we go through in building the intelligent system. The success of the design and development of our intelligent Chinese calligraphy generation system has come from our following the guidelines suggested by the synthesis reasoning model and its associated theory. Towards the end of this chapter, we discuss why our automatic calligraphy generation system can be viewed as a specialized instance of an intelligent shape design system based on the synthesis reasoning model. We also look at how constraints can affect the behavior of an intelligent system designed according to the synthesis reasoning model and conclude the chapter by proposing a generic methodology for developing synthesis reasoning based intelligent systems for computer aided design.

Chapter 10 looks at the issue of performance for our intelligent Chinese calligraphy system. We particularly focus on two algorithmic components which could significantly improve the system performance: 1) how to increase the system's calligraphy facsimile ability, which is reflected as the system's ability to parameterize existent calligraphy-writing samples for use as learning samples; 2) how to equip the intelligent calligraphy generation system with the capability to tell the beautiful looking calligraphy examples from the not so beautiful ones. By enhancing the first component, the amount of knowledge learnable by the intelligent system can be expanded to give better training to the intelligent system so that it will have the ability to explore and generate new calligraphy styles. Augmenting the second component can make the system better aware of the quality of its generated results, and capable of command visual scores approaching those conceived by humans. To enhance the first component, we adopt an integrated intelligence approach which uses and combines a multitude of existent algorithms. We further introduce an intelligent graphical user interface for utilizing human intelligence in the most economic fashion to increase the system's decomposition ability over cursive calligraphy writings. To strengthen the second component we design a sophisticated learning paradigm based on neural networks to teach the computer to grade calligraphy to best approximate the human grading. We integrate both improved components into our automatic calligraphy generation system and obtain a very encouraging performance gain in terms of the visual quality of the newly generated Chinese calligraphic artwork. We include a collection of experiment results for the readers to verify this claim. Finally, we give a sketch of an interactive calligraphy online tutoring system based on our automatic calligraphy generation system.

Principles of Automatic Generation of Artistic Chinese Calligraphy

8.1 Overview

In this chapter we will introduce a novel intelligent system which can automatically generate new Chinese calligraphic artwork to meet visually aesthetic requirements. The system first extracts the hierarchical parametric representations of Chinese characters from input images of existing calligraphic style to form a compact set of training examples. Using a six-layer hierarchical representation, the extraction results are stored in a small structural stroke database, which are then exploited to form a continuous calligraphy knowledge space. The space is spanned by character examples of different styles (knowledge sources) which are aggregated and aligned according to a proposed constraint-based analogous reasoning process. By also incorporating a set of simple and yet effective geometric constraints, the proposed system can generate novel calligraphic styles that are aesthetically appealing. Samples of novel calligraphic artwork produced using the system are presented to demonstrate the effectiveness of our approach. The combination of knowledge from various input sources creates a huge space for the intelligent system to explore and produce new styles of calligraphy. Possible applications of the proposed system are also discussed.

Without ambiguity we will abbreviate the term "automatic generation of artistic Chinese calligraphy" to "automatic calligraphy generation" from now on.

8.2 Introduction

Chinese calligraphy is among the finest and most important of all Chinese art forms, and an inseparable part of Chinese history. It can convey not just what was explicitly put in a written message but also the emotion of the writer. The very delicate aesthetic effects achievable by Chinese calligraphy are generally considered to be unique among all calligraphic arts because the normal shape and topological structure of the font in aesthetic Chinese calligraphy can be largely distorted for its better perceptual impression. Chinese calligraphy is also an integral part of traditional Chinese painting, e.g. Fig. 8.1(a). The calligraphy is there not just as an annotation, but also because it can affect the overall visual and perhaps also emotional perception of the viewer to the painting. As such, artistic Chinese calligraphy is often more preferred than printed types in Asian societies for banners and signs, and headers of newspapers, etc. (Fig. 8.1(b)). A latest example is the official logo of the 2008 Beijing Olympics Games (http://en.beijing-2008.org/).

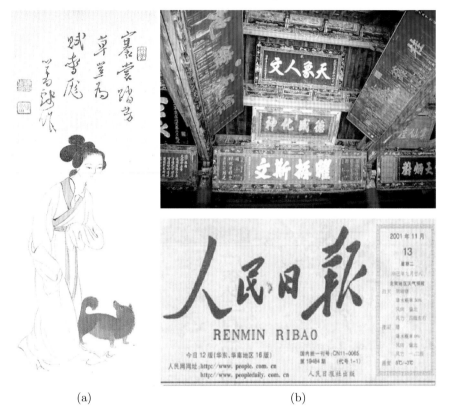

(a)   (b)

Fig. 8.1. Wide use of artistic Chinese calligraphy in Asian societies: (a) Chinese painting with calligraphy; (b) top: the roof of a Kong Zi (Confucius) temple; bottom: the header of the China Daily newspaper

Other than artists, it has also caught the attention of scientists who are interested in computer-assisted art. Chinese calligraphy is predominantly done using a brush. Computerizing Chinese calligraphy is challenging as the shapes of brush strokes as well as the topology over multiple strokes can be very complex. In comparison, Western calligraphy which is based on Latin alphabets is much simpler and easier to computerize.

The most common use of calligraphic art in the digital world is to create typographic or artistic fonts for display or printing, for which Knuth has done some pioneering work [Knu79]. Chinese calligraphy is predominantly carried out using a soft hair brush. Generating artistically appealing Chinese calligraphic artwork using the brush can be highly challenging. The large character set (consisting of 3,000+ commonly used characters) of the Chinese language itself presents a problem. Being able to master some of the characters does not mean that one can also write the other characters as satisfactorily. Similarly, one who is good in one or more styles is not necessarily also good in other styles, let alone able to create new styles in calligraphy. This is where the computer may step in and provide some help.

Calligraphic art is based on a font, which is a set of printer's type of the same size and face. Cubic Bézier curves and straight lines can be used to describe font shapes [Chu90, NTN93]. For artistic rendering, researchers have tried to model the brush used in calligraphy, such as [Str86] where the brush is modeled as a collection of bristles which evolve over the course of the stroke. In [XTLP02] a virtual brush based on solid modeling was demonstrated as a feasible interactive tool for creating realistic Chinese calligraphic writings. In [Blu67] the authors gave a detailed analysis of the writing effects that hairy brushes could produce. There have also been attempts at automatic generation of new fonts, such as [PMZS97] where the authors employed an algebra of geometric shapes to generate fonts by mixing existing fonts. But calligraphy can go beyond the boundaries of fonts; for example, it is possible to mix different styles and sizes of characters in a calligraphic artwork.

There has not been any published work on automatic creation (not just imitation) of beautiful calligraphic artwork using existing calligraphy as learning samples. This chapter proposes and describes such an intelligent system. We discuss the underlying principles and theories, and present the calligraphic results generated by a prototype we implemented. Our prototype system is able to generate brand new Chinese calligraphic artwork fully automatically. The number of input training samples used is very small.

In this chapter we propose an intelligent system which can automatically generate novel and yet artistically appealing Chinese calligraphic artwork based on a small number of training examples of existing calligraphic styles. The essential idea is to learn (good existing styles) and synthesize (beautiful new styles). The system first recovers the shapes of the training examples and represents them using a hierarchical parameterization. Then an analogous reasoning process is adopted to: 1) align the shape representations of the training examples to create a flexible model; 2) to generate novel calligraphic artwork; and 3) to remove aesthetically unacceptable candidates based on some simple but effective aesthetic constraints.

To demonstrate the feasibility of the proposed methodology, we have implemented a prototype system which can generate brand new Chinese calligraphic artwork fully automatically when given as input a small training set (typically below 10 for each character). To the best of our knowledge, there has not yet been any published work on the same approach. One remotely related project is the simulation of creativity in jazz performance [RG94], where artistic activities are also modeled using analogous reasoning.

The structure of the chapter is as follows. Sect. 8.3 formulates the problem and provides an overview of the system. Sect. 8.4 presents the hierarchical parametric representation of Chinese characters. Sect. 8.5 discusses how the training examples are analyzed and parameterized. Sect. 8.6 explains the proposed analogous reasoning process for automatic generation of new Chinese calligraphic characters. Sect. 8.7 discusses how aesthetic geometrical constraints can be incorporated into the system to reject unacceptable candidates from the output. Sect. 8.8 gives the experimental results. Sect. 8.9 discusses possible applications of our system in addition to generating Chinese calligraphy. Sect. 8.10 concludes the chapter and suggests some possible directions for future research.

8.3 Problem Formulation and Overall System Architecture

Let $\mathcal{P}$ denote a model with a parameterization $\mathbf{E}$ that is flexible enough to represent a class of highly deformable shapes (a Chinese character of different styles in our case). Normally, constructing a flexible model requires significant effort. On the other hand, an arbitrary instantiation from a flexible model could easily result in unacceptable results. Thus, generating novel and yet aesthetically appealing calligraphy using the model-based approach is by no means straightforward. Our approach is to make use of a constraint-based analogous reasoning process, which we apply to a set of given training examples. The basic idea of analogous reasoning is to fuse knowledge from multiple sources to support a restricted form of reasoning [Sim75]. In our case the *knowledge sources* are the *training examples* (which are in the form of images), and these two terms will be used interchangeably throughout this chapter.

Our proposed analogous reasoning process consists of three major phases: *shape decomposition, calligraphic model generation from examples,* and *artistic calligraphy generation.*

Calligraphic shape decomposition. *Shape decomposition* (or recovery) of a given training example is equivalent to the problem of extracting structural features for constructing a reference model $\mathbf{P}$. The reference model is an instance of the model $\mathcal{P}$ to best represent the input example. The underlying mechanism is character stroke segmentation/extraction.

Calligraphic model generation from examples. Given n reference models $\{\mathbf{P}_i\}$ constructed from a set of training examples, a family of novel shapes $\mathbf{P}(\omega)$ can be defined by *blending* the n reference models, $\{\mathbf{P}_i\}$, where the blending steps include: 1) identifying the correspondence of structure features among the reference models, and 2) combining the aligned models, by interpolation/extrapolation of the parameterization $\{\mathbf{E}\}$. Note that the newly derived shape family can be perceived as "re-parameterization" via the blending parameter, ω, which controls the contribution of each training example.

Artistic calligraphy generation. Given $\mathbf{P}(\omega)$ and a set of aesthetics-related geometrical constraints, artistic calligraphic artwork can be obtained by identifying some ω which satisfies the given constraints.

Fig. 8.2 shows the overall architecture of the proposed intelligent calligraphy generation system. At the heart of the system is an analogous reasoning

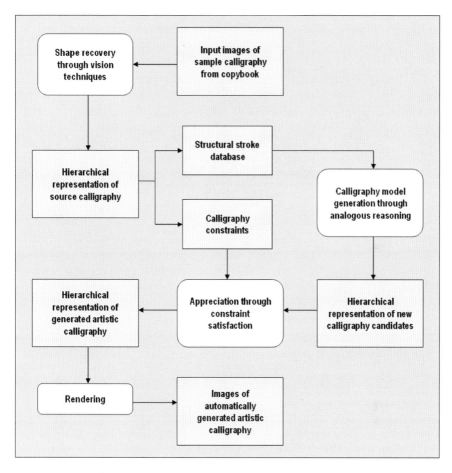

Fig. 8.2. Architecture of our intelligent calligraphy generation system

component that creates new calligraphy based on training examples and satisfying all the aesthetic constraints. In our experiments the training examples come from printed "copybooks" that present multiple calligraphic styles.

Our simulated analogous reasoning process is essentially data prediction (either interpolation or extrapolation) subject to the aesthetical constraints. For convenience we abbreviate "analogous reasoning process" to ARP and the current "simulated analogous reasoning process" to SARP.

The system has three main components. The first component learns and produces facsimiles of the existent calligraphic artwork in a hierarchical and parametric form; these facsimiles form a calligraphic knowledge base serving as the knowledge source for the SARP. The second component generates new calligraphic artwork automatically through the SARP. The third component applies constraint satisfaction to admit only those generated results that are aesthetically acceptable. The three components are referred to as the *facsimile component*, the *creation component*, and the *appreciation component*, respectively. The examination results led us to conclude that our approach is practical and the system is capable of generating acceptable outputs.

8.4 Hierarchical and Parametric Representation

No reasoning is possible and efficient without suitable knowledge representation. Before we elaborate on our intelligent calligraphy generation system based on analogous reasoning, we will first introduce our hierarchical and parametric representation of calligraphic artwork, which contributes tangibly to the overall system performance and reasoning capability.

In our system we treat Chinese characters and calligraphic artwork as images that are in a parametric form. This facilitates automatic processing of knowledge. Modern Chinese characters are derived from pictographs of complex shapes (see Fig. 8.5 for an example). The earliest Chinese characters are pictographs, which project meanings through shapes and images in an intuitive fashion. Over time these characters gradually became symbols and many basic features in different Chinese characters occur recurrently. To take advantage of this representation redundancy, we devise a hierarchical representation for Chinese characters.

8.4.1 Hierarchical Representation

It can be easily observed that many local features recur in many different Chinese characters frequently. To capitalize on this image information redundancy, we introduce a hierarchical representation of Chinese calligraphy. A piece of Chinese calligraphy as an image is decomposed into six layers (or levels): the constructive ellipse layer, the primitive stroke layer, the compound stroke layer, the radical layer, the single-character layer, and the complete artwork layer (see Fig. 8.3(b)).

This hierarchical representation can avoid much redundancy when storing the characters, and its various granularity makes SARP more effective and the input reasoning source as well as the output reasoning results more reusable. These six layers represent the calligraphic artwork parametrically. All the input parametric representations of the calligraphic artwork together form a reasoning space for the SARP to generate new aesthetic calligraphic artwork automatically.

The parametric representations adopted at all levels (to be described in the next subsection) together form the parameter space $\mathbf{E}$ for modeling Chinese calligraphic artwork.

For the prototype we have implemented 5 typical and most frequently occurring primitive strokes (point strokes, horizontal strokes, vertical strokes, left slanting strokes and right slanting strokes), 24 typical and most frequently occurring compound strokes, and 36 radicals are used, as shown in Fig. 8.4.

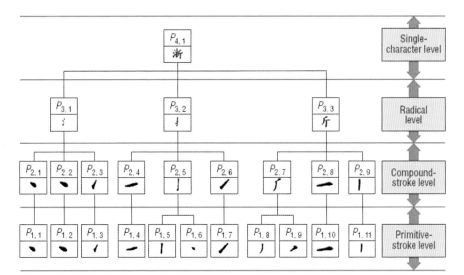

(a)

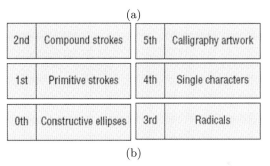

(b)

Fig. 8.3. (a) Hierarchical representation of a Chinese character (only four levels are shown); (b) Six-level hierarchical representation of calligraphy

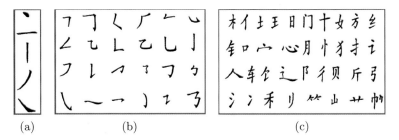

(a)   (b)   (c)

Fig. 8.4. (a) Five primitive strokes; (b) 24 compound strokes; (c) 36 radicals

Fig. 8.3(a) shows the hierarchical representation of the Chinese character "zhe", as in "Zhejiang", the beautiful coastal province well known for its wealth of scenic spots.

8.4.2 Six Levels of Parametric Representation

At Level 0 of the hierarchical representation, an artwork is viewed as a collection of ellipses. These ellipses are called the "constructive ellipses" of the artwork (Fig. 8.3(b)). The "image" of the artwork will be rendered as the regions in the image space that are covered by the constructive ellipses. This representation is inspired by the Blum model [Blu67], in which a zonary area is defined through an ellipse moving along a predefined curve. Each constructive ellipse is parameterized by a 4×1 matrix, in which two rows store the coordinates of the constructive ellipse's center and the other two rows store the lengths of the major and minor axes of the ellipse. When we traverse the hierarchy from bottom up, such constructive ellipses are first "lined" up to form "primitive strokes" (Level 1). Then primitive strokes are combined to form "compound strokes" (Level 2) and subsequently to radicals (Level 3). Shape grammar rules are used for the composition (see Sect. 8.5.2). By grouping radicals based on their spatial proximity, characters are formed (Level 4). The learned examples of the same character in different styles will be blended together to establish a flexible model of that character in the model creation step (see Sect. 8.6). Finally, at Level 5, there is the top-level constructive element, a calligraphy artwork, which may consist of more than one character.

8.4.3 Advantages of Our Representation

(1) Reasoning from a set of existent calligraphy styles to generate new writing styles belongs to the hard domain of qualitative reasoning. Our parametric representation offers a tool to attack the challenging qualitative reasoning problem through quantitative means—analogous reasoning together with aesthetic constraint satisfaction—to be described in the sequel.
(2) With the hierarchical representation, our intelligent system allows efficient local learning of constructive elements, and the huge global knowledge representation space is reduced to one characterizing only local shape variations. Besides, the hierarchical nature of our representation supports efficient retrieval (and thus reuse) of past calligraphic artwork reasoning results (to be described in the sequel) at different representation levels.
(3) With our hierarchical parametric representation, calligraphy in all styles, including the very cursive ones which are heavily deformed and distorted, can be represented in a uniform six-level hierarchy and processed using the same reasoning pipeline. This increases our system's capability to learn and generate cursive calligraphy, which is a very important aspect of aesthetic calligraphy and a hot area for calligraphy artists.

8.5 Calligraphic Shape Decomposition

This is the process in which the hierarchical and parametric representations are extracted from training examples—images of calligraphic artwork.

8.5.1 Extracting Levels 0–1 Elements

To extract primitive strokes and thus the corresponding constructive ellipses from a training example, we first compute the skeleton of the input image, that is to compute a close approximation to the actual trajectory of the brush when the calligraphic artwork was created. Various approaches have been proposed for skeletonizing binary images of characters. We employed the algorithm proposed in [HY00], where the extracted skeleton is composed of segmented *primitive strokes*. Fig. 8.5 gives a step-by-step illustration. Such a stroke decomposition is by no means optimal, and our system can benefit from any improved decomposition algorithm.[1] Once the skeletons of the primitive strokes are identified, all the constructive ellipses can be computed efficiently using the Bresenham ellipse rasterization algorithm.

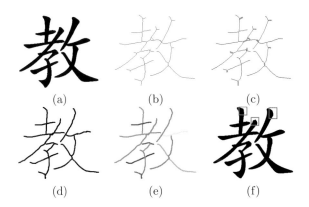

(a)   (b)   (c)

(d)   (e)   (f)

Fig. 8.5. Extracting Levels 0-1 elements of a character from its image: (a) The input image of a character, (b) the raw skeleton computed using a thinning algorithm, (c) the plausible short branches detected and color marked, (d) the short branches identified and removed, (e) the skeleton segmented into different strokes in the character and color coded, and (f) the reconstructed character using the extracted Levels 0-1 elements. Note that the reconstructed image (f) and the original image (a) have some slight differences at the ends of some of the strokes, e.g. areas indicated by the red rectangles

8.5.2 Extracting Levels 2–3 Elements

We identify compound strokes and radicals by analyzing the spatial relation between the primitive and compound strokes, respectively, through carefully designed shape grammar production rules. The syntactic description of any

---

[1] To further enhance the robustness of the stroke identification step, several structural variants of the five primitive strokes (Fig. 8.4) were used.

constructive element is represented using the syntax of the production system and generated by rule deduction. As an example, the shape production rule for the compound stroke in the upper leftmost corner of Fig. 8.4(b), denoted as $\mathbf{CS}_1$, is as follows:

> IF horizontal(a) AND vertical(b) AND ontop(a,b) AND onleft(a,b) AND touch(a,b)
> THEN $CS_1 := \{a,b\}$,

where horizontal(a), vertical(b), ontop(a,b), onleft(a,b) and touch(a,b) are the predicates indicating the relationships of horizontal primitive stroke, vertical primitive stroke, $\mathbf{a}$ on top of $\mathbf{b}$, $\mathbf{a}$ on left side of $\mathbf{b}$ and $\{\mathbf{a},\mathbf{b}\}$ touching each other, respectively.

To increase the reliability of the extraction process, we make use of fuzzy set theory as in [LHS98] so that a confidence value will be associated with each shape grammar production rule via the deduction process. The overall confidence of the shape grammar production can be derived by the confidences of all its statements. The rule that yields the highest overall confidence will be applied for the corresponding stroke composition.

8.5.3 Extracting Level 4 Elements

To extract the constructive elements at Level 4, we need to determine the radicals that can be grouped together to form a character. This is equivalent to the well-known problem of "character segmentation" in the pattern recognition field. In our system we use the standard projection analysis as in [YS94] to segment the individual characters in a calligraphy artwork.

8.6 Calligraphic Model Creation from Examples

8.6.1 Principles of Calligraphic Model Creation

To generate new calligraphic artwork, we apply an Analogous Reasoning Process (ARP) to a set of training examples of different calligraphic styles. The notion of generation/synthesis in artistic design was discussed by Simon [Sim75] in 1975. Keane [Kea88a] applied analogical mechanisms to problem solving. In general one can understand ARP as a process that synthesizes novel knowledge (shapes in our case) by fusing (blending in our case) together certain knowledge sources (the training examples). To support the fusion, establishing feature correspondence between the knowledge sources is needed.

In principle the ARP can be applied at different levels of the hierarchy, resulting in different artistic effects. Assume that the ARP is applied to $\mathbf{P}_{k,m}$, the m-th constructive element at the k-th level of the hierarchical representation and there are n different versions of $\mathbf{P}_{k,m}$: $\mathbf{P}_{k,m}^1, \cdots, \mathbf{P}_{k,m}^n$ derived from the n training examples, i.e., the independent knowledge sources in the ARP. The result of the ARP is denoted as $\mathbf{P}_{k,m}^r$. Then the general mathematical principle in the adopted ARP can be stated as:

$$\mathbf{P}^r_{k,m} = \sum_{i=1}^{n} \omega^i \mathbf{P}^i_{k,m}, \tag{8.1}$$

where ω^i $(i = 1, \cdots, n)$ is defined as the analogous reasoning intensity for $\mathbf{P}^i_{k,m}$ with the constraint that $\sum_{i=1}^{n} \omega^i = 1$. Obviously, $\mathbf{P}^i_{k,m}$ with a higher value of ω^i contributes more to the overall reasoning result.

The suggested ARP can be interpreted as either an interpolation or an extrapolation process. Note that here we assume a one-to-one correspondence among different versions of $\mathbf{P}_{k,m}$. In reality, a constructive element (a constructive ellipse, a primitive stroke, etc.) derived from a training example can correspond to one element in another training example in more than one way. A feature correspondence step (to be described in the next subsection) is therefore required before one can blend together features extracted from the different examples. In our intelligent calligraphy generation system, all the analogous reasoning intensities can be adjusted by the user manually through a graphical interface; or they can be generated randomly and fed to a subsequent phase that automatically filters out the ones violating some aesthetics-related constraints.

8.6.2 Fusing Knowledge Sources in ARP

To establish the feature correspondence between training examples for knowledge fusion, we first derive a discrete planar curve for each constructive element $\mathbf{P}^i_{k,m}$ using the centers of all the constructive ellipses associated with it. The curve forms the skeleton of the element, and critical points on the planar curves are detected using the algorithm in [ZC95] as the key points for setting up the correspondence.

In our application we first assume the shape of a constructive element in the font style "Kai" (GB2312) as used in the recent version of Microsoft Word to be the standard reference, which we denote as $\mathbf{P}^{\text{std}}_{k,m}$. Note that because the shape of the element $\mathbf{P}_{k,m}$ has already been extracted in the shape decomposition phase, we can easily compute the deviation $\mathbf{F}^i_{k,m}$ by which the shape of the i-th source $\mathbf{P}^i_{k,m}$ differs from that of $\mathbf{P}^{\text{std}}_{k,m}$ through applying the shape difference operator $\ominus$. The exact definition of this operator will be provided and explained in detail in the next chapter.

$$\mathbf{F}^i_{k,m} \triangleq \mathbf{P}^i_{k,m} \ominus \mathbf{P}^{\text{std}}_{k,m} \tag{8.2}$$

With all the deviations of the reasoning sources $\mathbf{F}^1_{k,m}, \cdots, \mathbf{F}^n_{k,m}$ computed, we can then derive the overall deviation $\mathbf{F}^r_{k,m}$, as follows:

$$\mathbf{F}^r_{k,m} = \oslash(\mathbf{F}^1_{k,m}, \cdots, \mathbf{F}^n_{k,m}, \overline{\omega}), \tag{8.3}$$

where $\oslash$ is defined as the analogous reasoning mechanism simulation operator, which is currently implemented as an interpolation/extrapolation process in our prototype system. $\overline{\omega}$ is the *aesthetic viewpoint sequence* dictating the weights and order of the contributions from different sources. The ordered set of the intensities forms what is called the "viewpoint sequence" of the ARP. So not only will different reasoning intensities affect the final output, but different orders of presenting the training examples will also lead to different calligraphy results.

Finally, by adding back the shape of $\mathbf{P}_{k,m}^{\text{std}}$, the standard constructive element associated with the reasoning result $\mathbf{P}_{k,m}^{\text{r}}$ in the ARP, we obtain:

$$\mathbf{P}_{k,m}^{\text{r}} = \mathbf{F}_{k,m}^{\text{r}} \oplus \mathbf{P}_{k,m}^{\text{std}}, \tag{8.4}$$

where the operator $\oplus$ is a reverse function of the operator $\ominus$.

Note that the ARP can be applied not only to the constructive elements from all the reasoning sources, but also to some topological constructors (in the form of geometric transformation matrices for the corresponding constructive elements) in order to further increase the reasoning power. Some simple ARP simulation operators for the topological constructors include arithmetic mean, geometric mean and harmonic mean.

8.6.3 A Computational Psychology Perspective

If all the intensities of the knowledge sources fall within $(0, 1)$, the ARP is in fact simulated using an interpolation process; otherwise it is simulated using an extrapolation process. From a psychological point of view, the existence of negative values for the reasoning intensities reflects the inverse reasoning of brain activities with certain input source knowledge being treated as negative examples. On the contrary, positive values correspond to exaggeration of brain activities where the larger an input example's reasoning intensity is, the more heavily the generated result will follow the style of that input source knowledge. When the number of knowledge sources is greater than two, the ARP mimics combined thinking activity, which will make use of several knowledge reference cases during the reasoning process.

8.7 Generating Artistic Calligraphy

With the mechanisms we describe above in place, candidates of novel calligraphic artwork can easily be generated by random perturbations of the reasoning intensities. As the analogous reasoning steps can be applied to something as fine as one single parameter of a constructive ellipse or something as coarse as all the parameters of a character, we have a highly flexible system to vary the shapes and generate many possible candidates. We describe next a filtering step to make sure that only the candidates which meet some aesthetic requirements would be output. The requirements would come from the training examples.

8.7.1 Extracting Aesthetic Constraints from Training Examples

Aesthetic constraints are criteria by which the aesthetic quality of a candidate or its parts is to be quantified and measured. They are categorized as:

1) constraints for visual appearance of a constructive element, and 2) constraints for spatial relationship between neighboring constructive elements. Fortunately the proposed ARP can automatically guarantee the satisfaction of the former one (at least under most circumstances) due to the parametric nature of the constructive elements. Therefore we only need to focus on deriving and applying constraints of the second type to guarantee the generation of visually pleasant novel calligraphy.

An important consideration for a quantifiable constraint on aesthetics is the *degree of overlapping* between two constructive elements. Three types of overlapping between a pair of elements, $\mathbf{a}$ and $\mathbf{b}$, are used in our system: the x dimensional overlapping $\vartheta_x(\mathbf{a}, \mathbf{b})$, the y dimensional overlapping $\vartheta_y(\mathbf{a}, \mathbf{b})$, and the area overlapping $\vartheta_s(\mathbf{a}, \mathbf{b})$. All three measures are computed based on the bounding boxes of the constructive elements. After the overlapping measures are computed for all the element pairs of the training examples, their upper and lower bounds are recorded. The upper bound is used to avoid two neighboring elements within a newly generated calligraphy artwork being squeezed together while the lower bound is to avoid the neighboring elements being too far apart. These overlapping measures are then used to direct the process of generating the upper-level constructive elements from the lower-level ones. The overall effect is to constrain the ARP so that it will not perturb too much the spatial relationships of the *sub-components* of each constructive element as they are found in the training examples. Thus, for example, if a newly generated calligraphy candidate from the ARP, contains some sub-constructive elements whose x dimensional overlapping is smaller than the derived lower bound, the calligraphy candidates will be rejected.

If needed, the upper and lower bound constraints of the ARP can be relaxed in order to allow for results of new styles that cannot be easily imagined. In our system the end user can interactively adjust these two bounds according to his/her preferences. Thus, choosing the best values for the two bounds becomes a matter of the reviewer's personal aesthetic taste. According to the experience of using the proposed system, relaxing or ignoring the constraints in our analogous reasoning process seems to correspond to the creation of a more cursive and running style writing. Further study on the psychological analogy of the above computational simulation should be an interesting future research direction (see Sect. 8.10.1).

8.7.2 Past Results Reuse for Efficient Reasoning

While the ARP can be simulated by a random process which could be computationally intensive, reuse of similar past reasoning results (as experience) can be incorporated to make the reasoning process more efficient. In addition, the hierarchical representation allows a whole or partial "experience" to be reused. Our proposed system therefore proposes a high degree of reusability of past reasoning results.

8.8 Experiment Results

Fig. 8.6 shows the results obtained by our prototype system based on six training examples as the input knowledge sources and linear interpolation is used to simulate the generation step of the proposed analogous reasoning process. Fig. 8.7 shows the results of using five training examples and a non-linear interpolation process. Fig. 8.8 shows another set of results. It can be

Fig. 8.6. A single character in many styles; the first row is the training examples, and the other rows are automatically generated by our system

easily observed that there is consistency in style among characters within the same newly-generated calligraphic piece.

The results we obtained demonstrate that our approach can yield novel calligraphy styles given some existing ones. To verify that the system was indeed able to generate quality outputs, we asked practicing artists, art school professors and amateurs to examine the outputs; most of them considered our generated calligraphy to be acceptable. In addition, we have also analyzed the sensitivity in terms of the "creativity" of the system when the number of training examples is varied. The experiment was done using training examples with a varying number of styles which include "Kai", "Li", "Xingshu", "Weibei", "Xingkai", "Xingchao", and "Kuangchao". We invited six calligraphic fans with at least more than 2 years' writing experience and four professional calligraphists to form a review committee. They cast votes on the calligraphic artwork generated by the system. If an artwork received more than seven votes, it was considered a new calligraphic work. With more training examples of different styles, the chance of generating a creative and yet aesthetically acceptable calligraphy pieces increases. Also, between linear and non-linear APR, the latter is found to be able to generate more creative

(a)

(b)   (c)   (d)   (e)   (f)

(g)   (h)   (i)   (j)   (k)

Fig. 8.7. A "couple" in many styles. (a) Training examples; (b)—(k) Some selected computer generated results

calligraphy pieces. Using 6 or 7 training examples, the linear ARP generated about 30 acceptable pieces of calligraphy, and the non-linear ARP generated more than 50.

We also analyzed the sensitivity in terms of the increase in creativity of the system when the number of learned samples was varied. Fig. 8.9 reports the results, where the sample styles learned are the shapes of the "Kai", "Li", "Xingshu", "Weibei", "Xingkai", "Xingchao", and "Kuangchao" styles.

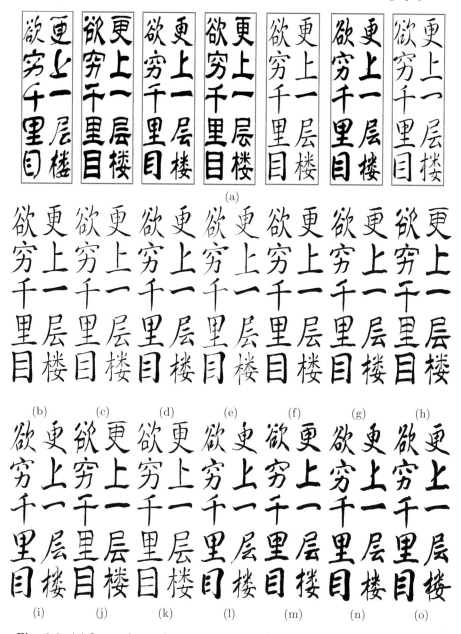

Fig. 8.8. (a) Learned samples in seven styles. (b to o) Some selected samples of newly-generated calligraphy

We invited six calligraphic fans with at least more than 2 years' writing experience and four professional calligraphists to form a review committee, including a professor major in calligraphy in an art school. They cast votes on the calligraphic artwork generated by the system. If an artwork received more than seven votes, it was considered a new calligraphic work. Fig. 8.9 clearly shows that with more learned samples, the chance of generating an acceptable calligraphic piece increases.

Fig. 8.10 presents an interesting example. The calligraphy (the character "forever" in Chinese) in the top of the picture was generated fully automatically using our prototype system. The horse was generated through human manipulation using paint-brush software [XTLP04]. The character is in a rapid-running style that is in the same spirit as that of the running horse. Without the use of the proposed intelligent system, generating a piece of calligraphy that would match perfectly the painting is almost impossible.

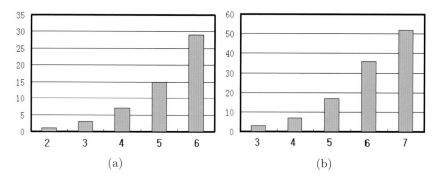

(a)   (b)

Fig. 8.9. System's creativity (vertical axis—number of acceptable results) against number of learned samples (horizontal axis) (a) Single-character level using linear reasoning (b) Single-character level using non-linear reasoning

8.9 Possible Applications

The system described in this chapter is an innovative and yet practical system for generating novel Chinese calligraphy. Its effectiveness has been rigorously tested with satisfactory results. Computer-generated novel artistic calligraphy has the following potential applications.

(1) **Personalized font generation**. By importing the fonts installed in a computer, our proposed system can first compute each character of a flexible model by aligning all the corresponding characters of the different fonts. Then the system can ask for a small set of characters written by the users as additional knowledge. Based on these knowledge sources, the proposed ARP is simulated but now with the additional criterion to best match the user inputs. Because of the uniformity of the chosen hierarchical representation, the resulting set of intensities can be directly

Fig. 8.10. "Forever running"

applied to the full character set of all the existing fonts, resulting in a font customized to the user's *handwriting*. We performed a simple test—the results are shown in Fig. 8.11. The top row shows the user's handwritten input characters and the ones below are generated by mimicking the writing style of the input. The results are surprisingly impressive. Of course, if the user's handwriting is so peculiar and unique that it lies outside the feasible space composed from all the existing fonts, the proposed system may still fail.

(2) **Handwriting beautification.** Handwriting is considered an important factor affecting people's impression of the writer. In many places, especially in Asia, handwriting is looked on as something that reflects the quality of a person. It is something like a speaking tone and accent in western society. To improve on one's handwriting could take a long time, which many VIPs often suffer by taking long hours of intensive and expensive personal coaching on handwriting during their own limited free-time. In situations where personal handwriting is preferred, our system can provide beautification of a person's handwriting. Our system can be applied to beautify people's handwriting. For instance, the user first writes his own handwriting, which is input as one source for the ARP. He then specifies some existing aesthetically appealing writing styles as the other

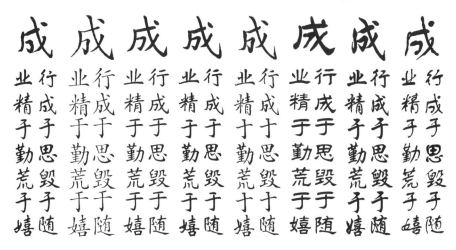

Fig. 8.11. Results of automatic handwriting style mimicking and calligraphy generation using the learned writing style from a single character: the first row of bigger characters are single characters written by different users in their respective handwriting styles, and the other rows are the automatically mimicked characters using the corresponding captured handwriting style

sources. By manually setting the reasoning intensities, he can choose the extent to which his personal handwriting would be rectified, while at the same time preserving some degree of his original personal handwriting style. The computer can remember the setting, and so in the future he can always generate his beautiful handwriting with the same consistent style. A preliminary market survey has revealed a strong welcome for handwriting software with such a functionality.

(3) **Handwriting recognition.** Artistic calligraphy tends to contain many distorted characters. Normal Optical Character Recognition (OCR) techniques cannot effectively deal with them because they are mostly based on templates of styles that are commonly used.

However, each person is likely to have his own personal handwriting style. Thus there are countless different styles in the world. With our system, a relationship between the shapes of the same character written in different styles can be established. Such a relationship between even a small number of typical handwriting styles would allow the shapes of the character in a wide range of styles to be predicted by the system. This mechanism can be used in a calligraphy recognition system.

The proposed system is essentially a specific version of a deformable model for modeling Chinese characters of different calligraphic styles. The representation power and yet visually appealing properties of the adopted model makes it suitable for deformable model based handwriting recognition [CYC98]. In addition, the modeling approach based on the unified ARP is an excellent candidate for writer adaptation in related handwriting recognition systems.

(4) **A Chinese CAPTCHA agent.** The CAPTCHA project at Carnegie Mellon University (http://www.captcha.net) presents a good case for possible adoption of our approach. A Chinese CAPTCHA agent can be developed to avoid web sites crawling with software robots. The agent would generate heavily distorted Chinese writings which are readable by humans but not by any machine-computable algorithm.

8.10 Conclusion and Future Work

8.10.1 Conclusion

In this chapter our thesis has been that with the parametric hierarchical knowledge representation of Chinese calligraphy, the computer is able to create new Chinese calligraphic artwork in a variety of styles fully automatically and in real time based on a compact set of printed calligraphic inputs. The creativity capability of the proposed intelligent calligraphy generation system is mainly due to the huge feasible space available for the simulated analogous reasoning process. The experiment results show that our approach can indeed generate calligraphic artwork that can stand among existing ones, regardless of whether they appear to be realistic or completely inventive.

8.10.2 Future Work

There are a number of possible extensions to our proposed system. Some immediate future extensions to our proposed system include: 1) extending our approach to cover other languages; 2) adding a feedback component to be used to fine tune the aesthetic constraints through reinforcement learning; 3) capturing and translating the "psychological" states of other media so that they can be linked to the corresponding states in calligraphy, and therefore letting one use music to direct the generation of calligraphy.

Although we focus on automatic generation of Chinese calligraphy in this chapter, the lure and challenge of automatic generation of artistic calligraphy should not be limited to the Chinese language. See Fig. 8.1 (b), where artistic English and Arabic numerals are also used. So an immediate future work item would be to extend our algorithm to cover calligraphy in more languages. Another future direction is to add a feedback component behind the constraint satisfaction component to automatically tune for the best thresholds to be used in the constraint satisfaction. The tuning can be based on the evaluation marks given by human reviewers on the visual quality of the automatically generated calligraphy. This backward reinforcement mechanism can make our system more able to cater to the personal aesthetic taste of the reviewers. Further improvement of the constraint types, and different tolerances for different parts acquired either via training examples , or prior knowledge about Chinese characters, may also improve our system's performance.

There is a tradeoff between the creativity and the practical acceptability of interpolation results. Too strict a set of constraints could limit the creativity, while too loose a set of constraints could harm the overall acceptability of the results. How to find the best tradeoff point should be a worthwhile future pursuit.

Another interesting extension of this project is to explore the relationship between the "psychological" state and the "creativity" as possessed by the different simulated analogous reasoning processes. We can call this "quantitative aesthetics". If such a relationship can be established for not only calligraphy but also other computer synthesized creative works, e.g. computer music, then there could emerge the possibility of an intelligent multimedia application that couples the "psychological" states of the two media; that is, the style of the aesthetic fonts generated by our system can be dynamically changed according to music being played and the mood of human beings. In such an application, the rhythm and the spiritual content of a piece of music are expected to be automatically associated with artistic fonts carrying the same spiritual interpretations. Such a bridge between audio and visual expressions based on their psychological contents could in turn contribute to a better understanding of the artistic thinking of human beings.

The input calligraphic artwork samples we used are in different well-disciplined styles in the Chinese calligraphy world, based on which our system can produce a large number of new writing styles. How to create a new writing style with a pre-specified constraint on its style (as opposed to a character) is a much harder and more challenging research issue. In order to solve the problem, we need to extract the relationships between the parameters driving the analogy; these parameters include the analogous reasoning's source intensities and quantitative definitions for the visual features of different writing styles. The degree of automation to which our system can learn the sample source knowledge from copybooks can be further improved, which is a non-trivial pattern recognition problem for characters in cursive writing style.

Another exciting direction is "quantitative aesthetics". Every piece of newly created calligraphic artwork has a set of source intensities associated with the reasoning. Some generated results are more beautiful than others. The task is to find out the relationships among these source intensities and how they translate into aesthetic values. This may develop into a very fundamental topic in computational cognition. We will present some of our preliminary attempts to quantitative aesthetics research in Chapter 10.

References

[Blu67] Harry Blum. A transformation for extracting new descriptors of shape. *Models for the Perception of Speech and Visual Form,* (ed. Wathen-Dunn, W.), 10(2):362–380, 1967.

[Chu90] Yap S. Chua. Bézier brushstrokes. *Computer-Aided Design,* 22(9): 556–573, 1990.

[CYC98] Kwok-Wai Cheung, Dit-Yan Yeung, and Roland T. Chin. A Bayesian framework for deformable pattern recognition with application to handwritten character recognition. *IEEE Transactions on Pattern Analysis and Machine Intelligence,* 20(12):1382–1388, 1998.

[HY00] Rong He and Hong Yan. Stroke extraction as pre-processing step to improve thinning results of Chinese characters. *Pattern Recogn. Lett.,* 21(8):817–825, 2000.

[Kea88a] Mark Keane. Analogical mechanisms. *Artificial Intelligence Review,* 2(4):229–250, 1988.

[Knu79] Donald E. Knuth. *Tex and Metafont: New Directions in Typesetting.* American Mathematical Society, and Bedford, MA, USA: Digital Press, Providence, RI, 1979.

[LHS98] H.M. Lee, C.W. Huang, and C.C. Sheu. A fuzzy rule-based system for handwritten Chinese characters recognition based on radical extraction. *Fuzzy Sets and Systems,* 100(1–3):59–70, 1998.

[NTN93] Tomoyuki Nishita, Shinichi Takita, and Eihachiro Nakamae. A display algorithm of brush strokes using Bézier functions. In *CGI'93: Proceedings of CG International,* Lausanne, Switzerland: Springer-Verlag, pages 244–257, 1993.

[PMZS97] Zhigeng Pan, Xiaohu Ma, Mingmin Zhang, and Jiaoying Shi. Chinese font composition method based on algebraic system of geometric shapes. *Computers and Graphics,* 21(3):321–328, 1997.

[RG94] Geber Ramalho and Jean-Gabriel Ganascia. Simulating creativity in jazz performance. In *AAAI '94: Proceedings of the Twelfth National Conference on Artificial Intelligence,* Menlo Park, CA, USA: American Association for Artificial Intelligence, volume 1, pages 108–113, 1994.

[Sim75] Herbert A. Simon. Style in design. *Spatial Synthesis in Computer-Aided Building Design,* ed. Charles M. Eastman, pages 287–309, 1975.

[Str86] Steve Strassmann. Hairy brushes. In *SIGGRAPH '86: Proceedings of the 13th Annual Conference on Computer Graphics and Interactive Techniques,* Dallas, TX, USA: ACM Press, pages 225–232, 1986.

[XTLP02] Songhua Xu, Min Tang, Francis C.M. Lau, and Yunhe Pan. A solid model based virtual hairy brush. *Computer Graphics Forum (Proceedings of Eurographics '02),* 21(3):299–308 & 625, 2002.

[XTLP04] Songhua Xu, Min Tang, Francis C.M. Lau, and Yunhe Pan. Virtual hairy brush for painterly rendering. *Graphical Models*, 66(5):263–302, 2004.

[YS94] Berrin A. Yanikoglu and Peter A. Sandon. Recognizing off-line cursive handwriting. In *Proc. Computer Vision and Pattern Recognition*, Seattle, WA, USA: IEEE Computer Society, pages 397–403, 1994.

[ZC95] Pengfei Zhu and Paul M. Chirlian. On critical point detection of digital shapes. *IEEE Transactions on Pattern Analysis and Machine Intelligence*, 17(8):737–748, 1995.

9

Two Perspectives on Automatic Generation of Artistic Chinese Calligraphy

9.1 Overview

In this chapter we offer two perspectives on the understanding of the system design and development practices we have gone through during the construction of our prototype system for automatic generation of artistic Chinese calligraphy: from a system engineering perspective (Sect. 9.2—Sect. 9.6) and from an artificial intelligence perspective (Sect. 9.7—Sect. 9.10). In the first part of the chapter we focus on the mathematical modeling of the cognitive process of calligraphy writing learning and novel style generation, aiming at providing sufficient technical details for the redevelopment of a similar prototype system; in the latter part of the chapter we concentrate on the study and experiments on a human being's creative thinking and the computational simulation of the intelligence involved in the process.

9.2 A System Engineering Perspective on Automatic Generation of Artistic Chinese Calligraphy

In this part of the chapter (Sect. 9.2—Sect. 9.6) we study in depth the system design and implementation issues of our automatic Chinese calligraphy generation system from a system engineering perspective. We hope this will not only shed light on understanding the working principles of our automatic Chinese calligraphy generation algorithm, but also provide some useful information for system engineers to develop a system equipped with similar functionalities.

The structure of this part is organized as follows. Sect. 9.3 provides the mathematical modeling and implementation details for Sect. 8.4. Similarly, Sect. 9.4 concretizes the technical details for Sect. 8.5; Sect. 9.5 supplements Sect. 8.6 and finally Sect. 9.6 details Sect. 8.7.

9.3 Hierarchical and Parametric Representation

9.3.1 Hierarchical Representation

We can give a definition over the hierarchic representation of calligraphic artwork based on the concept of equivalent relationship. If $\mathbf{R}$ is the equivalent relationship defined over the field of $\mathbf{P} = \{p_1, p_2, \cdots, p_n\}$, i.e. $\mathbf{R}$ is (1) self-reflective, (2) symmetrical, (3) transitive, field $\mathbf{P}$ can be divided into a collection of sub-sets $\mathbf{P}_1$, $\mathbf{P}_2$, $\cdots$, $\mathbf{P}_m$ under $\mathbf{R}$. We call p_i equivalent to p_j if $(p_i, p_j) \in \mathbf{R}$, $1 \leqslant i, j \leqslant n$. Using the concept of equivalent relationships, we can now introduce the formal definition for the multi-layer calligraphic artwork representation.

In an image of a piece of calligraphic artwork, we adopt the following five kinds of equivalent relationships to establish our six-level hierarchic representation for one piece of calligraphy: $\mathbf{R}_1$: all the constructive ellipses that compose to the same primitive strokes are equivalent to each other; $\mathbf{R}_2$: all the primitive strokes that compose to the same compound strokes are equivalent to each other; $\mathbf{R}_3$: all the compound strokes that compose the same radical are equivalent to each other; $\mathbf{R}_4$: all the radicals that compose the same Chinese character are equivalent to each other; $\mathbf{R}_5$: all the characters in the same piece of calligraphic artwork are equivalent to each other.

Suppose in the parametric representation of a calligraphic artwork $\mathbf{C}$, there are num_0 constructive ellipses, denoted as $\mathbf{F}_0 \triangleq \{\mathbf{P}_{0,1}, \cdots, \mathbf{P}_{0,num_0}\}$, where each $\mathbf{P}_{0,i}$ is a constructive ellipse. And $\mathbf{F}_0$ is divided into num_1 equivalent classes (of primitive strokes) under the equivalent relationship of $\mathbf{R}_1$, and denote these classes as $\mathbf{F}_1 \triangleq \{\mathbf{P}_{1,1}, \mathbf{P}_{1,2}, \cdots, \mathbf{P}_{1,num_1}\}$, where each $\mathbf{P}_{1,i}$ is a primitive stroke. These num_1 primitive strokes are further divided into num_2 equivalent classes (of compound strokes) under the equivalent relationship of $\mathbf{R}_2$, and denoted as $\mathbf{F}_2 \triangleq \{\mathbf{P}_{2,1}, \mathbf{P}_{2,2}, \cdots, \mathbf{P}_{2,num_2}\}$, where each $\mathbf{P}_{2,i}$ is a compound stroke. All the compound strokes are divided into num_3 equivalent classes (of radicals) under the equivalent relationship of $\mathbf{R}_3$, and denoted as $\mathbf{F}_3 \triangleq \{\mathbf{P}_{3,1}, \mathbf{P}_{3,2}, \cdots, \mathbf{P}_{3,num_3}\}$, where each $\mathbf{P}_{3,i}$ is a radical. Finally, all the radicals are divided into num_4 equivalent classes (of single Chinese characters) under the equivalent relationship of $\mathbf{R}_4$, and denoted as $\mathbf{F}_4 \triangleq \{\mathbf{P}_{4,1}, \mathbf{P}_{4,2}, \cdots, \mathbf{P}_{4,num_4}\}$, where each $\mathbf{P}_{4,i}$ is a single Chinese character. That is, in a certain calligraphic artwork of Chinese handwriting $\mathbf{C}$, there are num_0 constructive ellipses $\mathbf{P}_{0,i}$, $i \in \{1, 2, \cdots, num_0\}$. Or we can view $\mathbf{C}$ as being composed by num_1 primitive strokes $\mathbf{P}_{1,i}$, $i \in \{1, 2, \cdots, num_1\}$. Namely, $\mathbf{C}$ contains num_2 compound strokes $\mathbf{P}_{2,i}$, $i \in \{1, 2, \cdots, num_2\}$. Or we can say that $\mathbf{C}$ contains num_3 radicals $\mathbf{P}_{3,i}$, $i \in \{1, 2, \cdots, num_3\}$. We can also say that $\mathbf{C}$ contains num_4 single Chinese characters $\mathbf{P}_{4,i}$, $i \in \{1, 2, \cdots, num_4\}$. From the point of view of level 5 in the hierarchical representation, $\mathbf{C}$ is actually $\mathbf{P}_{5,1}$ with $num_5 = 1$.

The hierarchical structural knowledge representation of calligraphic artwork can be stated formally as Eq. (9.1):

$$\mathbf{P}_{k,l} \triangleq \begin{cases} \{\mathbf{P}_{k-1,i} | (\mathbf{P}_{k-1,i}, \mathbf{P}_{k-1,1}) \in \mathbf{R}_k\} \ (l = 1) & (9.1.1) \\ \{\mathbf{P}_{k-1,i} | (\mathbf{P}_{k-1,i}, \mathbf{P}_{k-1,q_{k,l}}) \in \mathbf{R}_k\} \ (l \neq 1) & (9.1.2) \end{cases}, \qquad (9.1)$$

where in Eq. (9.1.2), $q_{k,l} = \min\{t | \mathbf{P}_{k-1,t} \bar{\in} \bigcup_{s=1}^{l-1} \mathbf{P}_{k,s}, \mathbf{P}_{k-1,t} \in \mathbf{F}_{k-1}\}$; and throughout Eq. (9.1), $\mathbf{P}_{k-1,i} \in \mathbf{F}_{k-1}$, $k = 1, \cdots, 5$. We denote the number of elements in set $\mathbf{M}$ as $|\mathbf{M}|$, then the relationship Eq. (9.2) holds within the hierarchy of Chinese calligraphic artwork representation:

$$|\mathbf{F}_{k-1}| = \sum_{i=1}^{|\mathbf{F}_k|} |\mathbf{P}_{k,i}| = num_{k-1} \ (k = 1, \cdots, 5). \tag{9.2}$$

The hierarchical representation describes how an artwork is composed from constructive ellipses at the lowest level. Each higher level describes how to generate one level of representation from the information at one level down. It is essentially a tree-like knowledge representation.

Note that since the number of compound strokes and radicals implemented in the system is limited because of resource limitations, it is possible that some lower-layer element cannot be combined with other elements on the same level. In this case, that lower-layer element promotes itself to the next level. An example is the primitive stroke $\mathbf{P}_{1,1}$ on Fig. 8.3(a), which becomes the compound stroke $\mathbf{P}_{2,1}$ on the next level. Similarly, it is possible for a radical to degrade to a compound stroke, and then to a primitive stroke.

9.3.2 Six Levels of Parametric Representation

We denote the i-th constructive element on the k-th level as $\mathbf{P}_{k,i}$, and its matrix form parametric representation as $\mathbf{E}_{k,i}$. If $k \geqslant 1$, $\mathbf{P}_{k,i}$ must be composed of one or more constructive elements on one level down; we call the latter sub-constructive elements. All the information needed for the composition of $\mathbf{P}_{k,i}$ is stored in $\mathbf{T}_{k,i}$, the *topological constructor* of $\mathbf{P}_{k,i}$.

To derive $\mathbf{E}_{k,i}$, we need first to define several operators for calligraphic knowledge representation and operations to simulate the ARP. A quick index of these operators is in Table 9.1, which is a list over all the operators defined for knowledge representation and simulating ARP with constraint that satisfy the requirements of our system for generating artistic calligraphy automatically.

Table 9.1. Operators defined

Operators	Definition	Operators	Definition
$\ominus$	Eq. (9.18)	$\oslash$	Eq. (9.21)
$\oplus$	Eq. (9.25)	$\odot$	Eq. (9.27)
$\vartheta_x(), \vartheta_y(), \vartheta_s()$	Eq. (9.28)	$\theta_x(), \theta_y(), \theta_s()$	Eq. (9.29)
$\nabla_{m,n}^{b}()$	Eq. (9.7)	$\nabla_n^{c}()$	Eq. (9.9)
$\nabla_n^{o}()$	Eq. (9.10)	$\nabla_n^{d}()$	Eq. (9.11)
$\nabla_{n,m}^{e}()$	Eq. (9.12)	∇_t^{g}	Eq. (9.16), Eq. (9.17)
$\nabla_n^{f}()$	Eq. (9.19)	$\otimes$	Eq. (9.24)

We use $\overline{\mathbf{P}}_{k,i}$ to represent the bounding box of the image space that the element $\mathbf{P}_{k,i}$ occupies, that is, $\overline{\mathbf{P}}_{k,i} \triangleq \{\overline{\mathbf{P}}_{k,i}.h, \overline{\mathbf{P}}_{k,i}.w, \overline{\mathbf{P}}_{k,i}.x, \overline{\mathbf{P}}_{k,i}.y\}$, where

$\overline{\mathbf{P}}_{k,i}.h$ is the box's height, $\overline{\mathbf{P}}_{k,i}.w$ the box's width, and $(\overline{\mathbf{P}}_{k,i}.x, \overline{\mathbf{P}}_{k,i}.y)$ the box's center. All the coordinates are in the world coordinate system.

On the 0-th level, the calligraphy is viewed as a set of ellipses, denoted as $\mathbf{F}_0$. These ellipses are called the "constructive ellipses" of the calligraphic artwork (Fig. 8.3(b)). For each constructive ellipse, $\mathbf{P}_{0,i}$, let (x_i, y_i) be the center and a_i and b_i the lengths of its major and minor axis respectively. Then the "image" of the calligraphic artwork $\mathbf{C}$ can be represented as the image area covered by all its constructive ellipses, defined as Eq. (9.3).

$$Img(\mathbf{C}) \triangleq \{(x,y) \in \mathbf{R}^2 | \exists \mathbf{P}_{0,i} \in \mathbf{F}_0, \frac{(x-x_i)^2}{a_i{}^2} + \frac{(y-y_i)^2}{b_i{}^2} \leqslant 1\}. \qquad (9.3)$$

This representation is inspired by the Blum model [Blu67], in which a zonary area is defined through an ellipse moving along a predefined curve. The ranges for the horizontal and vertical coordinates x_i, y_i and the horizontal and vertical distances a_i, b_i are normalized with respect to the bounding box of the constructive ellipse $\overline{\mathbf{P}}_{0,i}$, as defined in Eq. (9.4). The resultant respective values for x_i, y_i, a_i, b_i are denoted as x'_i, y'_i, a'_i, b'_i and recorded in the matrix form representation of $\mathbf{P}_{0,i}$, such that $\mathbf{E}_{0,i} \triangleq (x'_i, y'_i, a'_i, b'_i)^{\mathrm{T}}$.

Suppose that the element $\mathbf{P}_{k+1,1}$ is composed of n elements on the next lower level, $\mathbf{P}_{k,l_1}, \cdots, \mathbf{P}_{k,l_n}$. Then $\mathbf{E}_{k+1,1}$ can be derived by concatenating the matrices $\mathbf{E}_{k,l_1}, \cdots, \mathbf{E}_{k,l_n}$ column by column in sequence. Since the parametric representation of a constructive ellipse is a 4×1 matrix, concatenation at the higher levels will produce matrices having exactly four rows. Each row of the matrix forming parametric representation of a constructive element is called a *field* of the element's parametric representation. Different fields of an element can be separately reasoned out.

The parametric representation of each constructive element only records the relative coordinates. The use of relative coordinates makes the representation independent of other elements' representations, and hence reusable in different SARPs. Also, because of the use of relative coordinates, coordinate transformation is necessary to convert the relative coordinates between different relative coordinate systems. We include the coordinate transformation associated with $\mathbf{E}_{k,l_i}$ in $\mathbf{P}_{k,l_i}$'s topological constructor, $\mathbf{T}_{k,l_i}$.

9.3.3 Deriving Parametric Representations for Constructive Elements

9.3.3.1 Level 0 of the parametric representation

For each constructive element on level 0, i.e. constructive ellipses $\mathbf{P}_{0,i}$ in our hierarchy, we use a procedure introduced at Sect. 9.4.1 to compute the ellipse's four parameters (x_i, y_i, a_i, b_i). We then employ Eq. (9.4) to convert the absolute coordinates (x_i, y_i, a_i, b_i) into relative coordinates (x'_i, y'_i, a'_i, b'_i), which are actually recorded by $\mathbf{E}_{0,i}$.

$$
\begin{pmatrix} x'_i \\ y'_i \\ a'_i \\ b'_i \end{pmatrix} = \begin{pmatrix} \frac{x_i - \overline{\mathbf{P}}_{0,j}.x}{\overline{\mathbf{P}}_{0,j}.w} + \frac{1}{2} \\ \frac{y_i - \overline{\mathbf{P}}_{0,j}.y}{\overline{\mathbf{P}}_{0,j}.h} + \frac{1}{2} \\ \frac{a_i}{\overline{\mathbf{P}}_{0,j}.w} \\ \frac{b_i}{\overline{\mathbf{P}}_{0,j}.h} \end{pmatrix}. \tag{9.4}
$$

9.3.3.2 Levels 1–5 of the parametric representation

To depict the order by which several constructive elements compose one piece of calligraphic artwork in a level-by-level method, we also introduce the topological constructor in our hierarchic representation. Each of the five levels (1-st level to 5-th level) in the representation has its individual topological constructor. All the topological constructors in one complete piece of calligraphic artwork are also managed on five levels, namely the primitive stroke level, the compound stroke level, the radical level, the single character level and the whole calligraphy level. All these form a topological tree.

Recall in Sect. 9.3.1, the i-th element on the k-th level in the hierarchy is denoted as $\mathbf{P}_{k,i}$, and $\mathbf{T}_{k,i}$ is the topological constructor associated with $\mathbf{P}_{k,i}$. $\mathbf{T}_{k,i}$ carries the topological constructive relationship to compose element $\mathbf{P}_{k,i}$ based on $\mathbf{P}_{k-1,1+l_{k,i}}$, $\mathbf{P}_{k-1,2+l_{k,i}}$, $\cdots$, $\mathbf{P}_{k-1,|\mathbf{P}_{k,i}|+l_{k,i}}$, where $l_{k,i} = \sum_{s=1}^{i-1} |\mathbf{P}_{k,s}|$. And we can derive the topological constructor $\mathbf{T}_{k,i}$ using matrix Eq. (9.5).

$$
\begin{cases}
\mathbf{T}_{k,i} \triangleq (\mathbf{TCR}_{k,i}, \mathbf{TCS}_{k,i}) \\
\mathbf{TCR}_{k,i} \triangleq \begin{pmatrix} \mathbf{TR}_{k,1+l_{k,i}} \\ \mathbf{TR}_{k,2+l_{k,i}} \\ \vdots \\ \mathbf{TR}_{k,|\mathbf{P}_{k,i}|+l_{k,i}} \end{pmatrix} \\
\mathbf{TCS}_{k,i} \triangleq \left(\mathbf{TS}_{k,1+l_{k,i}}, \mathbf{TS}_{k,2+l_{k,i}}, \cdots, \mathbf{TS}_{k,|\mathbf{P}_{k,i}|+l_{k,i}} \right)
\end{cases} \tag{9.5}
$$

In Eq. (9.5), $l_{k,i} \triangleq \sum_{s=1}^{i-1} |\mathbf{P}_{k,s}|$; $\mathbf{P}_{k,s} \in \mathbf{F}_k$; $k = 1, \cdots, 5$ and $\mathbf{TCR}_{k,i}, \mathbf{TCS}_{k,i}$ are the scale and transition transformation components of the topological constructor $\mathbf{T}_{k,i}$. The definitions for matrices $\mathbf{TR}_{k,z}, \mathbf{TS}_{k,z}$, which are the elements of $\mathbf{TCR}_{k,i}, \mathbf{TCS}_{k,i}$ are as Eq. (9.6),

$$
\begin{cases}
\mathbf{TR}_{k,z} \triangleq \begin{cases} \begin{pmatrix} \frac{\overline{\mathbf{P}}_{k,i}.w}{\overline{\mathbf{P}}_{k-1,z}.w} & 0 \\ 0 & \frac{\overline{\mathbf{P}}_{k,i}.h}{\overline{\mathbf{P}}_{k-1,z}.h} \end{pmatrix} & (k=2,3,4) \\ \mathbf{I}_{2\times2} & (k=1) \end{cases} \\
\mathbf{TS}_{k,z} \triangleq \begin{cases} \begin{pmatrix} \frac{\overline{\mathbf{P}}_{k-1,z}.x - \frac{\overline{\mathbf{P}}_{k-1,z}.w}{2} - \overline{\mathbf{P}}_{k,i}.x}{\overline{\mathbf{P}}_{k,i}.w} + \frac{1}{2} \\ \frac{\overline{\mathbf{P}}_{k-1,z}.y - \frac{\overline{\mathbf{P}}_{k-1,z}.h}{2} - \overline{\mathbf{P}}_{k,i}.y}{\overline{\mathbf{P}}_{k,i}.h} + \frac{1}{2} \end{pmatrix} & (k=2,3,4) \\ \mathbf{0}_{2\times1} & (k=1) \end{cases}
\end{cases}, \tag{9.6}
$$

where $z = 1 + l_{k,i}, 2 + l_{k,i}, \cdots, |\mathbf{P}_{k,i}| + l_{k,i}$, $\mathbf{I}$ is a unit matrix and $\mathbf{0}$ is a full zero matrix.

With topological constructors of the calligraphic artwork, a one-to-one mapping between points at different levels in its hierarchical representation can be established. That is any point $[x_{k,i}, y_{k,i}]$ in the image space taken up by $\mathbf{P}_{k,i}$ is uniquely mapped to the point $[x_{l,t}, y_{l,t}]$ in the image space taken up by $\mathbf{P}_{l,t}$. Without loss of generality, we assume $l > k$. According to our hierarchical representation, for any $[x_{k,i}, y_{k,i}]$ there must exist such a chain: $\mathbf{P}_{k,i} \in \mathbf{P}_{k+1,m_1} \in \cdots \in \mathbf{P}_{k+(l-k-1),m_{l-k-1}} \in \mathbf{P}_{l,t}$, where $\mathbf{P}_{k+j,m_j} \in \mathbf{F}_{k+j}$ $(j = 1, 2, \cdots, l - k - 1)$.

For any point $[x_{m,n}, y_{m,n}]$ on the m-th level in the hierarchy, which falls within the image space taken up by $\mathbf{P}_{m,n}$, we can use the matrix operator $\nabla_{m,n}^{\mathrm{b}}$ to find its correspondent point $\nabla_{m,n}^{\mathrm{b}}([x_{m,n}, y_{m,n}])$ on the $(m + 1)$-th level in the hierarchy:

$$\nabla_{m,n}^{\mathrm{b}}([x_{m,n}, y_{m,n}]) \triangleq (\mathbf{TR}_{m+1,n}[x_{m,n}, y_{m,n}]^{\mathrm{T}} + \mathbf{TS}_{m+1,n})^{\mathrm{T}}. \qquad (9.7)$$

We can also find the correspondent point $[x_{l,t}, y_{l,t}]$ on the l-th level in the hierarchical representation for any point $[x_{k,s}, y_{k,s}]$, which is on the k-th level in the hierarchy and falls within the image space taken up by $\mathbf{P}_{k,s}$ by applying the above relationship iteratively as Eq. (9.8).

$$[x_{l,t}, y_{l,t}] = \nabla_{l-1,m_{l-k-1}}^{\mathrm{b}} \left(\cdots \left(\nabla_{k+1,m_1}^{\mathrm{b}} \left(\nabla_{k,s}^{\mathrm{b}}([x_{k,s}, y_{k,s}]) \right) \right) \right) \qquad (9.8)$$

We introduce the matrix operator ∇_n^{c} which can generate an $f \times \sum_{l=1}^{n} d_l$ dimensional matrix $\mathbf{M} = (m_{i,j})_{f \times \sum_{l=1}^{n} d_l}$ by concatenating n input matrices $\mathbf{M}_l = (m_{l,i,j})_{f \times d_l}$, which is individually an $m \times d_l$ $(l = 1, 2, \cdots, n)$ dimensional matrix. That is, we can denote $\mathbf{M} \triangleq \nabla_n^{\mathrm{c}}(\mathbf{M}_1, \mathbf{M}_2, \cdots, \mathbf{M}_n)$ if, and only if, Eq. (9.9) holds.

$$m_{i,j} = \begin{cases} m_{z+1,i,j-\sum_{l=1}^{z} d_l} & (9.9.1) \\ m_{1,i,j} & (9.9.2) \end{cases} . \qquad (9.9)$$

In Eq. (9.9.1), $\sum_{l=1}^{z} d_l < j \leqslant \sum_{l=1}^{z+1} d_l$, $z = 1, 2, \cdots, n - 1$. In Eq. (9.9.2), $j \leqslant d_1$.

A slight variation of ∇_n^{c} leads to a new operator ∇_n^{o} defined in Eq. (9.10). ∇_n^{o} concatenates some matrices and transposes the resultant matrix. Based on the definition of ∇_n^{c}, we further define the matrix operator ∇_n^{d} as Eq. (9.11), which concatenates n copies of the input matrices.

$$\nabla_n^{\mathrm{o}}(\mathbf{M}_1, \mathbf{M}_2, \cdots, \mathbf{M}_n) \triangleq \left(\nabla_n^{\mathrm{c}}(\mathbf{M}_1, \mathbf{M}_2, \cdots, \mathbf{M}_n) \right)^{\mathrm{T}}, \qquad (9.10)$$

$$\nabla_n^{\mathrm{d}}(\mathbf{A}) \triangleq \nabla_n^{\mathrm{c}}(\underbrace{\mathbf{A}, \mathbf{A}, \cdots, \mathbf{A}}_{n \text{ matrices } \mathbf{A}s}). \qquad (9.11)$$

Once again, based on ∇_n^{d} a new matrix operator $\nabla_{n,m}^{\mathrm{e}}$ is defined as Eq. (9.12),

$$\nabla_{n,m}^{e}(\mathbf{E}_{n,m}) \triangleq \nabla_{2}^{c}\Big(\nabla_{2}^{o}(\mathbf{TR}_{n,m}, \mathbf{0}_{2\times 2}), \nabla_{2}^{o}(\mathbf{0}_{2\times 2}, \mathbf{TR}_{n,m})\Big)\mathbf{E}_{n,m}+ \\ \nabla_{col(\mathbf{E}_{n,m})}^{d}\Big(\nabla_{2}^{o}(\mathbf{TS}_{n,m}^{T}, \mathbf{0}_{1\times 2})\Big),$$

(9.12)

where $col(\mathbf{E}_{n,m})$ is the number of columns in matrix $\mathbf{E}_{n,m}$ and $\mathbf{0}_{2\times 2}$ is a 2×2 dimensional full zero matrix. $\nabla_{n,m}^{e}$ converts the matrix form parametric representation $\mathbf{E}_{n,m}$ for the constructive element $\mathbf{P}_{n,m}$ into its correspondent part in the matrix form parametric representation $\mathbf{E}_{n+1,l}$ for the constructive element $\mathbf{P}_{n+1,l}$, in which $\mathbf{P}_{n,m} \in \mathbf{P}_{n+1,l}$.

Now we can derive the formal definition for the hierarchical and parametric representation for calligraphic artwork as Eq. (9.13),

$$\begin{cases} \mathbf{E}_{k,i} = (x_i', y_i', a_i', b_i')^{T} \ (\mathbf{P}_{0,i} \in \mathbf{F}_0) \ (k = 0), \\ \mathbf{E}_{k,i} = \nabla_{|\mathbf{P}_{k,i}|}^{c}\Big(\nabla_{k-1,1+l_{k,i}}^{e}(\mathbf{E}_{k-1,1+l_{k,i}}), \\ \quad \nabla_{k-1,2+l_{k,i}}^{e}(\mathbf{E}_{k-1,2+l_{k,i}}), \cdots, \\ \quad \nabla_{k-1,|\mathbf{P}_{k,i}|+l_{k,i}}^{e}(\mathbf{E}_{k-1,|\mathbf{P}_{k,i}|+l_{k,i}})\Big) \ (k = 1, \cdots, 5), \end{cases}$$

(9.13)

where $l_{k,i} = \sum_{s=1}^{i-1} |\mathbf{P}_{k,s}|$.

9.4 Facsimiling Existent Calligraphy

This is the process in which the hierarchical parametric representations are extracted from input images of existent calligraphic artwork. The reason why we choose to process this kind of input rather than using tablet input devices is that many famous calligraphists in history only left their handwriting as static images. Obviously it is very easy to tailor our system to process parametric calligraphy directly sampled by tablet pen as input data.

9.4.1 Extracting Levels 0–1 Elements

To extract the ellipses from the input image, we first compute the skeleton of the calligraphy. This is the "character skeletonization" problem. The target is to extract a skeleton that is a close approximation to the actual trajectory of the brush when the calligraphy was created. Several existing papers discussed various approaches to automatic skeletonizing binary images of characters [Xia89, DSS98, KK02]. For the specific problem of handwritten Chinese character skeletonization, many approaches have also been proposed [HL90, LC95, CT99, ZY99, L'H00, SYTH01].

In our approach we employ the algorithm in [HY00] to extract skeletons of strokes from input images of Chinese characters. The strokes of a character are extracted first and then the isolated strokes are skeletonized. The algorithm can work effectively on characters written in most styles. However, for those largely distorted calligraphic styles, it will tend to commit mistakes. These mistakes occur during stroke segmentation, where multiple

strokes could be mistaken as being of the same stroke or a single stroke segmented into multiple strokes. This is a difficult problem to tackle, and an
important area for future research.

Once the skeleton of a primitive stroke is identified, each pixel on this
discrete curve is taken as the center of an ellipse, and the maximum ellipse
within the stroke area is computed. It is easy to compute all the constructive
ellipses using the Bresenham ellipse rasterization algorithm. In our approach
all the constructive ellipses do not have rotational freedom, i.e. their major
axes must be either horizontal or vertical.

We then determine the syntax of the identified stroke. This is through
comparing the shape of the stroke to the shapes of the five standard primitive strokes (Fig. 8.4(a)). The identified primitive stroke's syntax is recognized as one of the five standard primitive strokes with which the mutual shape similarity is maximum. The similarity between two 2D shapes
$\mathbf{a}$ and $\mathbf{b}$ is defined to be the maximum overlapping between $\mathbf{a}$ and $\mathbf{b}$, i.e,
$Similarity(\mathbf{a}, \mathbf{b}) \triangleq \max\{Over(\mathbf{a}, \mathbf{b})\}$ with the condition that shape $\mathbf{a}$ can be
arbitrarily rotated and scaled. The overlapping between $\mathbf{a}$ and $\mathbf{b}$ is defined
to be $Over(\mathbf{a}, \mathbf{b}) \triangleq (\mathbf{a} \cap \mathbf{b})/(\mathbf{a} \cup \mathbf{b})$, where $\mathbf{a} \cap \mathbf{b}$ and $\mathbf{a} \cup \mathbf{b}$ are respectively the
intersection and union of the image spaces taken up by $\mathbf{a}$ and $\mathbf{b}$ separately.

9.4.2 Extracting Levels 2–3 Elements

Based on the identified primitive strokes, we can use the spatial relation between them to compose constructive elements at higher levels through shape
grammar productions. We can therefore extract constructive elements on levels 2–3. The syntax of any constructive element produced this way can be
easily determined since each shape grammar production is associated with a
certain syntax. Inspired by [LHS98], the idea of a fuzzy set is used to increase
the reliability of the extraction process.

The shape grammar production for the compound stroke $\mathbf{CS}_1$ in the first
column and first row of Fig. 8.4(b) is:

IF {$\mathbf{a}$ is a horizontal primitive stroke} AND {$\mathbf{b}$ is a vertical primitive
stroke} AND {$\mathbf{a}$ is on top of $\mathbf{b}$} AND {$\mathbf{a}$ is on left side of $\mathbf{b}$} AND {$\mathbf{a}$
touches $\mathbf{b}$}
THEN {$\mathbf{a},\mathbf{b}$ should be combined to form the compound stroke $\mathbf{CS}_1$.}

And the shape grammar production for the radical $\mathbf{R}_{36}$ in the last column
and last row of Fig. 8.4(c) is:

IF {$\mathbf{a}$ is a degraded compound stroke, which resembles a vertical primitive
stroke} AND {$\mathbf{b}$ is a degraded compound stroke, which resembles a vertical
primitive stroke} AND {$\mathbf{c}$ is a compound stroke of the kind $\mathbf{S}_2$} AND {$\mathbf{a}$
is on the left side of $\mathbf{c}$} AND {$\mathbf{a}$ is on left side of $\mathbf{b}$} AND {$\mathbf{b}$ crosses $\mathbf{c}$}
AND {$\mathbf{a}$ touches $\mathbf{c}$}
THEN {$\mathbf{a},\mathbf{b},\mathbf{c}$ should be combined to form the radical $\mathbf{R}_{36}$.}

$\mathbf{S}_2$ refers to the compound stroke in the first row and the second column of
Fig. 8.4(b). Speaking of "a *degraded* compound stroke resembling a vertical

typed primitive stroke" is explained through a case example in the last paragraph of Sect. 9.3.1. Following [LHS98], during shape grammar production deduction, each statement in the production is associated with a confidence value. The overall confidence of the shape grammar production can be derived by the confidence of all its statements. Only the shape grammar production that yields the highest confidence will be applied.

The above processes of extracting compound strokes and radicals through shape grammar productions are not always correct when the calligraphy is cursive. Thus, during extraction of constructive elements on levels 2—3, direct user interaction is allowed through a friendly GUI. Due to space limitations, we omit the discussion about this GUI.

9.4.3 Extracting Level 4 Elements

To extract constructive elements on level 4, we need to determine which radicals belong to the same character, and whether the radicals are degraded or not. This is the well-known problem of "character segmentation" in pattern recognition research. In our system we use projection analysis to account for possible slanting of characters in order to segment the characters in a calligraphy piece, like what is done in [YS94]. More accurate and sophisticated character segmentation methods are introduced in [CL96], which could be incorporated into future versions of our system.

9.5 Generating New Calligraphy

9.5.1 Principle of New Calligraphy Generation

As early as 1968, Evan [Eva68] proposed a paradigm for solving geometric analogy intelligence test questions. In 1975 Simon [Sim75] pointed out that design and creation is a class of problems featured by their synthesis nature. In early 1980s Winston [Win80, Win82] published his pioneering results on the relationship between learning, reasoning and analogy. Other fundamental work on learning by analogy include [Car83, GH80, Kea88b]. Holyoak [Hol84] concluded that analogical thinking is an important feature of human intelligence. Keane [Kea85, Kea88a] applied analogical mechanisms to problem solving. Our approach is also based on analogical reasoning. We devised a *calligraphy creation component* by simulating the ARP using a computational approach.

Suppose that the SARP is applied to the k-th level in the hierarchical representation of calligraphic artwork. In the reasoning, there are n constructive elements $\mathbf{P}_{k,l_1}, \cdots, \mathbf{P}_{k,l_n}$ already learned by the computer, which are organized and stored in a small structural stroke database and activated as source knowledge for the SARP. Recall each element has four fields (Sect. 9.3.2). We denote the analogous reasoning intensity used against the s-th field of the i-th source knowledge ($\mathbf{P}_{k,l_i}$) during the SARP as $\omega_{l_i}^s$, where s's range is $1, \cdots, 4$. All the analogous reasoning intensities, $\omega_{l_i}^s$ ($s = 1, \cdots, 4$), together form the "viewpoint sequence" of the SARP: $\bar{\omega} = \{\omega_{l_i}^s | i = 1, \cdots, n; s = 1, \cdots, 4\}$. We denote the result of the SARP as $\mathbf{P}_{k,r}$ with its matrix form parametric representation being $\mathbf{E}_{k,r}$. Then the general mathematic principle we adopted in the SARP can be stated as Eq. (9.14),

$$\mathbf{E}_{k,r} = \sum_{i=1}^{n} \sum_{s=1}^{4} \omega_{l_i}^s \mathbf{E}_{k,l_i}, \qquad (9.14)$$

where $\mathbf{E}_{k,l_i}$ is the matrix form parametric representation of the constructive element $\mathbf{P}_{k,l_i}$. With Eq. (9.14) we can generate a new constructive element $\mathbf{P}_{k,r}$ based on all the machine-learned samples, $\mathbf{P}_{k,l_i}$ ($i = 1, \cdots, n$), and the viewpoint sequence $\bar{\omega}$ through our SARP. Note that Eq. (9.14) is not a strict mathematical equation. It is only a sketch showing the principle we adopted to generate new calligraphy through the SARP. Sect. 9.5.2 discusses in more details the principle.

Our SARP is essentially either an interpolation or an extrapolation process. That is, $\sum_{i=1}^{n} \omega_{l_i}^s = 1$ ($i = 1, \cdots, n; s = 1, \cdots, 4$). In our intelligent calligraphy generation system, all the analogous reasoning intensities can be inputed and adjusted by the user manually through a graphical interface; the computer would perform auto-normalization to scale the sum of all the input reasoning intensities to 1. Our system is also equipped with a component to generate random numbers to be used as reasoning intensities, and to filter out those "ugly looking" calligraphic outputs via a constraint satisfaction procedure. Sect. 8.7 has more details on this component.

9.5.2 New Calligraphy Generation System

9.5.2.1 Generating new constructive elements

To carry out the SARP, we need to equalize the dimensions of the reasoning sources. That is, if $\mathbf{P}_{k,s}$ and $\mathbf{P}_{k,t}$ are reasoning sources of SARP, their matrix representations $(\mathbf{E}_{k,s})_{4 \times n_1}$ and $(\mathbf{E}_{k,t})_{4 \times n_2}$ must be such that $n_1 = n_2$. To make the SARP also possible even when the dimensions of $\mathbf{P}_{k,s}$ and $\mathbf{P}_{k,t}$ are different, we introduce an equalization operator, ∇_t^g, to convert a matrix with any number of columns into a new matrix with t columns based on "key columns" in the original matrix.

Assume that $\mathbf{P}_{k,l_i}$ is a reasoning source in the SARP. We first derive a discrete planar curve composed of the centers of all the constructive ellipses that $\mathbf{P}_{k,l_i}$ contains by Eq. (9.15), denoted $\mathbf{C}_{k,l_i}$.

$$\begin{aligned}
\mathbf{C}_{k,l_s} &= \nabla_2^o \left((\mathbf{e}_{4,1}^{\mathrm{T}} \times \mathbf{E}_{k,l_s})^{\mathrm{T}}, (\mathbf{e}_{4,2}^{\mathrm{T}} \times \mathbf{E}_{k,l_s})^{\mathrm{T}} \right) \\
&= \begin{pmatrix} x_1 & x_2 & \cdots & x_{co} \\ y_1 & y_2 & \cdots & y_{co} \end{pmatrix}.
\end{aligned} \qquad (9.15)$$

In Eq. (9.15), $(\mathbf{e}_{n,i})_{n \times 1} \triangleq (\sigma(i,1), \cdots, \sigma(i,n))^{\mathrm{T}}$, where $\sigma(i,j) = 1$ if $i = j$, otherwise $\sigma(i,j) = 0$ and $co = col(\mathbf{E}_{k,l_s})$.

If the curve has $v + 1$ key points, with their occurrences in the curve being the sequence $u_0, u_1, \cdots, u_v$, the "key columns" in the matrix $\mathbf{E}_{k,l_i}$ are selected as the $u_0, u_1, \cdots, u_v$-th columns. That is, if the curve $\mathbf{C}_{k,l_s}$ has $v+1$ key points, with their individual coordinates as $\mathbf{C}_{k,l_s}\mathbf{e}_{co,u_0}, \mathbf{C}_{k,l_s}\mathbf{e}_{co,u_1}, \cdots,$ $\mathbf{C}_{k,l_s}\mathbf{e}_{co,u_v}$, the key columns in the matrix $\mathbf{E}_{k,l_s}$ are selected as $\mathbf{E}_{k,l_s}\mathbf{e}_{co,u_0},$ $\mathbf{E}_{k,l_s}\mathbf{e}_{co,u_1}, \cdots, \mathbf{E}_{k,l_s}\mathbf{e}_{co,u_v}$. We use the algorithm in [ZC95] to extract key points on the planar curve. With the key columns of the matrices for all the reasoning sources, a correspondence between related pieces of knowledge can be set up.

Suppose $\mathbf{E}_{k,l_s}$ is the matrix representation of a certain analogy source $\mathbf{P}_{k,l_s}$ with $v + 1$ key columns extracted. These key columns are the u_0-th, u_1-th, $\cdots$, u_v-th columns in the matrix $(1 = u_0 < u_1 < \cdots < u_v = col(\mathbf{E}_{k,l_s})$, $s = 1, 2, \cdots, n$). Then a matrix operator ∇_t^g can be defined as Eq. (9.16), which converts one matrix into a matrix having t columns:

$$\left(\nabla_t^g(\mathbf{E}_{k,l_s}) \right) \mathbf{e}_{t,i} \triangleq \mathbf{E}_{k,l_s}\mathbf{e}_{col(\mathbf{E}_{k,l_s}),\theta} \ (i = 1, 2, \cdots, t). \tag{9.16}$$

In the above, $\theta = \lceil u_j + \frac{u_{j+1}-u_j}{\lceil \frac{t\times(j+1)}{v} \rceil - \lceil \frac{t\times j}{v} \rceil} \times (i - \lceil \frac{t\times j}{v} \rceil) \rceil$; $\lceil \frac{t\times j}{v} \rceil < i \leqslant \lceil \frac{t\times(j+1)}{v} \rceil$; $j \in \{0, 1, \cdots, v - 1\}$; $s = 1, 2, \cdots, n$; $\lceil \cdot \rceil$ is a floor function. In particular, if each column in matrix $\mathbf{E}_{k,l_s}$ is selected as the key column, operator ∇_t^g can be simplified into Eq. (9.17):

$$\left(\nabla_t^g(\mathbf{E}_{k,l_s}) \right) \mathbf{e}_{t,i} \triangleq \mathbf{E}_{k,l_s}\mathbf{e}_{col(\mathbf{E}_{k,l_s}),\lceil \frac{i\times col(\mathbf{E}_{k,l_s})}{t} \rceil} (i = 1, 2, \cdots, t). \tag{9.17}$$

In the SARP, we assume the shape of a constructive element written in the font style "Kai" (GB2312) as used in recent versions of Microsoft Word to be the standard shape of the element. For each reasoning source $\mathbf{P}_{k,l_i}$ in the SARP, we denote its associated standard constructive element as $\mathbf{P}_{k,l_i}^{std}$ and its matrix form parametric representation as $\mathbf{E}_{k,l_i}^{std}$. We then compute the distance $\mathbf{E}_{k,l_i}^f$ by which the shape of $\mathbf{P}_{k,l_i}$ differs from that of $\mathbf{P}_{k,l_i}^{std}$, as expressed in Eq. (9.18).

$$\mathbf{E}_{k,l_i}^f \triangleq \mathbf{E}_{k,l_i} \ominus \mathbf{E}_{k,l_i}^{std}. \tag{9.18}$$

$\mathbf{E}_{k,l_i}^f$ is used as the feature of $\mathbf{P}_{k,l_i}$ in the SARP.

Based on the operator of ∇_t^g, we can define an active analogy source reaction operator ∇_n^f as:

$$\nabla_n^f(\mathbf{M}_1, \mathbf{M}_2, \cdots, \mathbf{M}_n) \triangleq \nabla_n^c \left(\nabla_h^g(\mathbf{M}_1), \nabla_h^g(\mathbf{M}_2), \cdots, \nabla_h^g(\mathbf{M}_n) \right), \tag{9.19}$$

where $h = \max\{col(\mathbf{M}_i) | i = 1, 2, \cdots, n\}$.

Applying the operator ∇_n^f can derive a feature matrix $\mathbf{E}_{k,\mathrm{src}}^f$ relating to all the activated analogous reasoning sources as Eq. (9.20):

$$\mathbf{E}_{k,\mathrm{src}}^f = \mathbf{E}_{k,\mathrm{src}} \ominus \mathbf{E}_{k,\mathrm{std}} \triangleq \mathbf{E}_{k,\mathrm{src}} - \nabla_n^f(\mathbf{E}_{k,l_1}^{std}, \cdots, \mathbf{E}_{k,l_n}^{std}). \tag{9.20}$$

Eq. (9.20) is a detailed version of Eq. (9.18), which gives the implementation of the operator $\ominus$. To evaluate ∇_n^f, we follow Eq. (9.19) in which h is derived as $h = \max\{col(\mathbf{E}_{k,l_i}) | i = 1, 2, \cdots, n\}$.

Recall that all the reasoning intensities in SARP are organized into the viewpoint sequence $\overline{\omega}$ (Sect. 9.5.1). We simulate ARP as an interpolation/extrapolation process. To derive $\mathbf{P}_{k,r}^{f}$, the feature of the reasoning result from the SARP, we take the reasoning intensity $\omega_{l_i}^{s}$ against the s-th field of the i-th reasoning source $\mathbf{P}_{k,l_i}$ as the weight for the s-th row of the feature matrix $\mathbf{E}_{k,l_i}^{f}$ of $\mathbf{P}_{k,l_i}$ in an interpolation/extrapolation process ($s = 1, \cdots, 4$; $i = 1, \cdots, n$). This means that $\mathbf{E}_{k,l_i}^{f}$s are the entities that are actually interpolated/extrapolated. The interpolation/extrapolation process we employ to simulate ARP is in the form of Eq. (9.21).

$$\mathbf{E}_{k,r}^{f} = \oslash(\mathbf{E}_{k,l_1}^{f}, \cdots, \mathbf{E}_{k,l_n}^{f}, \overline{\omega}), \tag{9.21}$$

where $\mathbf{E}_{k,r}^{f}$ is the matrix form parametric representation of $\mathbf{P}_{k,r}^{f}$; $\oslash$ is the analogous reasoning mechanism simulation operator, which is currently implemented as an interpolation/extrapolation process in our prototype system. Eq. (9.24) depicts the specific interpolation/extrapolation strategy we employed, to be explained later.

According to user specified reasoning intensities $\omega_{l_i}^{s}$ for each reasoning source in the hierarchy, we can derive an analogous reasoning viewpoint matrix $\mathbf{W}^s$ acting on the s-th fields of all the activated analogous reasoning sources in SARP as:

$$\mathbf{W}^s \triangleq \nabla_n^o(\omega_{l_1}^{s} \times \mathbf{I}_{h \times h}, \omega_{l_2}^{s} \times \mathbf{I}_{h \times h}, \cdots, \omega_{l_n}^{s} \times \mathbf{I}_{h \times h}), \tag{9.22}$$

where $h = \max\{col(\mathbf{E}_{k,l_i}) | i = 1, 2, \cdots, n\}$ and $\mathbf{I}_{h \times h}$ is a $h \times h$ dimensional unit matrix, $s = 1, \cdots, 4$.

Now we can get the reasoning feature result $\mathbf{E}_{k,r}^{f}$ from SARP as:

$$\begin{aligned} \mathbf{E}_{k,r}^{f} &= \oslash(\mathbf{E}_{k,l_1}^{f}, \cdots, \mathbf{E}_{k,l_n}^{f}, \overline{\omega}) \\ &\triangleq \left(\nabla_4^c \left((\mathbf{E}_{k,\text{src}}^{f} \otimes \mathbf{W}^1)^{\mathrm{T}} \mathbf{e}_{4,1}, \cdots, (\mathbf{E}_{k,\text{src}}^{f} \otimes \mathbf{W}^4)^{\mathrm{T}} \mathbf{e}_{4,4} \right) \right)^{\mathrm{T}}. \end{aligned} \tag{9.23}$$

Eq. (9.23) is a detailed version of Eq. (9.21), which gives the implementation of the operator $\otimes$.

In Eq. (9.23), $\otimes$ is the analogous reasoning mechanism simulation operator, defined at Eq. (9.24).

$$\mathbf{C}_{p \times r} = \mathbf{A}_{p \times q} \otimes \mathbf{B}_{q \times r} \triangleq \begin{cases} \mathbf{A}_{p \times q} \bullet \mathbf{B}_{q \times r} & (9.24.1) \\ c_{i,j} = \sqrt[z]{\sum_{k=1}^{q}(a_{i,k} \times b_{k,j})^z} & (9.24.2) \\ c_{i,j} = \sqrt[q]{\prod_{k=1}^{q}(a_{i,k} \times b_{k,j})} & (9.24.3) \end{cases} \tag{9.24}$$

In Eq. (9.24), $c_{i,j}$ is the element in the i-th row and j-th column of the matrix $\mathbf{C}_{p \times r}$. If the SARP is linear, $\otimes$ is defined as Eq. (9.24.1). In Eq. (9.24.1), $\bullet$ is the ordinary matrix multiplication operator. If the reasoning process is z-degree polynomial, $\otimes$ is defined as Eq. (9.24.2). If the process is non-polynomial, $\otimes$ can be defined as Eq. (9.24.3).

If all the intensities of reasoning sources fall within $(0,1)$, namely $0 \leqslant \omega_{l_i}^s \leqslant 1$ ($s = 1, \cdots, 4; i = 1, \cdots, n$), the ARP is simulated using an interpolation process; otherwise it is simulated using an extrapolation process. From a psychological point of view, if $\exists \omega_{l_i}^s < 0$, the SARP reflects the inverse reasoning of brain activity; if $\exists \omega_{l_i}^s > 1$, the SARP represents positive exaggeration of brain activity; and if $n \geqslant 3$, SARP mimics combined thinking activity.

Finally, by adding back the shape of $\mathbf{P}_{k,r}^{\text{std}}$, the standard constructive element associated with the feature $\mathbf{P}_{k,r}^f$ of the reasoning result $\mathbf{P}_{k,r}$ in the SARP, we obtain the parametric representation $\mathbf{E}_{k,r}$ of $\mathbf{P}_{k,r}$ as indicated by Eq. (9.25),

$$\mathbf{E}_{k,r} = \mathbf{E}_{k,r}^f \oplus \mathbf{E}_{k,r}^{\text{std}}, \tag{9.25}$$

where $\mathbf{E}_{k,r}^{\text{std}}$ is the matrix form parametric representation of the shape of $\mathbf{P}_{k,r}^{\text{std}}$. Eq. (9.26) is a detailed version of Eq. (9.25).

$$\mathbf{E}_{k,r} = \mathbf{E}_{k,r}^f \oplus \mathbf{E}_{k,r}^{\text{std}} \triangleq \mathbf{E}_{k,r}^f + \nabla_h^g \mathbf{E}_{k,r}^{\text{std}}, \tag{9.26}$$

which gives the implementation of the operator $\oplus$. With $\oplus$, the resultant knowledge (constructive elements in calligraphy) from the SARP can be derived. In Eq. (9.26), $h = \max\{col(\mathbf{E}_{k,l_i}) | i = 1, 2, \cdots, n\}$.

9.5.2.2 Generating new topological constructor

Note that the SARP can be applied not only to the matrix representations, $\mathbf{E}_{k,l_1}, \cdots, \mathbf{E}_{k,l_n}$, of all the reasoning sources, $\mathbf{P}_{k,l_1}, \cdots, \mathbf{P}_{k,l_n}$, by evaluating a series of matrix operations simulating the ARP, but can also be applied to the topological constructors of all the reasoning sources, $\mathbf{T}_{k,l_1}, \cdots, \mathbf{T}_{k,l_n}$. If the corresponding intensities of $\mathbf{T}_{k,l_1}, \cdots, \mathbf{T}_{k,l_n}$ are $\omega_{l_1}, \cdots, \omega_{l_n}$, where $\sum_{i=1}^n \omega_{l_i} = 1$, the newly generated topological constructor $\mathbf{T}_{k,r}$ can be given as: $\mathbf{T}_{k,r} \triangleq \odot(\mathbf{T}_{k,l_1}, \cdots, \mathbf{T}_{k,l_n}, \omega_{l_1}, \cdots, \omega_{l_n})$. Here $\odot$ is the ARP simulation operator for topological constructors. Similarly, we can overload the definition of the operator $\odot$ to simulate different types of creative thinking activities; some simple ones are: arithmetic mean, geometric mean and harmonic mean. The strict definition of the analogous reasoning simulation operator for topological constructors $\odot$ is as:

$$\mathbf{T}_{k,r} \triangleq \odot(\mathbf{T}_{k,l_1}, \cdots, \mathbf{T}_{k,l_n}, \omega_{l_1}, \cdots, \omega_{l_n})$$

$$\triangleq \begin{cases} \sum_{i=1}^n (\mathbf{T}_{k,l_i} \times \omega_{l_i}) & \text{ArithmeticMean} \\ \prod_{i=1}^n (\mathbf{T}_{k,l_i}^{\omega_{l_i}}) & \text{GeometricMean} \\ \left(\sum_{i=1}^n (\omega_{l_i}/\mathbf{T}_{k,l_i}) \right)^{-1} & \text{HarmonicMean} \end{cases} \tag{9.27}$$

9.6 Generating Artistic Calligraphy

9.6.1 Constraints on the Process

There are four constraints that are useful: $\mathbf{Con}_1$ is a rigid constraint, and $\mathbf{Con}_2$, $\mathbf{Con}_3$, and $\mathbf{Con}_4$ are soft constraints.

$\mathbf{Con}_1$ says that the source knowledge that is being reasoned must be homogeneous in terms of its compositive constructive elements; that is, they must be composed of the same number of sub-constructive elements from one level down. $\mathbf{Con}_2$ and $\mathbf{Con}_3$ suggest that all the reasoning sources in the SARP, namely parameterized constructive elements from existent calligraphy, must have similar syntax. $\mathbf{Con}_2$ requires all the constructive elements used in the reasoning process must be on the same level; specifically, when we apply reasoning on $\mathbf{P}_{m,s}$ and $\mathbf{P}_{n,t}$, we must guarantee $m = n$. $\mathbf{Con}_3$ dictates that the constructive elements being reasoned at should have similar properties. For instance, if we are reasoning at the level of "primitive strokes", the elements involved must be of the same type, which is one of the five possible types on level 1: a horizontal stroke, a vertical stroke, a left slanting stroke, a right slanting stroke or a point stroke, which are illustrated at Fig. 8.4(a). $\mathbf{Con}_4$ demands that the structure of the newly-generated calligraphy should not go beyond the maximum or minimum tolerable constraint extracted from all the samples learned. The details of maximum and minimum tolerable constraints will be discussed in Sect. 9.6.3.

9.6.2 Extracting Aesthetic Constraints from Existent Artwork

9.6.2.1 Interference between constructive elements

The need for a quantifiable constraint on aesthetics is the concept of the *degree of interference* between two constructive elements, which indicates the spatial inter-relationship between the elements. These degrees of interference supervise the process of generating an upper-level constructive element from several lower-level ones.

We denote the bounding boxes of two constructive elements $\mathbf{a}$ and $\mathbf{b}$ as $\overline{\mathbf{a}}$ and $\overline{\mathbf{b}}$. There are three kinds of degrees of interference possible between $\overline{\mathbf{a}}$ and $\overline{\mathbf{b}}$, as given in Eq. (9.28). $\vartheta_x(\overline{\mathbf{a}}, \overline{\mathbf{b}})$ is the x dimensional degree of interference; $\vartheta_y(\overline{\mathbf{a}}, \overline{\mathbf{b}})$ the y dimensional degree of interference; and $\vartheta_s(\overline{\mathbf{a}}, \overline{\mathbf{b}})$ the shaping degree of interference.

$$\begin{cases} \vartheta_x(\overline{\mathbf{a}}, \overline{\mathbf{b}}) \triangleq (\overline{\mathbf{a}}.x - \overline{\mathbf{b}}.x)/(\overline{\mathbf{a}}.w + \overline{\mathbf{b}}.w) & (9.28.1) \\ \vartheta_y(\overline{\mathbf{a}}, \overline{\mathbf{b}}) \triangleq (\overline{\mathbf{a}}.y - \overline{\mathbf{b}}.y)/(\overline{\mathbf{a}}.h + \overline{\mathbf{b}}.h) & (9.28.2) \\ \vartheta_s(\overline{\mathbf{a}}, \overline{\mathbf{b}}) \triangleq (I(\mathbf{a}) \cap I(\mathbf{b}))/(I(\mathbf{a}) \cup I(\mathbf{b})) & (9.28.3) \end{cases} \quad (9.28)$$

In Eq. (9.28.3), $I(\mathbf{a})$ and $I(\mathbf{b})$ are the image spaces that the constructive elements $\mathbf{a}$ and $\mathbf{b}$ take up; $I(\mathbf{a}) \cap I(\mathbf{b})$ and $I(\mathbf{a}) \cup I(\mathbf{b})$ are the intersection and union of these two image spaces respectively. With Eq. (9.28), the x, y directional spatial relativity between $\mathbf{a}$ and $\mathbf{b}$ can be compactly represented, and the shaping degree of interference $\vartheta_s(\overline{\mathbf{a}}, \overline{\mathbf{b}})$ can depict the degree of over-lapping of the two constructive elements $\mathbf{a}$ and $\mathbf{b}$.

Introducing these three kinds of degrees of interference not only provides much convenience in describing the spatial relativity between the two constructive elements concerned quantitatively, but also helps express the spatial relativity qualitatively. Take $\vartheta_x(\overline{\mathbf{a}}, \overline{\mathbf{b}})$ for example, if $\vartheta_x(\overline{\mathbf{a}}, \overline{\mathbf{b}}) < -\frac{1}{2}$, $\overline{\mathbf{a}}$ is on the left side of $\overline{\mathbf{b}}$, not overlapping; if $\vartheta_x(\overline{\mathbf{a}}, \overline{\mathbf{b}}) = -\frac{1}{2}$, $\overline{\mathbf{a}}$ is on the left side of $\overline{\mathbf{b}}$, just overlapping; if $\vartheta_x(\overline{\mathbf{a}}, \overline{\mathbf{b}}) \in [-\frac{1}{2}, \frac{1}{2}]$, $\overline{\mathbf{a}}$ overlaps $\overline{\mathbf{b}}$; if $\vartheta_x(\overline{\mathbf{a}}, \overline{\mathbf{b}}) = \frac{1}{2}$, $\overline{\mathbf{a}}$ is on the right side of $\overline{\mathbf{b}}$, just overlapping; if $\vartheta_x(\overline{\mathbf{a}}, \overline{\mathbf{b}}) > \frac{1}{2}$, $\overline{\mathbf{a}}$ is on the right side of $\overline{\mathbf{b}}$, not overlapping. In the same manner, with $\vartheta_y(\overline{\mathbf{a}}, \overline{\mathbf{b}})$, the spatial relativity between $\overline{\mathbf{a}}$ and $\overline{\mathbf{b}}$ along the y dimension can be conveniently derived. $\vartheta_s(\overline{\mathbf{a}}, \overline{\mathbf{b}})$ also reveals whether the two constructive elements overlap: if $\vartheta_s(\overline{\mathbf{a}}, \overline{\mathbf{b}}) > 0$, the two constructive elements overlap.

9.6.2.2 Structure matrix of a constructive element

Based on the degrees of interference between two constructive elements just defined, we introduce the *structure matrix* of a constructive element. Let $\overline{\mathbf{P}}_{k+1,1}$ be the bounding box of a constructive element $\mathbf{P}_{k+1,1}$, which is composed of m constructive elements $\mathbf{P}_{k,l_1}, \cdots, \mathbf{P}_{k,l_m}$ on the next lower level. We use three matrices, $\theta_x(\mathbf{P}_{k+1,1})$, $\theta_y(\mathbf{P}_{k+1,1})$, and $\theta_s(\mathbf{P}_{k+1,1})$, to represent the structure of $\mathbf{P}_{k+1,1}$, as given in Eq. (9.29).

$$
\begin{cases}
\theta_x(\mathbf{P}_{k+1,1}) \triangleq (\theta_{k,x}^{i,j})_{m \times m}; \ \theta_{k,x}^{i,j} = \vartheta_x(\overline{\mathbf{P}}_{k,l_i}, \overline{\mathbf{P}}_{k,l_j}) \\
\theta_y(\mathbf{P}_{k+1,1}) \triangleq (\theta_{k,y}^{i,j})_{m \times m}; \ \theta_{k,y}^{i,j} = \vartheta_y(\overline{\mathbf{P}}_{k,l_i}, \overline{\mathbf{P}}_{k,l_j}) \\
\theta_s(\mathbf{P}_{k+1,1}) \triangleq (\theta_{k,s}^{i,j})_{m \times m}; \ \theta_{k,s}^{i,j} = \vartheta_s(\overline{\mathbf{P}}_{k,l_i}, \overline{\mathbf{P}}_{k,l_j}) \\
\quad (i = 1, \cdots, m; \ j = 1, \cdots, m)
\end{cases}
\tag{9.29}
$$

The three matrices are essentially made up of the x, y dimensional and shaping degrees of interference between every pair of $\overline{\mathbf{P}}_{k,l_i}$ and $\overline{\mathbf{P}}_{k,l_j}$.

9.6.3 Constraint Satisfaction for Calligraphy Generation

In Sect. 9.5.1, we assumed there are n knowledge sources, $\mathbf{P}_{k,l_1}, \cdots, \mathbf{P}_{k,l_n}$, in the SARP. With the structure matrices of these n samples computed according to Eq. (9.29), we can derive constraint matrices for the SARP needed for the generation of artistic calligraphy. Without loss of generality, we discuss how to derive two x-dimensional constraint matrices based on $\theta_x(\mathbf{P}_{k,l_1}), \cdots,$ $\theta_x(\mathbf{P}_{k,l_n})$. Among the two constraint matrices, one is the matrix of the maximum tolerable structure $\theta_x^{\max}$ and the other is the matrix of the minimum tolerable structure $\theta_x^{\min}$. Assume each of $\mathbf{P}_{k,l_1}, \cdots, \mathbf{P}_{k,l_n}$ is composed of m constructive elements of the next lower level; then $\theta_x^{\max}$ and $\theta_x^{\min}$ are both $m \times m$ dimensional matrices. In $\theta_x^{\max}$, the element in the i-th row and the j-th column ($\theta_x^{\max}(i,j)$) is the maximum value of all the n elements in the i-th row and the j-th column of $\theta_x(\mathbf{P}_{k,l_1}), \cdots, \theta_x(\mathbf{P}_{k,l_n})$. Similarly, $\theta_x^{\min}(i,j)$, the element in the i-th row and the j-th column of $\theta_x^{\min}$, is the minimum value of all the elements in the i-th row and the j-th column of $\theta_x(\mathbf{P}_{k,l_1})$, $\cdots, \theta_x(\mathbf{P}_{k,l_n})$. The use of the two constraint matrices in the SARP is simple: during the SARP, each time the system automatically generates a new constructive element $\mathbf{P}_{k,r}$, the x-dimensional structure matrix of this element is computed as $\theta_x(\mathbf{P}_{k,r})$. The system will output this newly generated constructive element only if $\theta_x(\mathbf{P}_{k,r})$ is no smaller than $\theta_x^{\min}$ under the tolerance $\tau^{\min}$ and no larger than $\theta_x^{\max}$ under the tolerance $\tau^{\max}$. We say a matrix is larger (resp. smaller) than another matrix under a certain tolerance τ only if all of its elements are at least (resp. at most) τ times that of the corresponding elements in another matrix and these other elements are non-zero. In our experiments, we set $\tau^{\max} = 0.8$ and $\tau^{\min} = 1.2$. Similarly, we also derive $\theta_y^{\min}, \theta_y^{\max}, \theta_s^{\min}, \theta_s^{\max}$ to constrain the randomly generated intensities of the SARP to forbid the system to output a calligraphy that violates the aesthetic constraints extracted from existent calligraphy.

9.6.4 Relaxing the Aesthetic Constraints

The constraints of the SARP can be relaxed in order to allow for results with new styles that are not so imaginable. To relax $\mathbf{Con}_1$, constructive elements that are heterogeneous can be turned into homogeneous ones by combining some sub-constructive elements together. [CC92] gives an optimized strategy to do the combining using fuzzy-attribute graphs. To relax $\mathbf{Con}_2$, we apply the SARP simultaneously to constructive elements belonging to different layers. To relax $\mathbf{Con}_3$, we apply the SARP to constructive elements with different syntaxes, such as reasoning between a point and a vertical stroke. To relax $\mathbf{Con}_4$, we can adjust the thresholds $\tau^{\min}$ and $\tau^{\max}$ when comparing the structure matrix of the newly-generated constructive element against the maximum and minimum tolerance matrices.

From a computational psychology perspective, relaxing or ignoring the constraints in our analogous reasoning process corresponds to creative brain activity of the calligraphists such as when performing cursive and running style writing. Such a loose SARP could well be the reflection of the thinking process of a calligraphist while creating an artwork of running style, a style which is considered to be the freest of all forms. Without the constraints or with them relaxed, there is a huge space in which reasoning could lead to plenty of fancy results. Going to the extreme with the relaxation, however, might give rise to ugly handwriting results. When such a situation arises, some human intervention to filter out the unacceptable might be necessary.

9.7 An Artificial Intelligence's Perspective on Automatic Generation of Artistic Chinese Calligraphy

In the second part of this chapter (Sect. 9.7—Sect. 9.10) we will analyze the system design and developing practices from an artificial intelligence point of view. Following that angle, we will use our system development experiences as a case study to address the demanding task of developing intelligent systems equipped with machine creativity that can perform design tasks automatically. The main challenge we concentrate on in this latter part of the chapter is how to model human beings' creativity mathematically and mimic such creativity computationally. We adopt the "synthesis reasoning model" as the underlying mechanism to simulate human beings' creative thinking when they are handling design tasks.

The structure of this part is organized as follows: We will first briefly look at some background research on simulating machine creativity through analogous reasoning (Sect. 9.8). And then we present the theory of the synthesis reasoning model (Sect. 9.9).At last, based on implementation experiences of the calligraphy generation system as well as a few other systems for solving real-world problems, we suggest a generic methodology for constructing intelligent systems using the synthesis reasoning model (Sect. 9.10).

9.8 Background

What is creative thinking? What is the mechanism that underlines human beings' creative thinking? How can one experiment with the purportedly biological creative thinking process through a computational approach? These questions pose challenges for researchers in the fields of AI and cognitive science. Researchers in intelligent CAD (ICAD) systems in particular have a strong interest in these problems. This chapter can be considered a step towards understanding the human creative process. We use a computer-based automatic reasoning system to mimic artistic creativity. Such a task for the computer is highly demanding as the implemented system has to satisfy both the theoretical soundness of machine intelligence and performance benchmarks.

There is a large body of existent work on simulating creative thinking for solving real-world problems. In 1975 Simon [Sim75] pointed out that design and creation is a class of problems based on the synthesis of existing ideas. Qian [Qia86] argued that the synthesis process (using qualitative or quantitative approaches) is an important aspect of brain activities. Hall [Hal89] comprehensively surveyed the computational efforts to simulate analogous reasoning. Kapur [KM88] explored the application of artificial intelligence in geometrical reasoning. Pan et al. [Pan93, XP95, LPJ96, PG96, GP96, ZP97] has researched modeling visual information for intelligent computer-aided design.

9.9 The Synthesis Reasoning Model

The synthesis reasoning model [XP95], or simply synthesis reasoning, is a model we propose to simulate human beings' creative thinking activities when performing design tasks involving images of one kind or another. In the following we briefly survey the basic theory and concepts of the synthesis reasoning model.

9.9.1 Features of the Model

Synthesis reasoning is a generation oriented reasoning mechanism for simulating human creative thinking. Concepts essential to synthesis reasoning include: synthesis reasoning source, reasoning source intensity field, synthesis reasoning space, synthesis reasoning viewpoint and synthesis reasoning process. It is an attempt to relax the constraints of traditional reasoning mechanisms in artificial intelligence to solve problems by using a more flexible reasoning method. Because of the flexibility, synthesis reasoning is particularly suitable for reasoning tasks on shape design as in an Intelligent Computer-Aided Design system (ICAD system). Essentially, synthesis reasoning searches the feasible synthesis reasoning space to identify satisfying viewpoints in the space. A core step in applying the synthesis reasoning model therefore is to establish a synthesis reasoning space, usually by superimposing several input synthesis reasoning sources.

9.9.2 Key Concepts of the Model

In the following we briefly overview some key concepts employed in the synthesis reasoning model. Synthesis reasoning source: A synthesis reasoning source $\mathbf{S}$ is a structure of the form: $\mathbf{S} = \{\mathbf{P}, \mathbf{m}, \mathbf{F}\}$. $\mathbf{P}$ is a collection of n components $\mathbf{P} = \{\mathbf{P}_1, \mathbf{P}_2, \cdots, \mathbf{P}_n\}$. $\mathbf{m}$ is a structure which describes how the above n components can be combined together into a reasoning source. And $\mathbf{F}$ is a reasoning source intensity field.

Reasoning source intensity field: A reasoning source intensity field $\mathbf{F}$ describes the intensity distribution of different reasoning sources during a synthesis reasoning process. $\mathbf{F}$ is composed of two parts: $\mathbf{F} = \{\mathbf{FP}, \mathbf{Fm}\}$. $\mathbf{FP}$ is a collection of reasoning intensities, each of which is associated with one component of the reasoning source, i.e. $\mathbf{FP} = \{\mathbf{FP}_1, \cdots, \mathbf{FP}_n\}$. $\mathbf{Fm}$ is a structure, which records how multiple components can be combined together. The intensity field $\mathbf{F}$ can be classified into two broad types: discrete intensity field where any reasoning intensity is either 0 or 1, and continuous intensity field where intensity can be an arbitrary real number, possibly negative or bigger than 1. With a discrete intensity field, a reasoning source will be either adopted (intensity=1) or ignored (intensity=0).

Synthesis reasoning space: The synthesis reasoning space $\mathbf{SS}$ is the result of superimposing multiple reasoning sources. Each position selected in a synthesis reasoning process is a potential synthesis reasoning result, denoted as $\mathbf{SS}(x, y, z)$. A synthesis reasoning space, which is composed of m reasoning sources, can thus be defined as:

$$\mathbf{SS}(x, y, z) = \sum_{j=1}^{m} \sum_{i=1}^{n} (\mathbf{FP}_{ij}(x, y, z) \cdot \mathbf{P}_{ij}, \mathbf{Fm}_j \cdot \mathbf{m}_j). \qquad (9.30)$$

Synthesis reasoning process: In general we need to carry out two steps to set up a synthesis reasoning model. First we need to construct a synthesis reasoning space using multiple synthesis reasoning sources. And then we need to identify a certain viewpoint/viewpoints in the synthesis reasoning space. There are two inputs to the synthesis reasoning model: one is the multiple reasoning sources and another is requirements for the synthesis reasoning process, if any. Specifically, a two-valued synthesis reasoning process is a process that reasons simply by component replacement. For example, for a language being the experiment target, the word selection and sentence touchup process by rhymists forms a two-valued synthesis reasoning process. Two-valued synthesis reasoning is a degenerate case of the more general and sophisticated continuous valued synthesis reasoning process.

9.9.3 The Computational Model of Synthesis Reasoning

Definition. If there is a correspondence between $\mathbf{T}$ and $\mathbf{B}$, then $\mathbf{T}$ is similar to $\mathbf{B}$ (in a broad sense), which can be denoted as $\mathbf{T} \sim \mathbf{B}$.

Let $\mathbf{B}_1, \cdots, \mathbf{B}_N$ be N pieces of synthesis reasoning source knowledge and $\mathbf{T}$ be the reasoning result, where each of $\mathbf{B}_i$ and $\mathbf{T}$ is composed of M components (parts). We can then represent the synthesis reasoning process and its result using the form:

$$\begin{cases} \mathbf{B}_i = \{b_{ij} | j = 1, \cdots, M\} \\ \mathbf{T} = \{t_j | j = 1, \cdots, M\} \end{cases} \quad (i = 1, \cdots, N).$$

If the synthesis reasoning process is of one source, i.e. $N = 1$, the reasoning equation is simplified to be:

$$\begin{cases} t_1 = f_1(b_{11}) \\ \quad \vdots \\ t_M = f_M(b_{1M}) \end{cases} .$$

If there are multiple pieces of synthesis reasoning source knowledge, the reasoning process can be defined mathematically as follows:

$$\mathbf{A} = \begin{pmatrix} a_{11} & \cdots & a_{1M} \\ a_{21} & \cdots & a_{2M} \\ \vdots & & \vdots \\ a_{N1} & \cdots & a_{NM} \end{pmatrix}_{N \times M} = \begin{pmatrix} \mathbf{a}_1 \\ \mathbf{a}_2 \\ \vdots \\ \mathbf{a}_N \end{pmatrix},$$

$$\mathbf{B} = \begin{pmatrix} b_{11} & \cdots & b_{N1} \\ b_{12} & \cdots & b_{N2} \\ \vdots & & \vdots \\ b_{1M} & \cdots & b_{NM} \end{pmatrix}_{M \times N} = (\mathbf{B}_1, \mathbf{B}_2, \cdots, \mathbf{B}_N),$$

where $\mathbf{a}_i$ is the similarity metric vector of $\mathbf{T}$ to the i-th reasoning source. Then the general form of synthesis reasoning equation $\mathbf{T} = \mathbf{F}(\mathbf{B}_1, \mathbf{B}_2, \cdots, \mathbf{B}_N)$ can be instantiated as:

$$
\begin{cases}
\mathbf{T} = \{t_1, t_2, \cdots, t_M\} = \sum_{i=1}^{n} \mathbf{A}_i \mathbf{B}_i, \\[4pt]
\mathbf{A}_i = \begin{pmatrix} a_{i1} & 0 & \cdots & 0 \\ 0 & a_{i2} & \ddots & \vdots \\ \vdots & \ddots & \ddots & 0 \\ 0 & \cdots & 0 & a_{iM} \end{pmatrix}_{M \times M} & (9.31.1) \\[10pt]
\sum_{i=1}^{n} \mathbf{A}_i = \mathbf{I}_{M \times M} & (9.31.2) \\[6pt]
\begin{cases} a_{ij} \in \{0_F, 1_F\} \subset F \\ \quad\quad \text{or} \\ a_{ij} \in [0_F, 1_F] \subset F \end{cases} & (9.31.3)
\end{cases}
\qquad (9.31)
$$

This equation can be expanded for ease of interpretation as:

$$
\begin{cases}
\mathbf{T} = \mathbf{B}\mathbf{A} = (\mathbf{B}_1, \mathbf{B}_2, \cdots, \mathbf{B}_N) \begin{pmatrix} a_{11} & \cdots & a_{1M} \\ a_{21} & \cdots & a_{2M} \\ \vdots & & \vdots \\ a_{N1} & \cdots & a_{NM} \end{pmatrix}_{N \times M} \\[14pt]
\begin{cases} a_{ij} \in \{0_F, 1_F\} \subset F \\ \quad\quad \text{or} \\ a_{ij} \in [0_F, 1_F] \subset F \end{cases}
\end{cases}
\qquad (9.32)
$$

In the above, Eq. (9.31.1) defines the degree of similarity between $\mathbf{T}$ and $\mathbf{B}_i$. Eq. (9.31.2) guarantees that the scale of $\mathbf{T}$ is synchronized with that of $\mathbf{B}_i$. And Eq. (9.31.3) ensures that $\mathbf{T}$ is more or less similar to $\mathbf{B}_i$ (similarity in a narrow sense).

If $\mathbf{B}_i, \mathbf{T} \in V$, $\oplus$ is closed in V, then $(V, \oplus)$ is an algebraic structure and an exchangeable group, where the involved addition operation is realized through the continuous operator $\oplus$ that satisfies the following properties:

$$
\begin{cases}
1) & t_1 \oplus (t_2 \oplus t_3) = (t_1 \oplus t_2) \oplus t_3 \\
2) & \exists 0 \in V, \exists x \in V \Rightarrow 0 \oplus x = x \oplus 0 = x \\
3) & \forall x \in V, \exists y \in V, \text{ s.t. } x \oplus y = y \oplus x = 0 \\
4) & \forall t_1, t_2 \in V, t_1 \oplus t_2 = t_2 \oplus t_1
\end{cases}
$$

Here V is a vector space on field F, i.e.:

a) $(V, \oplus)$ is an exchangeable group;

b) $\forall a, b \in F \Rightarrow \begin{cases} (a \oplus b)x = ax \oplus bx \\ a(x \oplus y) = ax \oplus ay \\ (ab)x = a(bx) \\ 1_F x = x \end{cases}$

For simplicity we will first study situations where there are only two reasoning sources $\mathbf{B}_1$ and $\mathbf{B}_2$, each of which has only one component, i.e. the synthesis reasoning process when $M = 1$ and $N = 2$. Under this circumstance the form is:

$$\begin{cases} \mathbf{T} = \mathbf{A}_1\mathbf{B}_1 \oplus \mathbf{A}_2\mathbf{B}_2 \\ \mathbf{A}_1 \oplus \mathbf{A}_2 = \mathbf{I}_M \\ a_{ij} \in F; i = 1,2; j = 1,\cdots,M \end{cases} \quad (9.33)$$

To verify that such an equation satisfies the properties mentioned above, we assume $\mathbf{B}_1$ is unknown while $\mathbf{T}$ and $\mathbf{B}_2$ are both known. Then the synthesis reasoning process takes the form:

$$\begin{cases} a_{11}^{-1}a_{11}\mathbf{B}_1 = a_{11}^{-1}\mathbf{T} - a_{21}a_{11}^{-1}\mathbf{B}_2 \\ a_{11} \oplus a_{21} = 1_F \\ a_{11}, a_{21} \in [0_F, 1_F] \end{cases} \quad .$$

Letting $k_1 = a_{11}^{-1}, k_2 = -a_{21}a_{11}^{-1}$, we will then have:

$$\begin{cases} \mathbf{B}_1 = k_1\mathbf{T} \oplus k_2\mathbf{B}_2 \\ a_{11}^{-1}a_{11} = 1_F, 1_F x = x \\ k_1 \oplus k_2 = a_{11}^{-1}(1_F \oplus (-a_{21})) = a_{11}^{-1}(a_{11} \oplus (a_{21} \oplus (-a_{21}))) = a_{11}^{-1}a_{11} = 1_F \\ k_1, k_2 \in F(k_2 < 0_F) \end{cases} \quad .$$

Therefore the synthesis reasoning process with two one-component reasoning sources is of the form:

$$\begin{cases} \mathbf{T} = a_{11}\mathbf{B}_1 \oplus a_{21}\mathbf{B}_2 \\ a_{11} \oplus a_{21} = 1_F \\ a_{11}, a_{21} \in F \end{cases} \quad ,$$

which shows that the synthesis reasoning process we defined does satisfy all the properties as described above.

To take this a step further, suppose there are N reasoning sources, each of which has M components; the synthesis reasoning process is then of the form:

$$\begin{cases} \mathbf{T} = \mathbf{A}_1\mathbf{B}_1 \oplus \mathbf{A}_2\mathbf{B}_2 \oplus \cdots \oplus \mathbf{A}_N\mathbf{B}_N = \sum_{i=1}^{N} \mathbf{A}_i\mathbf{B}_i \quad (9.34.1) \\ \sum_{i=1}^{N} \mathbf{A}_i = \mathbf{I}_M \quad\quad\quad\quad\quad\quad\quad\quad (9.34.2) \\ a_{ij} \in F \quad\quad\quad\quad\quad\quad\quad\quad\quad\quad (9.34.3) \end{cases} \quad (9.34)$$

where $\mathbf{A}_i = \begin{pmatrix} a_{i1} & 0 & \cdots & \cdots & 0 \\ 0 & a_{i2} & 0 & \cdots & \vdots \\ \vdots & 0 & \ddots & 0 & \vdots \\ \vdots & & \ddots & 0 & \ddots & 0 \\ 0 & \cdots & \cdots & 0 & a_{iM} \end{pmatrix}_{M \times M}$.

In the above equations, a_{ij} is the coefficient of $\mathbf{T}'$s similarity metric matrix to the j-th component of the i-th reasoning source. $\mathbf{A}_i$ is the similarity metric matrix of $\mathbf{T}$ to the i-th reasoning source. Eq. (9.34.1) defines the similarity of $\mathbf{A}_i$ to each $\mathbf{B}_i$. So $\mathbf{T}$ is analogically generated by all the $\mathbf{B}'_i$s. Eq. (9.34.2) aligns the scale of $\mathbf{T}$ with each $\mathbf{B}_i$. Eq. (9.34.3) shows that the similarity metric can be either similar (positive) or dissimilar (negative), i.e. similarity in a broad sense.

9.10 A Generic Methodology to Developing Synthesis Reasoning-based Intelligent Systems

Now we will generalize the experiences gained from the system development to propose a generic methodology for designing synthesis reasoning based intelligent CAD systems for solving real-world problems.

The synthesis reasoning model we have proposed is capable of solving a class of shape reasoning problems. We have successfully applied the model to resolve many real world design problems. The automatic Chinese calligraphy generation system introduced in previous sections is one of these systems. Other successful problem solving systems developed, based on the synthesis reasoning model ,include an intelligent advertisement design system [XP95], an intelligent decoration design system [LPJ96] and an intelligent chair design system [PG96]. Although each of these systems has its own problem solving semantics and background knowledge, the synthesis reasoning approaches they employed are very similar. Based on the practices and experiences we accumulated through designing and developing those systems, we propose a generic methodology for developing a synthesis reasoning-based intelligent system for solving any particular type of design problem in the real world, as follows.

(1) According to the specific application domain, choose the synthesis reasoning sources and its properties. By superimposing all the synthesis reasoning sources together, we can construct the synthesis reasoning space.

(2) Introduce a hierarchy of knowledge representation by picking a suitable granularity of knowledge for the different levels in the hierarchy so that the reusability of the reasoning sources and the reasoning results, as well as the reasoning efficiency, can all be improved.

(3) Derive the operators to convert between knowledge representations at different levels in the hierarchy.

(4) Based on the work done in steps 1–3, a full parametric and hierarchical knowledge representation of the complete synthesis reasoning space can be derived.

(5) According to the semantics of the specific application problem to be solved, construct operators to instantiate the synthesis reasoning model as a concrete computable algorithmic framework, based on which the overall system architecture can be deduced. These operators include the synthesis reasoning source superimposing operator, the reasoning source equalization operator, the synthesis reasoning evaluation operator, etc.

References

[Blu67] Harry Blum. A transformation for extracting new descriptors of shape. *Models for the Perception of Speech and Visual Form,* ed. Wathen-Dunn, W., 10(2):362–380, 1967.

[Car83] Jaime G. Carbonell. Learning by analogy: formulating and generalizing plans from past experience. *Machine Learning II.*, Kaufmann, Los Angeles, CA, USA: pages 415–435, 1983.

[CC92] K.P. Chan and Y.S. Cheung. Fuzzy-attribute graph with application to Chinese character recognition. *IEEE Transactions on Pattern Analysis and Machine Intelligence*, 22(1):153–160, 1992.

[CL96] Richard G. Casey and Eric Lecolinet. A survey of methods and strategies in character segmentation. *IEEE Transactions on Pattern Analysis and Machine Intelligence*, 18(7):690–706, 1996.

[CT99] Hung-Pin Chiu and Din-Chang Tseng. A novel stroke-based feature extraction for handwritten Chinese character recognition. *Pattern Recognition*, 32(12):1947–1959, 1999.

[DSS98] Marc Pierrot Deseilligny, Georges Stamon, and Ching Y. Suen. Veinerization: a new shape description for flexible skeletonization. *IEEE Transactions on Pattern Analysis and Machine Intelligence*, 20(5):505–521, 1998.

[Eva68] Thomas G. Evans. ed. M. Minsk, A program for the solution of a class of geometric-analogy intelligence-test questions. *Semantic Information Processing*, The MIT Press, 1968.

[GH80] Mary L. Gick and Keith J. Holyoak. Analogical problem solving. *Cognitive Psychology*, 12:279–306, 1980.

[GP96] Weidong Geng and Yunhe Pan. Multi-dimension theory of knowledge representation. *Science in China: Series E*, 26(3):266–275, 1996.

[Hal89] Rogers P. Hall. Computational approaches to analogical reasoning —a comparative analysis. *Artificial Intelligence*, 39(1): 39–120, 1989.

[HL90] Chia-Wei Liao and Jun S. Huang. Stroke segmentation by Bernstein-Bézier curve fitting. *Pattern Recognition*, 23(5):475–484, 1990.

[Hol84] Keith J. Holyoak. Analogical thinking and human intelligence. *Advances in the Psychology of Human Intelligence*, ed. R.H. Sternberg, Hillsdale, NJ, USA: Lawrence Erlbauum Associates, 2:199–230, 1984.

[HY00] Rong He and Hong Yan. Stroke extraction as pre-processing step to improve thinning results of Chinese characters. *Pattern Recogn. Lett.*, 21(8):817–825, 2000.

[Kea85] Mark T. Keane. On drawing analogies when solving problems: a theory and test of solution generation in an analogical problem solving task. *British Journal of Psychology*, 76(4):449–458, 1985.

[Kea88a] Mark Keane. Analogical mechanisms. *Artificial Intelligence Review*, 2(4):229–250, 1988.

[Kea88b] Mark T. Keane. *Analogical Problem Solving*. New York, NY, USA: John Wiley & Sons, Inc., 1988.

[KK02] Balazs Kegl and Adam Krzyzak. Piecewise linear skeletonization using principal curves. *IEEE Transactions on Pattern Analysis and Machine Intelligence*, 24(1):59–74, 2002.

[KM88] Deepak Kapur and Joseph L. Mundy. Geometric reasoning and artificial intelligence: introduction to the special volume. *Geometric reasoning*, 37(1–3):1–11, 1988.

[Knu79] Donald E. Knuth. *Tex and Metafont: New Directions in Typesetting*. American Mathematical Society, and Bedford, MA, USA: Digital Press, Providence, RI, 1979.

[LC95] Jenn-Yih Lin and Zen Chen. A Chinese-character thinning algorithm based on global features and contour information. *Pattern Recognition*, 28(4):493–512, 1995.

[L'H00] Eric L'Homer. Extraction of strokes in handwritten characters. *Pattern Recognition*, 33(7):1147–1160, 2000.

[LHS98] H.M. Lee, C.W. Huang, and C.C. Sheu. A fuzzy rule-based system for handwritten Chinese characters recognition based on radical extraction. *Fuzzy Sets and Systems*, 100(1–3):59–70, 1998.

[LPJ96] Weilin Lu, Yunhe Pan, and Dongjian Jiang. Fuzzy grammar based image generation mechanism (in Chinese). *Chinese Journal of Computers*, 19(8):636–640, 1996.

[Pan93] Yunhe Pan. Thinking pattern when solving shape design problems. *Journal of Zhejiang University*, 27(3):363–368, 1993.

[PG96] Yunhe Pan and Weidong Geng. Intelligent CAD oriented automatic hierarchic prototype generation method. *Journal of Software*, 7(5):280–285, 1996.

[Qia86] Xuesheng Qian. *Science About Thinking*. Shanghai, China: Shanghai People's Press, 1986.

[RG94] Geber Ramalho and Jean-Gabriel Ganascia. Simulating creativity in jazz performance. In *AAAI '94: Proceedings of the Twelfth National Conference on Artificial Intelligence*, Menlo Park, CA, USA: American Association for Artificial Intelligence, volume 1, pages 108–113,1994.

[Sim75] Herbert A. Simon. Style in design. *Spatial Synthesis in Computer-Aided Building Design*, ed. Charles M. Eastman, pages 287–309, 1975.

[Str86] Steve Strassmann. Hairy brushes. In *SIGGRAPH '86: Proceedings of the 13th Annual Conference on Computer Graphics and Interactive Techniques*, Dellas, TX, USA: ACM Press, pages 225–232, 1986.

[SYTH01] Xingming Sun, Lihua Yang, Yuanyan Tang, and Yunfa Hu. A new stroke extraction method of Chinese characters. *International Journal of Pattern Recognition and Artificial Intelligence*, 15(4):707–721, 2001.

[Win80] Patrick H. Winston. Learning and reasoning by analogy. *Commun. ACM*, 23(12):689–703, 1980.

[Win82] Patrick H. Winston. Learning new principles from precedents and exercises. *Artificial Intelligence*, 19:321–350, 1982.

[Xia89] Yun Xia. Skeletonization via the realization of the fire front's propagation and extinction in digital binary shapes. *IEEE Transactions on Pattern Analysis and Machine Intelligence*, 11(10):1076–1086, 1989.

[XP95] Dongrong Xu and Yunhe Pan. Generation-oriented analogy reasoning. *Science in China*, 38(9):150–167, 1995.

[YS94] Berrin A. Yanikoglu and Peter A. Sandon. Recognizing off-line cursive handwriting. In *Proc. Computer Vision and Pattern Recognition*, Seattle, WA, USA: IEEE Computer Society, pages 397–403, 1994.

[ZC95] Pengfei Zhu and Paul M. Chirlian. On critical point detection of digital shapes. *IEEE Transactions on Pattern Analysis and Machine Intelligence*, 17(8):737–748, 1995.

[ZP97] Geyuan Zhu and Yunhe Pan. Mental image-based knowledge representation for artistic images. *Journal of Software*, 8(10):738–744, 1997.

[ZY99] Jujia Zou and Hong Yan. Extracting strokes from static line images based on selective searching. *Pattern Recognition*, 32(6):935–946, 1999.

10

A Preliminary Attempt at Evaluating the Beauty of Chinese Calligraphy

10.1 Overview

This chapter presents our preliminary efforts at automatic appreciation of the aesthetics of Chinese traditional calligraphy using artificial intelligence. This work is motivated by our wish to equip a computer with the ability to judge the aesthetic quality of calligraphic characters and then to create innovative calligraphic writing styles autonomously.

In terms of knowledge representation for calligraphic characters, we adopt the hierarchical ellipse-based parametric model as examined in the previous two chapters, which approximates how a paintbrush is moved and pressed during the calligraphic writing process. In order to derive characters in this model from copybooks, a two-phased semi-automatic mechanism is introduced for decomposing strokes from existent calligraphy images. For most regular styled calligraphy samples, a fully automatic extraction is possible using only the first phase where heuristic search is applied to derive an optimal stroke-to-stroke matching with the corresponding standard font; for those highly cursive and deformed styles of calligraphic writing, the second phase offers an intelligent user interface to allow the computer to extract strokes based on minimum user input.

Having derived parametric representations for calligraphic characters, we then apply a collection of machine learning techniques to train the computer to be able to numerically evaluate the aesthetics of calligraphic characters based on human labeled sample characters, each carrying a visual quality score. Features considered in the numerical aesthetics evaluation process include the shape of individual strokes, the spatial relationship between strokes, as well as the style consistency among all the strokes in a character. After training the underlying neural networks, the computer is able to evaluate visual qualities of calligraphic characters automatically. The visual quality evaluation has as output three probabilistic values for a character, denoting the likelihood of the character to be attractive, ordinary or ugly. Also, the system optionally offers to synthesize these three scores into a single number for ease of human reading or further algorithmic processing. This work represents our first step towards understanding the human process of appreciating beauty through modeling the process with an integration of available AI techniques.

Once the automatic calligraphy aesthetic quality grading function is developed, we integrate it into the automatic Chinese calligraphy generation prototype system which we have introduced in the previous two chapters. This integration is expected to significantly improve the visual quality of the generated calligraphy. Experiments show that our automatic calligraphy aesthetics evaluating algorithm can yield visual quality scores very similar to those given by the human experts.

10.2 Introduction

10.2.1 Motivation

In this increasingly digitalized society, more and more people choose to stay away from traditional writing tools such as pen, pencil, eraser and brush in their everyday work and life. Instead, they rely on such gadgets as keyboards and mice. This results in a significant improvement in working efficiency. However, up till now the practice of the creation of traditional art forms remains very conservative and distant from digital technologies.

The motivation of our work stems from our dream to computerize the art and process of Chinese traditional calligraphy, which includes the support for an artist to produce new artwork on the computer fully electronically, as discussed in the previous part of this book on interactive painting and calligraphy creation, as well as the goal for a computer to perform art creation autonomously after some learning process. This chapter presents a preliminary attempt to bridge the art of Chinese traditional calligraphy with computer science through an integrated intelligence approach.

Our dream is not only to preserve the ancient calligraphic art in this information era with assistance from computing technologies, but more ambitiously to try to propose novel forms of practising Chinese calligraphy art with active involvement of the computer. Our basic strategy is to develop a novel computer calligraphy creation ability based on applying the machine learning process to hundreds or thousands of calligraphic samples in different styles. This created ability can not only write calligraphic characters with visually acceptable quality, but also could be very innovative in styles. Given that we have already introduced an algorithmic framework capable of automatically generating calligraphy in the previous two chapters, in this chapter we focus our effects on how to evaluate the visual quality of calligraphy writing from an aesthetics point of view. Once this new goal is attained, we can then integrate the numerical grading component into the existent calligraphy generation system to achieve greater performance.

Aside from adding values to computer art, our study in this chapter also provides a good reference for general artificial intelligence research. The field of computer vision is predominantly concerned with recognizing shapes and meanings of objects by their images. But there is more than just knowing *what* things are. In everyday life, our visual perception also leads to a sense of how beautiful things are. Recently there has been an increased interest in affective computing [Pic00]. To the best of our knowledge, however, there has not been a solution to beauty appreciation by numerical means. Turing once said in his innovative paper [Tur50] that "We do not wish to penalize the machine for its inability to shine in beauty competitions, ..." But witnessing the advancement of photo-realistic techniques in computer graphics nowadays, we feel that if computers can tell the beautiful from what is not, beauty contests could certainly be open to them as well. Such contests will probably not feature a cat-walking computer, but rather computer-generated images of beauty, or such images versus real, human-generated ones. This might sound like going overboard, but to imbue the computer with the ability to recognize beauty will likely win general support. Furthermore, the ultimate intelligent machine in people's mind is one that can create results of beauty on its own, which certainly represents a nice challenge for artificial intelligence researchers.

We feel entailing the computer to understand or even produce outputs of beauty that are visible, such as painting, calligraphy and sculpture, may be a reasonable first step in the long journey to arrive at the ultimate intelligent machine which can deal with beauty in any form. This chapter presents such a "first step" of ours—an approach to the problem of understanding the beauty of Chinese calligraphy and its facsimile by the computer. We picked Chinese calligraphy because of its great importance in Chinese art and history and the many interesting challenges it presents to the computer. Our solution demonstrates the power of integrated intelligence.

Overall, our work in this chapter attempts to simulate a series of human psychological processes in learning, creation and appreciation. In our algorithmic design work, we are especially interested in exploring the potential styles that would contribute to the beauty of calligraphy. These potential rules may reflect also the writer's personality and his emotion at the time of writing. Our system has wide applications, for example to tutor a calligraphy beginner to write beautiful characters, to automatically imitate a person's writing styles, or to discover the possible relationship between people's handwriting and their gender, career, personality, health condition, etc.

10.2.2 Chapter Organization

This chapter features our work in three parts: 1) a two-phased decomposition method for deriving the parametric representation of Chinese calligraphy; 2) an integration of machine learning techniques to learn the ability to evaluate aesthetics of calligraphic characters; 3) automatic generation of aesthetic artistic calligraphy with the assistance of the proposed evaluation function. Fig. 10.1 shows an overview of the contents and their flow in this chapter.

First of all, we review the related work in Sect. 10.3. We then briefly discuss the calligraphic representation we use in Sect.10.4. After that a two-phase semi-automatic stroke decomposition algorithm for extracting hierarchically parametric representation is presented in Sect.10.5. With a large amount of parameterized calligraphy samples being accumulated, we asked

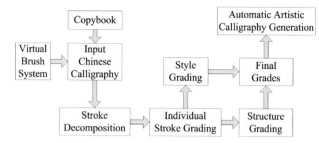

Fig. 10.1. An overview of the work in this chapter

several calligraphy experts and a few others to grade their aesthetic quality. All those samples are fed into the machine learning structures for training the computer's aesthetic ability; both the shape of each individual stroke and the spatial structure of the whole character are considered, plus the style consistency among all of its strokes. We introduce our calligraphy grading approach in Sect. 10.6. It is the core part of this chapter. Once the evaluation functionality is made available, we integrate it into an automatic artistic calligraphy generation system which can produce significantly higher quality new fonts given the scoring feedbacks from the grading module. This is introduced in Sect. 10.7. Relevant experiment results and statistics are given in their corresponding sections. A preliminary calligraphy tutoring system is also introduced, which is made possible by the calligraphy aesthetics evaluation function (Sect. 10.8). Finally, we conclude the chapter and discuss some future extension work (Sect. 10.9).

10.3 Previous Work

The closest related work to our own is the automatic artistic Chinese calligraphy generation system in [XLP03, XLCP04, XLCP05], which we have already looked at in the previous two chapters. That work, however, is concerned mainly with using constraint-based reasoning to generate stylistic calligraphic characters, but paid very little attention to the aesthetic aspects of the generated results; the latter is a major issue to be addressed in this chapter. Avizzano, et al. [ASB02] proposed a calligraphy tutoring system using a haptic interface. Lai et al. [LYP95] studied the problem of numerically evaluating the beauty of calligraphic characters through a heuristical approach. They identified four rules in Chinese calligraphy writing, based on which they implemented a rule-based beauty grading function. The function simply computes the weighted sum of the scores corresponding to these four rules. People have also tried fuzzy methods, e.g. [OAI93]. They devised membership functions for the calligraphists, but the design of these membership functions are fully manual and are fixed all the way through.

In contrast with the above, our calligraphy evaluation is realized through learning the underlying numerical relationships behind the training set. It is known to many who work with expert systems that the high-level expert rules do not always work, are not always known by the experts themselves and even impossible to be summarized sometimes. We feel that our data driven approach based on the learning techniques could thus provide a machine evaluation capability more similar to the actual brain functioning of real human experts.

In the field of computer graphics, there has been some work on automatic painting creation which however is mostly done with reference to a given photograph [Her03]. Others have explored using a combination of artificial intelligence and interactive techniques to produce painting-style animation [XXK+06]. The book [McC90] provides a comprehensive treatment of artificial intelligence art. Outside the domain of visual arts, computer music is probably the single most successful research area in which AI techniques have been employed to do or assist music composition [Roa85]. In IJCAI 2007 there was an independent track called MUSIC-AI 2007 devoted to the topic. It is important to notice that existent research on computer music includes both automatic music composition and music evaluation, which serves as a good inspiration for our work on calligraphy. Their problems in some respects are easier than ours because there are well-established music theories for judging music; that is not the case for visual arts including calligraphy. There is also an abundant collection of work on story generation, believable agents [Bat94], the interactive story, and the like, which aim at capturing aesthetics computationally. Finally, our work is also remotely related to Knuth's pioneering work on Metafont [Knu86]. Knuth's work focuses on the definition and interpretation of fonts, but leaves font creation to the end users; in contrast, our work emphasizes the generation of fonts.

10.4 Calligraphy Representation

Choosing a suitable form of knowledge representation is key to the success of an intelligent system design. Following the practice in computer vision, having a parametric curve-based representation may provide an efficient and effective support for solving our domain specific problem. Such a representation has two immediate benefits: 1) The representation is not per-pixel based, and thus is robust in the face of local noises; and it has more descriptive power on the overall shape and tends to better reflect high-level visual features; 2) The automatically-generated shapes would look more elegant because a parametric representation naturally can overcome the shape aliasing problem. We adopt the hierarchical representation method which we proposed in [XLP03, XLCP04, XLCP05], which iteratively constructs the representation of a character from individual strokes level after level.

Fig. 10.2 shows an example of our ellipse-based parametric representation for a calligraphic character. The idea comes from observations on the brush movements and experiences during human calligraphy production. From another viewpoint, the ellipses can be regarded as a moving ellipse along the skeleton trajectory of the character, which strictly simulates the brush movements during calligraphy.

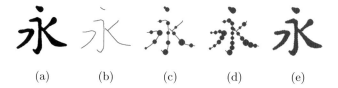

(a)   (b)   (c)   (d)   (e)

Fig. 10.2. An example of ellipse-based calligraphic character representation. (a) The original character, (b) the stroke trajectories, (c to e) characters with covering ellipses every 50, 20, 5 pixels respectively, where (e) is almost actually the presented shape of the character

10.5 Extracting Calligraphy Representation through a Two-phased Method

To derive the above representation, we introduce a two-phase, semi-automatic processing routine. In the first phase we combine several decomposition algorithms which are based on various AI techniques to perform a best-effort automatic stroke extraction. In the second phase, through an intelligent user interface we provide to the user, some remedial user interaction would convert the best-effort result to the desired hierarchical parametric representation.

10.5.1 Best-effort Automatic Stroke Extraction

Stroke decomposition for a Chinese character is a more difficult problem than its recognition. Researchers have proposed various methods, and several algorithms run well for most cases including regular and irregular characters. However, these mature algorithms still cannot achieve satisfying results for Chinese calligraphy whose complexity is exponentially higher, especially those highly random, cursive, or distorted styles. In this section we combine and improve several existent works for stroke extraction of Chinese characters, and propose a complete framework to automatically apply them to Chinese calligraphy. Our method is built on structural matching, so first of all we explain how to extract the structural features of each single font from the calligraphic piece. Since no thinning method is without loss when applied to brush writings such as calligraphy, this problem seems not easy, which we discuss in Sect. 10.5.1.1. After the structure analysis, in Sect. 10.5.1.2, we compare this with the standard font and seek a best-effort stroke match through an heuristic search (based on a probabilistic definition).

10.5.1.1 Structure extraction

All the input calligraphic images are split into single characters and then normalized into a binary image with a standard size, in our experiments a resolution of 300×300 pixels. Like any other image processing approaches for a handwritten character, the first thing to do is thinning for skeletonization. We apply a non-iterative thinning algorithm suggested in [NO94] to get its skeleton, which is faster than the other iteration-based thinning algorithm.

It first of all calculates the distance-to-edge function value for each black point, and then extracts a few points with the local maximal values, namely "pre-skeleton". Finally the pre-skeleton is connected into a complete skeleton with increasing paths.

After thinning, several points with small scales of distance-to-edge values are deleted from the skeleton. The scale threshold is determined by the average width of the whole character, where the width can be estimated through the distance-to-edge values of all the pixels on the skeleton. All pixels whose distance-to-edge values are less than the threshold are removed. This step hopes to remove the noisy signals in the character image, which are usually caused by the ink spreading effect during handwriting or the weathering and erosion of old stones for carved calligraphy. A few thinning results are given in Fig. 10.3(b).

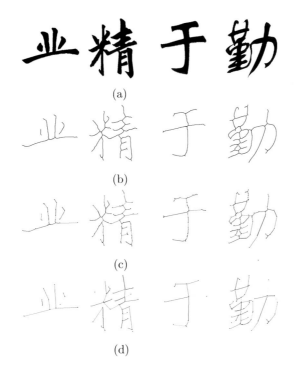

(a)

(b)

(c)

(d)

Fig. 10.3. Examples of extracting the structures of calligraphic characters. (a) the input calligraphic characters; (b) the skeleton images after applying a non-iterative thinning algorithm; (c) the geometric graph of characters after the feature point detection and line segments approximation, where lots of noisy and spurious branches are left behind; (d) the pruned graph by deleting noisy and merging spurious branches

The skeleton is still just a series of pixels. Borrowing the definition of the feature point in [LHS99], we divide the entire skeleton into several discrete curves through these feature points. Having derived several feature points, we trace the discrete curves from each feature point via a depth-first search, until all the curves have been traversed.

In succession, we employ a modified Hough transform to approximate each individual discrete curve with a few line segments. This process converts the pixel-based signals into geometric objects, effectively extracting the spatial structures of the character. Thus for each character we can construct a graph G from these line segments, where

$$G =< V, E >, E = \{(v_1, v_2)|v_1, v_2 \in V\}. \tag{10.1}$$

Here E is the set of line segments derived from the Hough transform and V consists of all the ending points on those line segments. This is more than a topological graph in normal graph theory, where each vertex has its coordinates on a 2D plane. This kind of graph is called a *"geometric graph"* for which the definition is adapted as:

$$\widehat{G} =< \widehat{V}, E >, \widehat{V} = \{< v_i, x_i, y_i > |v_i \in V\}, \tag{10.2}$$

where (x_i, y_i) are the coordinates of vertex v_i. By comparing Fig. 10.3(b) and (c), we can see the result of feature points detection and line segments approximation.

However, the thinning and line approximation process brings in many fragments of short segments on the skeleton and the geometric graph. Another problem is a spurious branch: for example a crossing of two perpendicular strokes might be split into two feature points in the skeleton image. These problems are illustrated in Fig. 10.3(c), which motivate us to prune and revise the graph.

The first pruning plan is to merge successive collinear segments into one. Any pair of adjacent segments, connected by a 2-degree vertex, is merged into one segment if the angle between them is nearly 180 degrees or one of them is much shorter than the other. Once such a condition is met, these two segments and their common vertex are removed from the graph while the new merged segment is added, except for any part of the new segment which lies outside the black area of the original character trajectory. This merging step repeats until no pair meets the condition.

For the other "spurious branch" problem, we apply the "maximal circle criterion" [LHS99] on each pair of adjacent feature points. The two adjacent vertices are merged into one if, and only if, the "maximal circle criterion" is satisfied. As shown in Fig. 10.3(c to d), we can see that the pruning techniques improve the accuracy of the geometric graph significantly.

Fig. 10.3 illustrates the complete process of structure extraction step by step. Finally we get a geometric graph for each calligraphic character. In order to extract each stroke from this graph, we apply a structural matching method based on an heuristic search by making a comparison with the graph of its standard font, which we introduce next.

10.5.1.2 Best-effort stroke matching

After the geometric graph is extracted from the character, for every character in its standard font we employ the knowledge-based rules suggested in [LHS97] to extract its primitive strokes from the graph. During the experiment this method works well for almost all the characters of standard fonts whose skeletons are completely normal but not satisfactorily for the other fonts. As we already have the strokes of standard fonts, we can apply a structural matching algorithm to each new character to seek a stroke-to-stroke match in the graph of its corresponding standard font. Our structural matching algorithm is implemented with a heuristic search, based on the definitions of several probabilistic variables.

Borrowing from [YLL97], we define three groups of probabilistic values, i.e. STROKE_LENGTH, STROKE_TYPE, STROKE_LOCATION, to describe a primitive stroke, and two other groups, i.e. CROSSING_RELATION, POSITIONAL_RELATION, to describe the relation between a pair of strokes. Table 10.1 gives a list of these groups.

Table 10.1. Feature groups

Group	Feature Name
STROKE_LENGTH	short, normal, long
STROKE_TYPE	vertical(Shu), horizontal(Heng), slanting(Pie), anti-slanting(Na), dots(Dian)
STROKE_LOCATION	left-up, up, right-up, left, middle, right, left-down, down, right-down
CROSSING_RELATION	isolated, end-to-end, middle-to-end, end-to-middle, middle-to-middle(crossing), overlapped
POSITIONAL_RELATION	left, right, up, down, parallel

STROKE_LENGTH. In this group, three features recording the degree of the length of stroke are of concern. By comparing the specified stroke with the length of the character, the features concerning the length can be obtained by using the membership functions shown in Fig. 10.4, where the length of a character stands for the diagonal length of its bounding box.

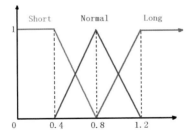

Fig. 10.4. Membership functions for STROKE_LENGTH feature group

STROKE_TYPE. In this group there are five features concerning the slope of the strokes. As shown in Fig. 10.5, the four features, vertical (V), horizontal (H), slanting (S), and anti-slanting (AS), are determined by the obliquity of the stroke. The fifth type is the dots (D) which are determined by the length of the stroke but not influenced by the obliquity, as also shown in Fig. 10.5. For example, a stroke with the angle of 22.5 degrees has the feature vector $(0.5/H, 0.5/S, 0/V, 0/AS)$. But if it is a short one with the 1/12 diagonal length, it has a probability of 0.5 to be a dot. After all, it has a feature vector $(0.25/H, 0.25/S, 0/V, 0/AS, 0.5/D)$.

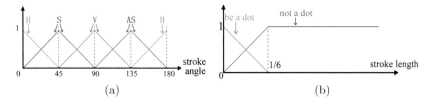

Fig. 10.5. Membership functions of STROKE_TYPE: (a) the probabilities for horizontal (H), vertical (V), slanting (S), anti-slanting (AS); t (b) the dot's probability

STROKE_LOCATION. The features in this group represent the location of the center of the specified stroke. In both x- and y-direction, we divide the projective line segment of the character into three parts, left (up), middle and right (down), as shown in Fig. 10.6. Then using a Descartes' multiplication, the whole image is split into 9 zones.

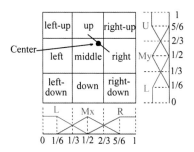

Fig. 10.6. Probabilistic membership functions of the nine zones, inspired by [YLL97]

The three membership groups described above represent the attributes of a single stroke. In most handwritten character images, a stroke is distorted in its length, location or obliquity. In fact in a character the inter-stroke relations are far more important than the individual strokes. In order to describe them exactly, two more functions are brought in, introduced below.

CROSSING_RELATION. This feature is used to represent the intersection relations between a pair of strokes. Under the assumption that the length of each stroke is one, the distance from the two ends to the intersection point (if it exists) for each stroke can be measured. With its help, we can divide the stroke into two parts, ending and middle, which are shown with probabilistic values in Fig. 10.7. So far the relationship could be classified six classes: not touched, end-to-end touched, end-to-middle touched, middle-to-end touched, crossing (middle-to-middle touching) and overlapped (intersecting not only at a point). Each stroke owns such a specific probabilistic vector which contains six probabilistic scales for the six types.

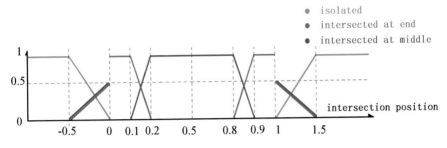

Fig. 10.7. Membership functions used for CROSSING_RELATION

POSITIONAL_RELATION. This procedure is similar to CROSSING_RELATION, except that the measure is not about the intersections but rather the relative positions. The probabilistic functions are shown in Fig. 10.8. Similar to STROKE_LOCATION, the projective segment in both x- and y-direction is divided into three parts, according to the relative locations between a pair of strokes.

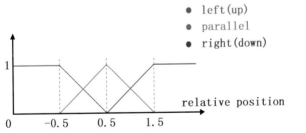

Fig. 10.8. Membership functions used for POSITIONAL_RELATION

10.5.1.3 Structural matching with heuristic search

With the probabilistic representation of the stroke's attributes and the relations between strokes, we can find a matching for each respective stroke from its standard font. Liu et al. [LKK01] have done some work on stroke matching for handwritten Chinese character recognition. Here we borrow their idea to extract the strokes in a calligraphic character. The matching consists of two phases. At first the probabilistic attributes of every combination of consecutive line segments in the structure graph are computed and compared with every stroke in the graph of the standard font. Limited combinations of similar attributes with a stroke in the standard font are added in its candidates set. This is a coarse classification to reject all the obviously incorrect stroke matching combinations. Secondly, an heuristic search is employed to select one stroke from the candidates set for each stroke in the standard font. The searching target is to find a best-effort matching based on the probabilistic definitions. In this phase, both the individual attributes and the relations between strokes are considered.

CANDIDATE_STROKE_EXTRACTION. Any stroke in the graph is an edge (line segment) or a path (poly-line) in the graph. All the candidate strokes for matching a stroke in the standard graph are stored in a list, where only these candidate strokes will be considered in the STROKE_MATCHING phase. All the combinations of edges in the graph are enumerated as a stroke, which can be traversed through a depth-first search on the graph. For each enumerated stroke, we calculate its distance from every stroke in the standard graph, defined as follows:

$$D(s, s') = a|\mathbf{len} - \mathbf{len}'| + b|\mathbf{loc} - \mathbf{loc}'| + c|\mathbf{type} - \mathbf{type}'|, \tag{10.3}$$

where **len**, **loc**, and **type** are the probabilistic vectors of a stroke (referred to in Sect. 10.5.1.2), and a, b and c are coefficients. With the definition for each stroke needed for matching, only enumerated strokes whose distances from the standard one are smaller than a tolerance threshold will be added in the candidates set. There are also three threshold values for the single distances between **len**, **loc** and **type**. The restriction due to these thresholds is quite loose, so that it just cuts off the strokes which do not match the standard one. (During experiments, every candidate set of a standard stroke has a limited capacity.)

STROKE_MATCHING. In stroke matching, each standard stroke is matched with a stroke in its candidate set. Moreover, the matched stroke in its graph must be consistent with the inter-stroke relations in the standard graph. We define the distance between two relations for two pairs of strokes as:

$$D'((s, s'), (t, t')) = d|\mathbf{cro}(s, s') - \mathbf{cro}(t, t')| + e|\mathbf{pos}(s, s') - \mathbf{pos}(t, t')| \tag{10.4}$$

where $\mathbf{cro}(s, s')$ represents the crossing relation vector between stroke s and s', and $\mathbf{pos}(s, s')$ represents the positional relation between s and s' (and d, e are coefficients). Since in most Chinese characters the inter-stroke relations are more crucial, the coefficients d and e here are quantitatively much larger than the coefficients a, b and c. So far we can achieve the definition of distance between two geometric graphs which comes from two character images, as follows:

$$Dis(\widehat{G}, \widehat{G}') = \sum_{i=1}^{n}(D(s_i, s_i') + \sum_{j=1}^{n} D'((s_i, s_j), (s_i', s_j'))), \tag{10.5}$$

where n is the number of strokes in both $\widehat{G}$ and $\widehat{G}'$, s is a stroke in $\widehat{G}$ and s' is a stroke in $\widehat{G}'$.

Now the matching problem comes to an optimization problem: to seek a mapping so that the distance between all the matched strokes and the graph of the standard character are minimized. A naive way is to enumerate all the possible matches, but for most Chinese characters this would be too slow. In order to reduce the computation complexity, we employ a heuristic search of the A* algorithm, instead of a complete enumeration.

In an A* search, the sum of distances under the current partial search is estimated as (assuming (s, s') is the current searching pair):

$$f(s, s') = c(s, s') + h(s, s'), \tag{10.6}$$

where $c(s, s')$ is the summed up distance from the beginning to the current matching pair and $h(s, s')$ is the heuristic function to estimate the summed up distance in all the remaining pairs. To ensure the final result will be optimal, $h(s, s') \leqslant H(s, s')$ must be guaranteed according to, the constraints of A*, where $H(s, s')$ is the actual summed up distance on the remaining path which is unknown currently. Here we assign the heuristic function $h(s, s')$ to be:

$$h(s_i, s_i') = \sum_{j=i+1}^{n} \min_{s_j'} \{ D(s_j, s_j') + \sum_{k=1}^{i} D'((s_j, s_k), (s_j', s_k')) \}. \tag{10.7}$$

Obviously the h here satisfies the optimal restriction $h \leqslant H$, which means we can get the best-effort matching through such a heuristic search. During implementation we have to consider the lost strokes in a character, since the situation appears commonly in Chinese calligraphy. We input a special stroke, "*null stroke*", which is a candidate for any standard stroke and always consistent with any crossing and positional relations, but with a large scale in distance from anyone else.

After the minimal summed up distance is found, there might still be a few line segments left which do not match any standard strokes. However, all the segments in the graph should be matched with the standard graph if the matching is actually perfect. For those remaining collected segments, we simply classify them into their nearest matched strokes.

So far we are able to arrive at a series of segments resembling the skeleton of the strokes. The last step is to construct the ellipse parametric representation for each stroke from these segments (skeleton). A pixel on the skeleton is regarded as the center of an ellipse and we draw the maximal ellipse within the black area of the original trajectory centered on each pixel. All the parameters of these maximal ellipses are recorded for representing the strokes. During practical operation there is another "spur" problem occurring in the intersection area of two or more strokes, where we use a B-spline curve to smooth both the skeleton and the stroke contour. Due to time and space limitations, we will not give the details of this problem here. An example to illustrate the structural matching process is shown in Fig. 10.9.

10.5.2 Intelligent User Interface for the Difficult Cases

We could not rely on a fully automatic processing routine because aesthetic calligraphy tends to be highly cursive and severely distorted, which renders

(a)	(b)	(c)	(d)

Fig. 10.9. An example of structural matching based on heuristic search: (a) the input character; (b) the geometric graph of the character after structure extraction; (c) comparing with the graph of standard font; (d) the matched strokes on the graph via the heuristic search; (e) the final stroke decomposition results

an automatic decomposition process based on available pattern recognition techniques practically impossible. Fig. 10.10 shows some difficult cases that are highly distorted and have almost completely lost original features.

(a)	(b)	(c)	(d)	(e)	(f)

Fig. 10.10. Difficult cases: (b) (d) (f) are the standard fonts of the three characters (a) (c) (e) respectively, where (a) (c) (e) are severely distorted which cannot be successfully decomposed by our automatic stroke matching algorithm

Our intelligent user interface allows the user to optionally correct or refine the automatic stroke decomposition results, especially the difficult cases. The "intelligence" of this UI component lies in its ability to solve the last bits of the puzzle based on the user's very sketchy hints. We show one example, in Fig. 10.11, to explain this process step by step.

We ask the user to draw just a few suggestive sketches to help the computer. We have developed an intelligent user interface for this purpose. The interface does not expect strokes to be drawn to high accuracy, as can be seen in Fig. 10.11(e). Given the user's sketches, we adopt the heuristic A* search to look for an optimal stroke matching between the user input and the remainder of the sub-stroke graph in Fig. 10.11(f). During this search process we also assign probabilistic values to stroke attributes and their spatial relationships in a fashion similar to our automatic approach. With this algorithmic processing in the background, our intelligent user interface gets all the strokes decomposed, as in Fig. 10.11(g to h). The decomposition results for the other two difficult cases referred to in Fig. 10.10 are shown in Fig. 10.12, with the help of skeleton stretches drawn through the user interface. Fig. 10.13 shows a few more examples of decomposition results.

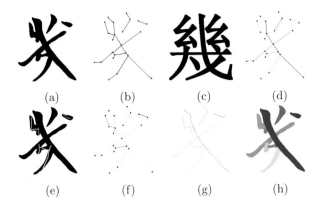

(a)   (b)   (c)   (d)

(e)   (f)   (g)   (h)

Fig. 10.11. An example of decomposing a calligraphic character by our two-phase decomposition method which utilizes an automatic analysis mechanism and an intelligent user interface. The input calligraphic character (a), its geometric graph (b), the shape of the character written in the standard style (c), the automatic stroke segmentation result by stroke topology analysis and matching, which only extracts three strokes (d). The remaining strokes are too difficult to be extracted by any automatic algorithm due to their great deviation from the standard way of writing. We turn to the intelligent interface, with which the user only sketches several simple strokes (e), according to which we can have all the strokes in the geometric graph identified (f); the corresponding stroke trajectories (g), and shapes (h), can thus be all extracted

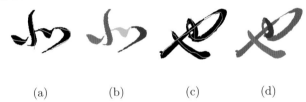

(a)   (b)   (c)   (d)

Fig. 10.12. The examples of stroke decomposition with the intelligent user interface. (a) and (c) show the sketches drawn by user; (b) and (d) show the decomposition results for (a) and (c) respectively

10.6 Calligraphy Aesthetics Evaluation

In this section we discuss how to rate the aesthetic quality of a calligraphic character, according to both the shapes of its constituent strokes in Sect. 10.6.1 and the spatial relationship between its strokes in Sect. 10.6.2, plus its style analysis compared with the existent well-known styles in Sect. 10.6.3.

First of all, we acquire a number of calligraphic character writing samples from both calligraphy copybooks and student practice books to compose the training set for our learning algorithm. After the sample collection, we invited five calligraphists to play experts to label each of the sample characters by their visual quality. To keep it simple, only three labels, "good", "so-so" and "bad" are used. For each labeled character, three values in the range of 0% to 100% for the three label types are computed following a Bayesian estima-

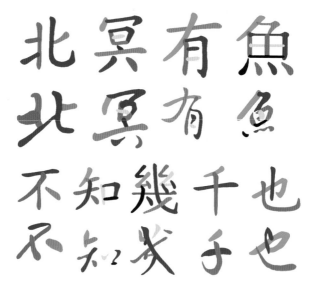

Fig. 10.13. A few more examples of decomposition results

tion method [WK01]. Each value indicates the probability of a calligraphic character being considered "good", "so-so" or "bad".

Based on discussion with practising calligraphists, we take into account three aspects when designing our calligraphy aesthetics evaluation algorithm: 1) the shape of single strokes, 2) the topological relationship between strokes, and 3) the correlation among the strokes' styles. After the calligraphic samples are decomposed, represented parametrically and labeled, a collection of machine learning algorithms are employed to capture the underlying rules governing the impression of beauty or ugliness of the characters. With such learned criteria, we can then evaluate new calligraphic writings. We demonstrate the practical value of the automatic aesthetics evaluation algorithm by integrating it into an existent automatic calligraphy generation system that we introduced in the previous two chapters. Better visual quality and more controlled output in high quality can be achieved after the integration.

10.6.1 Evaluating Shapes of Individual Strokes

In the first step we grade individual strokes. This agrees with the general learning process where one of the basic learning objectives for calligraphy beginners is to learn to write decent looking single strokes. The reason is simply that a single ugly stroke is enough to destroy the overall beauty of a character. So when grading a character we first estimate a visual appearance score for each of the individual strokes.

In our ellipse-based representation of a stroke, each stroke contains a series of points on its skeleton, and each point has a corresponding covering ellipse. We thus have a 2D curve, K, for the skeleton of the stroke and another two 1D curves, Ma and Mi, for the major and minor radii of the covering ellipse. We compute a minimum distance from a point on the skeleton to a point on the stroke contour for each pixel on the skeleton, which results in an offset distance curve D. Before extracting any features for these curves, we apply a Fourier transformation to discard the low frequency components from the curve of K to get the curve S which only indicates the local shape of the skeleton. This can discard much of the semantics of the particular stroke and thus yield a more compact representation for shape feature comparison across different strokes; this effectively increases the generality of our training samples. For Chinese characters in particular there can be easily hundreds of distinct shapes for a single stroke. Without such a content invariant representation, we would have labored intensively to collect a large number of training samples.

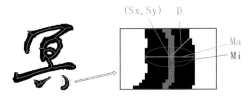

Fig. 10.14. The stroke signals used for shape grading: $\omega = \{S_x, S_y, Ma, Mi, D\}$

Now we have a set of curves $\omega = (S_x, S_y, Ma, Mi, D)$, where S_x and S_y are the x, y components of the 2D curve S, as shown in Fig. 10.14. We then compute the associated derivative curves for each of them, getting another set of curves $\omega' = (S'_x, S'_y, Ma', Mi', D')$. With both ω and ω', we can compute the shape features of the curves for use in both the learning and the grading process. For each curve C above, which is a 1D signal, we obtain its largest element $C_{\max}$, the average value C_{ave} and its median value C_{med}. The set of features for inputting into the neural network is derived as:

$$F \triangleq \{C_{\max}|C \in \Theta\} \cup \{C_{\text{ave}}|C \in \Theta\} \cup \{C_{\text{med}}|C \in \Theta\} \cup \theta, \qquad (10.8)$$

where $\Theta \triangleq \omega \cup \omega'$, and θ is defined below in Eq. 10.9. In our experiments we find those feature terms in θ_{ave} work most discriminatively.

$$\begin{cases} \theta & \triangleq \theta_{\text{ave}} \cup \theta_{\max} \cup \theta_{\text{med}} \\ \theta_{\text{ave}} & \triangleq \{\frac{C'_{\max}}{C'_{\text{ave}}}, \frac{C'_{\text{ave}}}{C'_{\text{ave}}}, \frac{C'_{\text{med}}}{C'_{\text{ave}}} | C \in \omega\} \\ \theta_{\max} & \triangleq \{\frac{C'_{\max}}{C'_{\max}}, \frac{C'_{\text{ave}}}{C'_{\max}}, \frac{C'_{\text{med}}}{C'_{\max}} | C \in \omega\} \\ \theta_{\text{med}} & \triangleq \{\frac{C'_{\max}}{C'_{\text{med}}}, \frac{C'_{\text{ave}}}{C'_{\text{med}}}, \frac{C'_{\text{med}}}{C'_{\text{med}}} | C \in \omega\} \end{cases} \qquad (10.9)$$

To provide labels for the training examples we ask our experts to mark each individual stroke with a label, "good", "so-so" or "bad". After the probabilistic grades are computed from these manual labels, we feed a training set containing a total of 2,500 such labeled single stroke examples, collected from around 500 single characters, into the back-propagation neural network and train it iteratively. As well as the labeled samples, three probabilistic values in the range of [0%, 100%] are in the output, corresponding to whether the single strokes are "good", "so-so" or "bad". Several grading results of individual strokes are shown in Fig. 10.15 and 10.16.

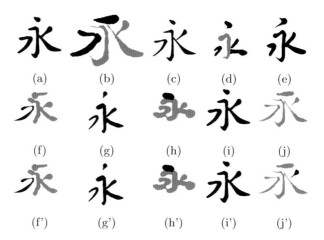

Fig. 10.15. Single stroke grading. (a to e) are five example characters among a set of ten sample characters, from which fifty single strokes are extracted to form the training set for single stroke grading. The red ones are aesthetically unacceptable strokes and the black ones are acceptable strokes. (f to j) are five new characters unknown to the training set. They are colored according to the grading results produced by our algorithm. (f' to j') are the corresponding human expert graded results. Our algorithm only makes one mistake for a stroke, in (j), where the stroke is rejected because it is not connected; the human expert feels in this situation the stroke still looks beautiful even though it is against some general rule of calligraphy

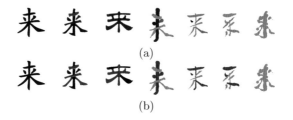

Fig. 10.16. Examples of individual strokes evaluation where the bottom one comes from human experts evaluation and the upper one is given by our algorithm. For visualization convenience, the evaluating results are represented with colorful strokes. A completely black stroke indicates it is "good" while a completely red one means "bad". As can be seen in this comparison, in general, our algorithmic grading results are very similar to those given by the human experts

An alternative way is to split a single stroke into pieces before the learning. This is inspired by our knowledge in Chinese calligraphy that a stroke in each style has abundant features around its two tips, which might be helpful for producing more convincing results. Normally we can divide the entire stroke into three pieces, its two tips and its central part. For each part we can do the same things as stated above.

10.6.2 Evaluating Spatial Layout of Strokes

As important as the appearance of single strokes is the way the strokes are spatially arranged to compose a character. The visual qualities of these individual strokes interact with one another to form the overall visual impression of the whole character, in much the same way as the looks of our facial parts mutually interact to form the overall appearance of a human face. For Chinese characters, these spatial arrangements not only affect the aesthetic appearance but can also lead to different readings as to what the characters are. Sometimes a minute change of the spatial relationship between strokes can result in an entirely different character being perceived, and not merely the same character written in a different style. This poses a great challenge to our algorithmic design. This will be easy to understand: a pair of charming eyes, a pretty nose, and perfect red lips together do not necessarily make a good-looking face if these various features are not in the right proportions and layout. Another issue is whether the styles of different strokes cooperate harmoniously, i.e. a pretty face probably will not result if mixing a pair of European eyes with an Indian nose, Japanese lips and black skin. We discuss the style coherence aspect in Sect. 10.6.3.

For every pair of strokes, x, y, we compute the maximum, minimum and mean distances, $l_{\max}(x,y)$, $l_{\min}(x.y)$, $l_{\mean}(x,y)$ from a point on one curve to a point on the other curve. These values can describe both the topological and the spatial relationships between the strokes. For example, we can easily determine by these values whether the two strokes intersect or how much they overlap if intersecting. However, these three values may not tell us the strokes' relative position precisely, which is important for the overall visual appearance or for determining the identity of the character. To capture that, we draw a bounding box for each stroke (a bounding box is the minimum rectangle that includes all the parts of the stroke), and then compute the horizontal, vertical, and planar overlaps of the pair of bounding boxes. We denote the computed values as $B_{\mathrm{h}}(x,y)$, $B_{\mathrm{v}}(x,y)$, $B_{\mathrm{p}}(x,y)$. This is similar to the measurement of the degree of overlap between shapes in [XLCP05]. The difference is that our bounding box is free in orientation, and is not confined to being parallel to the $X-Y$ axes. For a long and cursive stroke in particular, where its bounding box contains much blank area, we compute these values according to its original trajectory without the bounding box. In addition, we also consider the crossing relationship between a pair of strokes, which is another key factor for the whole visual effect. As referred to in Table 10.1 of Sect. 10.5.1.2, we use the CROSSING_RELATION value to represent the crossing relationship between a pair of strokes but directly use the numerically real numbers on the X-axis in Fig. 10.7 instead of the probabilistic features, denoted as $B_{\mathrm{c}}(x,y)$. Assume a character has n strokes, doing the above gives us seven $n \times n$ matrices $M_{\max}$, $M_{\min}$, $M_{\mean}$, M_{h}, M_{v}, M_{p}, M_{c} where the element in the i-th row and j-th column of M is taken from a corresponding value computed for the stroke pair of the i-th stroke and the j-th stroke.

In the experiments we discover that a majority of the strokes have little contribution to the architecture of a character while one or two strokes out of the character mostly determine its literal sense and its aesthetics. For a character with n strokes, we set up a series of weight values $V = \{v_i | i = 1, 2, \ldots, n\}$ to indicate the structural contribution of the each stroke, where v_i equals the space ratio of the i-th stroke's bounding box to the sum of the area of all the strokes' bounding boxes. On the other hand, inspired by the "radical" layer in the hierarchical representation in [XLCP05], we establish a weight matrix $\mathbf{W}$ for all the six matrices above, where the element in the i-th row and j-th column indicates the weight of the corresponding elements in all the six matrices. The elements of matrix $\mathbf{W}$ come from the radical structures from the character hierarchy. If a pair of strokes are in the same radical, the corresponding element in matrix $\mathbf{W}$ is assigned are 1, otherwise 0.5. With these weight definitions, we compute six new matrices $\mathbf{P}_{max}$, $\mathbf{P}_{min}$, $\mathbf{P}_{mean}$, $\mathbf{P}_h$, $\mathbf{P}_v$, $\mathbf{P}_p$. For each element $p_{i,j}$ in each matrix $\mathbf{P}$,

$$p_{i,j} = \min(v_i, v_j) \cdot w_{i,j} \cdot m_{i,j} \qquad (i, j = 1, 2, ..., n), \qquad (10.10)$$

where $w_{i,j}$ and $m_{i,j}$ are respectively the corresponding elements in $\mathbf{W}$ and each matrix $\mathbf{M}$ out of the six matrices referred to in the previous paragraph.

The next step is to compute the features of these matrices. For a character α we can find its corresponding character $\tilde{\alpha}$ written in the Kai style. We then compute the above six matrices for each of them, and then do a matrix deduction between the corresponding pair of matrices. The results are denoted as $\mathbf{Q}_{max}$, $\mathbf{Q}_{min}$, $\mathbf{Q}_{mean}$, $\mathbf{Q}_h$, $\mathbf{Q}_v$, $\mathbf{Q}_p$, $\mathbf{Q}_c$. Such a deduction operation attempts to derive a more or less content invariant version of the spatial relationships between the composing strokes in a character; the benefit is similar to the gain from removing the low frequency components when grading shapes of individual strokes. For each of the resultant matrices, we compute its maximum element value φ_{max}, minimum element value φ_{min}, maximum absolute value φ_{maxa}, mean element value φ_{mean}, median element value φ_{med}, and its first three eigenvalues, λ_1, λ_2, λ_3. In total we have $8 \times 7 = 56$ features for a character. Again we use a back-propagation neural network and train it through 10,000 iterations. We feed the network with over 500 character samples for 50 most frequently used characters, all of which come from different people with different experience levels in calligraphy; the samples include also a few ugly or naively written ones. Like what we do in individual stroke grading, only three levels, "good", "so-so" and "bad" are actually assigned according to people's opinion. Figs. 10.17 and 10.18 show a few experiment results for spatial-layout grading.

We should point out that the scores so produced depend on which font is used as the standard font to supply the standard shape of the character $\tilde{\alpha}$ as needed in the above processing. At present we always use the Kai style. We noticed for the same character written in other styles, it could appear very differently from that of the Kai style. To solve this problem we employ a topology matching algorithm to get a one-to-one stroke matching between the

Fig. 10.17. Stroke spatial relationship grading example. (a to e) are five training characters used in this experiment. (a to c) are positive examples and (d) and (e) are negative examples. (f to j) are the characters graded as aesthetically unacceptable by the spatial relationship analysis. Their respective scores are: 44.7, 12.7, 7.3, 64.7, 5.4. (k to o) are aesthetically acceptable results as judged by our grading algorithm. Their respective scores are: 80.1, 99.0, 99.6, 88.5, 99.8

Fig. 10.18. Spatial layout evaluation examples. The statistics in Table 10.2 show the evaluating details. Each percentage scale represents the probability that the sample is "good", "so-so" or "bad". For comparison, two probabilistic grades are listed in each unit where the bottom one comes from human experts and the upper one is given by our algorithm. As can be seen in this experiment, for the majority of the cases, the algorithmic grading results agree well with those given by human experts

Table 10.2. Statistics of spatial layout evaluation results for characters in Fig. 10.18

Figure	Good	So-so	Bad	Figure	Good	So-so	Bad
(a)	100%	0%	0%	(k)	100%	0%	0%
	100%	0%	0%		60%	40%	0%
(b)	61.6%	38.4%	0%	(l)	50.3%	49.7%	0%
	70%	30%	0%		70%	30%	0%
(c)	86.8%	13.2%	0%	(m)	94.0%	6.0%	0%
	100%	0%	0%		80%	20%	0%
(d)	35.5%	60.0%	4.5%	(n)	57.6%	42.4%	0%
	40%	60%	0%		70%	30%	0%
(e)	31.3%	60.0%	8.7%	(o)	90.2%	9.8%	0%
	70%	30%	0%		80%	20%	0%
(f)	55.0%	45.0%	0%	(p)	48.1%	51.9%	0%
	90%	10%	0%		50%	50%	0%
(g)	0%	54.3%	45.7%	(q)	0%	0%	100%
	50%	50%	0%		0%	40%	60%
(h)	0%	54.3%	45.7%	(r)	0%	0%	100%
	20%	60%	20%		0%	0%	100%
(i)	0%	50.7%	49.3%	(s)	0%	0%	100%
	20%	60%	20%		0%	0%	100%
(j)	98.4%	1.6%	0%	(t)	0%	5.9%	94.1%
	100%	0%	0%		0%	0%	100%

character and its standard style before going through the shape comparison and deduction process as discussed in the above paragraph. An alternative is to classify all the samples into different styles and use different standard fonts for reference purposes during feature extraction rather than always sticking to the Kai style. One way to execute this classification process automatically is to compare the shape of the character with its counterparts in different sample writing styles and choose the one yielding the highest score.

10.6.3 Evaluating Coherence of Stroke Styles

During our experiments we found that an ugly character could be composed of good-looking strokes. From a numerical point of view several high-score strokes with high-score spatial layout could still form an ugly character, since some of the strokes might be in different styles. Fig. 10.19 shows some samples on this issue.

Normally strokes in the same style would lead to a good-looking character in that style (if the strokes and their spatial layout are both "good"). And in some cases, where the styles of strokes are different, but "consistent", the strokes could still form a good-looking character. We need to consider and evaluate the style correlation among strokes, which is also important for the overall quality of the character.

For simplicity, assume there are always m well recognized writing styles available, which could come from multiple copybooks by different calligraphists.

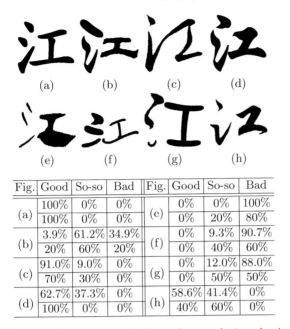

Fig. 10.19. The evaluation results of stroke styles correlation. As similar as in Fig. 10.18, both probabilistic grades from computer and human are given for comparison where the bottom one comes from human experts and the upper one is given by our algorithm

For each stroke in each writing sample, we calculate the probability for it to be written in a certain sample style. We thus get an m-dimensional vector measuring the probability for an individual stroke to be in the sample writing styles, i.e. $G = \{g_i | i = 1, 2, ..., m\}$. For a character with n strokes, an $n \times m$ matrix $\mathbf{R}$ is established, where the element in the i-th row and j-th column is the value of g_j for the i-th stroke. In our experiments we select six most frequent styles for each type of stroke and use all the $6n$ elements in $\mathbf{R}$ as the input to a Bayesian network. The outputs of the network are three real numbers between 0 and 1, denoting the probabilities of the stroke correlation as "good", "so-so" or "bad". To collect the training set, we first developed a program which could generate new characters in "novel" styles based on some given sample writing styles following an interpolation based method. We then asked several human experts to rate each training sample using one of three labels—good, so-so and bad. These novel and yet not necessarily beautiful fonts with their labels are fed into the network for training. Fig. 10.19 shows some training samples and evaluation results for stroke style coherence grading.

10.6.4 The Overall Evaluation

Finally, the overall evaluation of a character is obtained through a rule-based method. The training examples are also labeled by a human expert while the input to the system is just the topological score of the character, the style correlation grade and the single stroke shape grades for all its composite strokes. We employ a decision tree to produce rules for synthesizing the overall grades of characters with a certain number of strokes.

We also offer the option to give a single numeric number to indicate the overall aesthetics recommendation for a calligraphy piece. If that option is chosen, then we need to go through an additional algorithmic stage in which the overall score of a character is obtained through yet another neural network. Similarly, the training examples are labeled by a human expert while the input to the network is just the topological score of the character and all the shape scores for its composite strokes. We use a dedicated neural network for producing the overall scores of characters having a certain number of strokes. The examples used for training each of these neural networks are 50 characters, of which each character is written in six different styles.

For comparison convenience, we merge the three probabilities into an overall score which denotes the probability of whether the whole character is "good". These single probabilistic values are compared with the human labeling results. The overall grading results and the comparison results are shown in Fig. 10.20. Over 500 fonts for 50 different characters are employed in conducting this experiment.

Fig. 10.20. Synthesizing an overall aesthetics score for calligraphic characters, where the scoring statistics are listed in Table 10.3. Due to space limitations, we didn't list scores for individual single strokes in this experiment. The scores in columns "Spatial G.", "Spatial S.", "Spatial B." denote the possibility that the spatial layout is "good", "so-so" and "bad" respectively. Similarly, columns entitled "Style" and "Overall" are for the scores on stroke style coherence and the overall score of the character where the postfixes G, S and B stand for the category of "good", "so-so" and "bad" respectively. For comparison, the overall scores given by the user are listed in the columns starting with "User". The postfixes hold the same meaning. Overall scores for these characters 5 are shown in Table 10.3

10.7 Automatic Generation of Aesthetic Calligraphy

In the previous two chapters, we introduced a system which is able to generate a variety of stylistic calligraphic characters following an analogous reasoning-

Table 10.3. Overall scores for the characters shown in Fig. 10.20

Fig.	Spatial G.	Spatial S.	Spatial B.	Style G.	Style S.	Style S.
(a)	100%	0%	0%	100%	0%	0%
(b)	74.7%	25.3%	0%	56.3%	43.7%	0%
(c)	34.3%	65.7%	0%	49.4%	50.6%	0%
(d)	83.5%	16.5%	0%	93.5%	6.5%	0%
(e)	75.7%	24.2%	0%	62.1%	37.9%	0%
(f)	0%	10.7%	89.3%	26.7%	55.5%	17.8%
(g)	100%	0%	0%	100%	0%	0%
(h)	66.2%	33.8%	0%	87.0%	13.0%	0%
(i)	40.7%	58.4%	0.9%	78.3%	21.7%	0%
(j)	92.5%	7.5%	0%	29.6%	56.0%	14.4%
(k)	63.5%	36.5%	0%	8.8%	53.8%	37.4%
(l)	9.6%	60.2%	30.2%	14.9%	46.2%	38.9%
(m)	0%	26.5%	73.5%	28.6%	66.4%	5.0%
(n)	100%	0%	0%	100%	0%	0%
(o)	29.8%	64.0%	6.2%	66.4%	33.6%	0%
(p)	93.2%	6.8%	0%	81.3%	18.7%	0%

Fig.	Overall G.	Overall S.	Overall B.	User G.	User S.	User B.
(a)	100%	0%	0%	100%	0%	0%
(b)	64.5%	35.5%	0%	60%	40%	0%
(c)	55.7%	44.3%	0%	60%	40%	0%
(d)	67.8%	32.2%	0%	70%	30%	0%
(e)	71.1%	28.9%	0%	80%	20%	0%
(f)	0%	16.4%	83.6%	0%	0%	100%
(g)	100%	0%	0%	100%	0%	0%
(h)	34.7%	58.9%	6.4%	20%	80%	0%
(i)	43.8%	56.2%	0%	20%	80%	0%
(j)	53.7%	46.3%	0%	10%	90%	0%
(k)	24.4%	67.3%	8.3%	30%	70%	0%
(l)	14.2%	57.5%	28.3%	20%	60%	20%
(m)	0%	57.0%	43.0%	0%	10%	90%
(n)	100%	0%	0%	100%	0%	0%
(o)	44.2%	55.8%	0%	30%	60%	10%
(p)	85.6%	14.4%	0%	100%	0%	0%

based approach. However, only a subset of the generated results are truly aesthetically pleasing. This is due to the lack of a powerful built-in judging mechanism. Given our proposed calligraphy aesthetics grading method, we can add an elaborate and practical visual quality control module to that system. We have integrated these algorithms into our experimental system. For each font produced by their generation system, we evaluate it with our grading algorithm. According to the overall visual quality score, the involved generation parameters are varied from their original settings to yield a new font with a higher aesthetics score. Such a process functions as a typical optimization problem. Assume there are n generation parameters in a character

C, thus an n-dimensional function $f(C)$ is given, whose value is the overall score of the character. The task of calligraphy beautification is namely to find a maximal point in the n-dimensional space, which is reasonably close to the initial given generation point that corresponds to the original font. We employ a gradient descendent method that iteratively optimizes the target function to search for the best possible quality improvement for the given initial calligraphic writing.

Integrating our calligraphy aesthetics evaluation algorithm into their system results in a significant performance improvement in terms of the quality of the calligraphy being generated and output. We thus call our system an "aesthetic calligraphy generation system". Figs. 10.21, 10.22, 10.24 and 10.25 show several automatically-generated calligraphy characters.

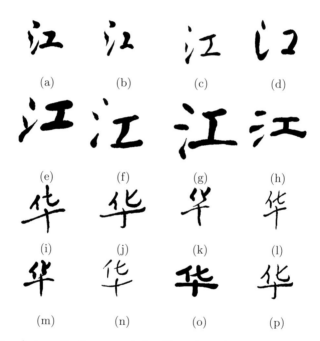

Fig. 10.21. Automatically-generated calligraphy using our system with the proposed grading method serving as visual quality control

10.8 Intelligent Calligraphy Tutoring System

We have also developed a very preliminary calligraphy tutoring system to support interactive calligraphy learning and writing. The major functionality of our tutoring system is to alert a novice to visually unpleasing strokes and to suggest improvements. Although our tutoring system cannot at this stage create calligraphy in the conventional sense (just like a human calligrapher), it provides prompt feedback and useful exemplifications to assist the

Fig. 10.22. The evaluating algorithm helps improve the aesthetic quality of automatic calligraphy generation. For every four consecutive figures (I to IV), the evaluating grades increase from left to right (a to d), corresponding to incremental improvements on the appearance

human learning process. A screen shot of the running system is shown in Fig. 10.26(a). With the system the end user manipulates a tablet pen corresponding to a hairy brush to do calligraphy writing. Signals from the tablet pen carrying 5 degrees of freedom are processed in the system in real time to control the position, orientation and elevation of the virtual brush. Fig. 10.26(b) shows some "e-calligraphy" written using our system. The intelligence of this tutoring system can be easily seen during the online interactive user writing process, when the score for the current writing stroke is fed back to the user in real time. This suggests an opportunity for them to make corrections to the strokes on the spot. The feedback includes suggestions for the appearance of both the individual strokes and the spatial relationships between the strokes. Fig. 10.26(c to f) show an example of the tutoring functionality. The system would identify strokes that are potentially unpleasing, and supply a candidate set of automatic correction plans for the user to choose from or for the user's reference. Such an interactive feedback is enormously helpful for calligraphy beginners.

Fig. 10.23. Source examples input into our automatic Chinese calligraphy generation system. Some generation results are shown in Fig. 10.24 and Fig. 10.25

10.9 Conclusion and Future Work

10.9.1 Conclusion

Our work links Chinese calligraphy to computer science through an integrated intelligence approach. We first extract strokes of existent calligraphy using a semi-automatic, two-phase mechanism: the first phase tries to do the best possible extraction using a combination of algorithmic techniques; the second phase presents an intelligent user interface to allow the user to provide input to the extraction process for the difficult cases such as those in highly random, cursive, or distorted styles. Having derived a parametric representation of calligraphy, we employ a supervised learning-based method to explore the space of visually pleasing calligraphy. A numeric grading method for judging the beauty of calligraphy is then applied to the space. We integrate such a grading unit into an existent constraint-based reasoning system for calligraphy generation, which results in a significant enhancement in terms of visual quality in the automatically generated calligraphic characters. Finally, we construct an intelligent calligraphy tutoring system making use of the above.

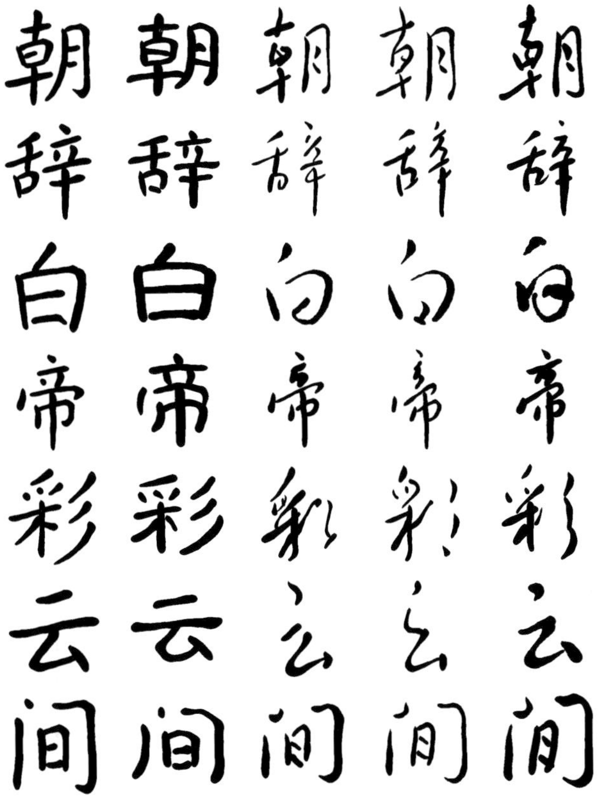

Fig. 10.24. Automatically generated calligraphy of an ancient poem in Tang Dynasty of China (8th century), based on the learning sources in Fig. 10.23

This work represents our first step towards understanding the human process of appreciating beauty through modeling the process with an integration of available AI techniques.

10.9.2 Discussion and Future Work

We have described a learning based approach for evaluating the aesthetics of Chinese calligraphy. The study of this topic could both lead to many practical applications, like automatic generation of aesthetic Chinese calligraphy, as demonstrated in this chapter, and could also shed light on the intriguing issue of numerical beauty appreciation. We have obtained very encouraging results from the experiments on the quantitative accuracy of our algorithmic attempts at automatic aesthetics evaluation of calligraphic objects.

In this chapter we are mainly concerned with evaluating the visual appeal of single calligraphic characters. In a complete piece of calligraphic artwork, the spatial relationship between adjacent characters in the entire artwork could affect the overall visual appearance in a profound manner. Thus, extending our current aesthetics appreciation work to account for the layout of

Fig. 10.25. (Continued from Fig. 10.24) Some more automatically generated calligraphy of the poem based on the learning sources in Fig. 10.23

characters in a complete piece of calligraphic writing is a major item in our future work.

Currently, when providing the sample set of calligraphy, human experts are asked to pick from three values indicating the visual quality of a certain calligraphic character. This is by no means a natural way for human experts. From time to time we noticed there were wrongly labeled training samples. In reality people are probably more accustomed to ranking characters in terms of their aesthetics, rather than assigning a numerical value for their relative visual quality. We feel that relational grading, instead of the absolute grades as in our current algorithm design, could significantly increase the reliability of the labeling over the training set itself. Revising the learning algorithms introduced in this chapter, to utilize the relational scores in the training samples, calls for some non-trivial algorithmic efforts. However, this represents a worthwhile step forward for improving the overall system performance.

Right now, the acquisition of the training set consumes a major portion of our experiment time. This is mostly because stroke extraction from input images of Chinese calligraphic characters is not fully automatic. As a result we are only able to establish a training set for those most frequently used

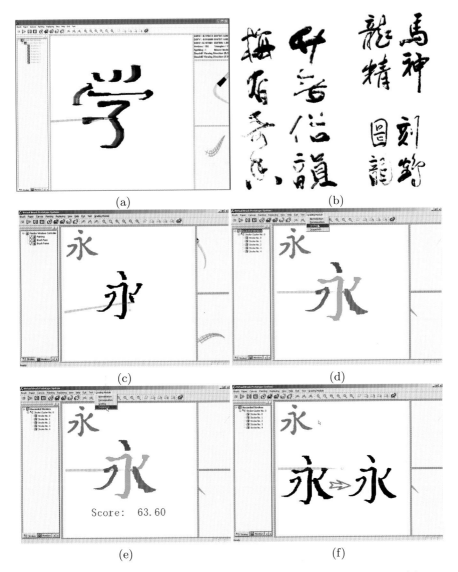

Fig. 10.26. Intelligent calligraphy writing tutoring system: a screen-shot (a), and some calligraphy created interactively using the system (b). (c to f) show a series of screen shots of how the tutoring function works. The user can write a calligraphic character with the virtual brush provided by the system (c). At first the character is decomposed into individual strokes (d). The grading result is given by both the shapes of individual strokes and spatial features of the character (e). According to the scoring, the system can suggest how to improve the writing (f)

characters. The limited size of the training set might also reduce the learning capability of automatic calligraphy aesthetics evaluation. Of course, enlarging the size of the calligraphic character training set is absolutely necessary for developing a commercially valuable system based on our algorithm. We thus plan to explore the problem of automatic calligraphic character recognition and stroke segmentation.

At present, when determining whether different strokes in a character follow the same writing style, we rely heavily on the predefined styles from existent copybooks and font libraries. In the future it would be interesting and meaningful to look at the problem of how to define writing styles from a numerical point of view and, moreover, how to imitate the writing style of a person after seeing a limited portion of characters in his writing. Once a person's writing style could be defined quantitatively, we could even try to tackle the more challenging problem of discovering a potential relationship between people's handwriting and their gender, career, personality, health condition, etc.

References

[ASB02] Carlo A. Avizzano, Jorge Solis, and Massimo Bergamasco. Teaching to write Japanese characters using a haptic interface. In *Proc. of the 10th Symposium on Haptic Interfaces for Virtual Environment and Teleoperator Systems*, Orlando, FL, USA: IEEE Computer Society, pages 255–262, 2002.

[Bat94] Joseph Bates. The role of emotion in believable agents. *Commun. ACM*, 37(7):122–125, 1994.

[Her03] Aaron Hertzmann. Tutorial: a survey of stroke-based rendering. *IEEE Computer Graphics and Applications*, 23(4):70–81, 2003.

[Knu86] Donald E. Knuth. *The METAFONTbook*. Massachusetts, MA, USA: Addison-Wesley, 1986.

[LHS97] Ke Liu, Yea S. Huang, and Ching Y. Suen. Robust stroke segmentation method for handwritten Chinese character recognition. In *Proc. of the 4th International Conference on Document Analysis and Recognition*, Ulm, Germany, 1997.

[LHS99] Ke Liu, Yea S. Huang, and Ching Y. Suen. Identification of fork points on the skeletons of handwritten Chinese characters. *IEEE Transactions on Pattern Analysis and Machine Intelligence*, 21(10):1095–1100, 1999.

[LKK01] Cheng-Lin Liu, In-Jung Kim, and Jin H. Kim. Model-based stroke extraction and matching for handwritten chinese character recognition. *Pattern Recognition*, 34(12):2339–2352, 2001.

[LYP95] Pak-Keung Lai, Dit-Yan Yeung, and Man-Chi Pong. Chinese glyph generation using character composition and beauty evaluation metrics. In *ICCPOL'95: Proceedings of the International Conference on Computer Processing of Oriental Languages*, Honolulu, Hawaii, pages 92–99, 1995.

[McC90] Pamela McCorduck. *Aaron's Code: Meta-Art, Artificial Intelligence and the Work of Harold Cohen*. W.H. Freeman & Co., 1990.

[NO94] Christian Neusius and Jan Olszewski. A noniterative thinning algorithm. *ACM Transactions on Mathematical Software*, 20(1):5–20, 1994.

[OAI93] Masahiro Ozaki, Yoshinori Adachi, and Naohiro Ishii. Fuzzy theory in hand writing learning system. In *Proceedings of International Joint Conference on Neural Networks*, Nagoya, Japan: IEEE Computer Society, pages 766–769, 1993.

[Pic00] Rosalind W. Picard. *Affective Computing*. The MIT Press, 2000.

[Roa85] Curtis Roads. Research in music and artificial intelligence. *ACM Computing Survey*, 17(2):163–190, 1985.

[Tur50] Alan M. Turing. Computing machinery and intelligence. *Mind*, 49:433–460, 1950.

[WK01] Michael Werman and Daniel Keren. A Bayesian method for fitting parametric and nonparametric models to noisy data. *IEEE Transactions on Pattern Analysis and Machine Intelligence*, 23(5):528–534, 2001.

[XLCP04] Songhua Xu, Francis C.M. Lau, Kwok-Wai Cheung, and Yunhe Pan. Automatic generation of artistic Chinese calligraphy. In *Proceedings of the 19th National Conference on Artificial Intelligence and the 16th Conference on Innovative Applications of Artificial Intelligence (AAAI/IAAI)*, San Jose, CA, USA: AAAI Press/The MIT Press, pages 937–943, 2004.

[XLCP05] Songhua Xu, Francis C. M. Lau, William K. Cheung, and Yunhe Pan. Automatic generation of artistic Chinese calligraphy. *IEEE Intelligent Systems*, 20(3):32–39, 2005.

[XLP03] Songhua Xu, Francis C.M. Lau, and Yunhe Pan. Automatic artistic calligraphy generation. Technical Report HKU-CS-TR-2003-02, Department of Computer Science, The University of Hong Kong, 2003.

[XXK⁺06] Songhua Xu, Yingqing Xu, Sing-Bing Kang, David H. Salesin, Yunhe Pan, and Heung-Yeung Shum. Animating Chinese paintings through stroke-based decomposition. *ACM Transactions on Graphics*, 25(2):239–267, 2006.

[YLL97] Hsin-Tai Yang, Jue-Wen Lin, and Shie-Jue Lee. A handwritten Chinese character recognition system based on neural-fuzzy theory. In *IEEE International Conference on Systems, Man, and Cybernetics*, Orlando, FL, USA: IEEE Computer Society, pages 1492–1497, 1997.

Part V

Animating Chinese Paintings

11

Animating Chinese Paintings through Stroke-based Decomposition

11.1 Overview

This chapter proposes a technique to animate a "Chinese style" painting given its image. We first extract descriptions of the brush strokes that hypothetically produced it. The key to the extraction process is the use of a brush stroke library, which is obtained by digitizing single brush strokes drawn by an experienced artist. The steps in our extraction technique are to first segment the input image, to then find the best set of brush strokes that fit the regions, and finally to refine these strokes to account for local appearance. We model a single brush stroke using its skeleton and contour, and we characterize texture variation within each stroke by sampling perpendicularly along its skeleton. Once these brush descriptions have been obtained, the painting can be animated at the brush stroke level. In this chapter we focus on Chinese paintings with relatively sparse strokes. The animation is produced using a graphical application we developed. We present several animations of real paintings using our technique.

11.2 Introduction

What if paintings could move? In this chapter we propose a way of animating Chinese paintings by automatically decomposing an image of a painting into its hypothetical brush stroke constituents. Most Chinese paintings are typically sparse, with each brush stroke drawn very purposefully [SL97]. Our method is specifically geared for handling paintings that employ brush strokes economically; in addition to most Chinese paintings, other suitable styles include Sumi-e and certain watercolor and oil paintings, such as those of van Gogh.

In Chinese paintings each stroke is often introduced to depict something specific in the real world. Thus the output of our stroke-based decomposition of these paintings is a set of graphical objects that are meaningful with regard to the set of real objects the paintings depict. As a result, animators would likely feel comfortable manipulating these graphical objects. In addition, the number of strokes in each painting is usually small, and hence manageable.

Our approach uses segmentation techniques and a library of brush strokes for fitting. The recovered brush strokes are basically vectorized elements, which are easy to animate (Fig. 11.1). In addition to animation, the set of recovered brush strokes can be used for synthesis of paintings or for manipulating images of paintings.

(a)   (b)   (c)   (d)

(e)   (f)

Fig. 11.1. Animating a flower painting. A painting is animated by decomposing it into a set of vectorized brush strokes. The brush strokes are produced by taking the input image (a) and over-segmenting it initially (b). These segments are then merged into coherent strokes (c), which are chosen to match strokes in a "brush stroke library." These strokes are then textured (d) using the input image as a texture source. Finally, the strokes are individually animated as vectorized elements (e), (f)

Our automatic stroke decomposition technique has other potential uses. For example, a system utilizing a camera or scanner along with the traditional media of paper, brush and paint can be thought of as a kind of "natural tablet" (as opposed to a digital tablet). Another application is compression—an animation sequence of a painting can be more efficiently represented and transmitted across a network. This is a direct consequence of the decomposition process producing a set of vectorized stroke elements. The resulting compressed representation could be used, for instance, to augment a textual chat system with little additional required bandwidth. Finally, the recovered representation could be analyzed to identify artistic style and identity.

To our knowledge there has been little or no work on automatically decomposing images of paintings into brush strokes. However, several related topics have been explored. One such example is that of "optical character recognition" (OCR) systems, where stroke analysis techniques are used for segmenting handwriting purely on the basis of shape (e.g. [WJ93]). Another related line of research is diagram recognition, which includes recognizing engineering drawings [JP92], mail pieces [WS88], sketch maps [MMH88], maths expressions [ZBC02], and music symbols [BH99]. However, the targets in diagram recognition are usually limited to symbols or objects drawn using thin lines, which are not nearly as visually rich as brush strokes in paintings.

In computer graphics, electronic virtual brushes have been developed to simulate the effects of brush painting on a computer. One of the earliest works in this area is that of Strassman [Str86], where paint brushes are modeled as a collection of bristles that evolve over the course of a stroke. Hsu and Lee [HL94] introduced the concept of the "skeletal stroke," which allows strokes to be textured. This idea was later used in a 2D stroke-based animation system called LivingCels [HLLS99]. The Deep Canvas system [Dan99] allows brush strokes to be digitally created on 3D surfaces and then animated. The virtual brush for oil painting was proposed by Baxter, et al. [BSLM01]. The virtual hairy brush for Oriental painting was suggested by Xu, et al. [XTLP04]. Kalnins, et al. [KMM+02] presented a system that supports the drawing of strokes over a 3D model.

Our stroke decomposition work is related to the extensively researched problem of image segmentation in computer vision (see [Jai89] and [FP02]). One particularly relevant approach is that of Neumann [Neu03]. He proposed an image segmentation technique that uses predefined graphical shape models. However, the technique requires manual selection of corresponding key points, which is non-trivial for large-scale data sets. Wang and Siskind [WS03] proposed the cut ratio method (a graph-based method) for segmenting images, which supports efficient iterated region-based segmentation and pixel-based segmentation. Marroquin et al. [MSB03] proposed a Bayesian formulation for modeling image partitioning and local variation within each region. All these methods either require manual input or assume non-overlapping regions.

Our brush stroke extraction approach involves over-segmenting the image and incrementally merging parts. This technique is common in computer vision and has been used in computer graphics as well. For instance, DeCarlo and Santella [DS02] progressively group regions based on similarity of color modulated by region size. Liu and Sclaroff [LS01] used a deformable, model-guided, split-and-merge approach to segment image regions. We used a similar approach, except that we consider the similarity with brush strokes from a library as well as color distributions on region boundaries.

There are other object-based editing systems that do not involve brush strokes. In Litwinowicz and Williams's image editing system [LW94], users can align features such as points, lines and curves to the image and distort the image by moving these features. Salisbury et al. [SABS94] developed an interactive image-based non-photorealistic rendering system that creates pen-and-ink illustrations using a photograph as the reference for outline and tone. In Horry et al.'s "Tour-into-the-picture" system [HAA97], the user can interactively create 2.5 D layers, after which flythrough animations can be generated. Barrett and Cheney [BC02] developed an image editing system that allows the user to interactively segment out objects in the image and manipulate them to generate animations.

The closest work to ours is probably that of Gooch et al. [GCS02] because of some similarity with two important parts of our algorithms — image segmentation and medial axis extraction — and the shared goal of generating brush strokes. However, Gooch et al. addressed a very different problem: they wish to convert one image — photographs or views of synthetic 3D scenes — to another — a non-photorealistic rendering — without preserving the image's *exact* appearance. Moreover, their system's output is a static image. As such it is not important for them whether or not the extracted strokes are amenable to animation. Also, correct recovery of overlapping strokes is not an issue for them because they are not trying to replicate exactly the appearance of the input image. By comparison, we wish to decompose an image of a painting to separate vectorized elements, or strokes, such that rendering those strokes reproduces the original image's appearance. In addition, in order to facilitate more "natural-looking" animation, the extracted strokes have to be plausible strokes that the artist may have made. Figs. 11.2 and 11.3 show the results of applying Gooch et al.'s [GCS02] algorithm to two images of paintings. As can be seen, the extracted strokes do not depict anything that corresponds to the real world. This makes "proper" animation of the painting significantly more labor-intensive than if the correct original strokes were extracted. In addition, the original appearance of the painting is not preserved.

11.3 Painting Decomposition Approach

Before we animate a painting, we first decompose its image into a plausible set of brush strokes. A graphical overview of our decomposition approach is depicted in Fig. 11.4, which also shows an example image, the intermediate results and the final output. The basic idea is simple: we segment the image, use a brush library to find the best fit for each region and refine the brush

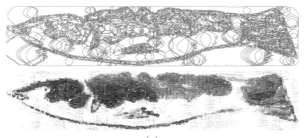

(a)

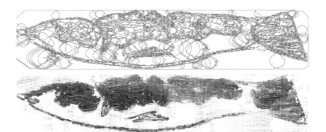

(b)

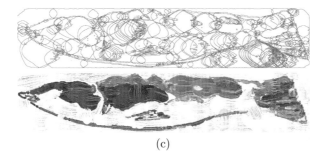

(c)

Test	Segmentation level (maximum 255)	Number of strokes
a	255	1,769
b	120	1,255
c	25	403

Fig. 11.2. Stroke extraction results of the fish painting using Gooch et al.'s algorithm. The original painting is Fig. 11.15(a). Three typical segmentation levels are tested: fine (a); medium (b) and coarse (c). The contours of extracted strokes for each test are shown on the top, while their corresponding rendered results are shown on the bottom. The statistics for these results are listed in the table below

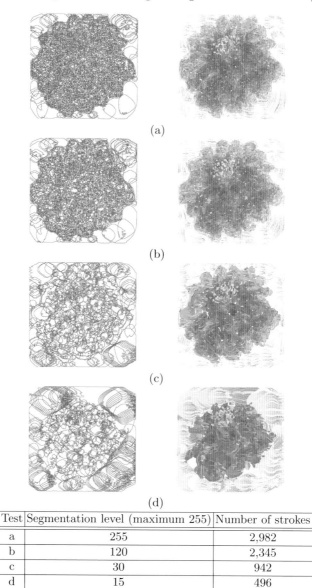

(a)

(b)

(c)

(d)

Test	Segmentation level (maximum 255)	Number of strokes
a	255	2,982
b	120	2,345
c	30	942
d	15	496

Fig. 11.3. Stroke extraction results of the flower painting using Gooch et al.'s algorithm. The original painting is Fig. 11.4. Four typical segmentation levels are tested: (a to d). The left row shows the contours of extracted strokes, while their corresponding rendered results are shown in the right row. The segmentation parameter and number of strokes extracted are listed in the table below

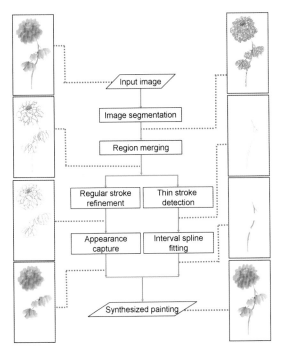

Fig. 11.4. Steps involved in our painting analysis and reconstruction approach

strokes found directly from the input image. The brush library used was created with the help of a painter who specializes in Chinese paintings.

11.3.1 Image Segmentation

Given an image of a painting, we first segment the image into regions of similar color intensities. This segmentation is done to speed up the processing for brush decomposition. We tune the mean-shift algorithm [CM02] to produce an over-segmented image because similarity of color intensity is a necessary but not sufficient condition for brush stroke segmentation. The overly conservative segmentation ensures that each region does not straddle multiple brush strokes unless they overlap.

11.3.2 Stroke Extraction by Region Merging

After over-segmentation is done, we merge contiguous regions that likely belong to the same brush strokes. Our merging process is inspired by domain-dependent image segmentation techniques proposed by Feldman and Yakimovsky [FY74] and Tenenbaum and Barrow [TB77] (and more recently, Kumar and Desai [KD99] and Sclaroff and Liu [SL01]). In these techniques the image is initially partitioned without the use of domain knowledge. Subsequently, pairs of adjacent regions are iteratively merged based on the likelihood of being single world objects.

In our approach the domain knowledge is derived from two sources: the intuition that color gradients are low along brush strokes (the directional smoothness assumption), and a stroke library containing the range of valid stroke shapes (the shape priors). The directional smoothness assumption is implemented using average gradients and the difference between the average color intensities along mutual boundaries. The stroke library is obtained by digitizing single strokes drawn by an expert artist, and the resulting shape priors are used to avoid implausible shapes. The shape priors also handle brush stroke overlap and, as such, our technique goes beyond conventional segmentation.

Before merging takes place, the *region merging criterion* ε (explained shortly) is computed for each pair of adjacent regions. Pairs of adjacent regions are then merged in ascending order of ε. In addition, we merge (or "steal") neighboring regions if the best-fit brush stroke straddles them.

We now define the region merging criterion ε. Suppose we have two adjacent regions γ_i and γ_j. The boundary region of γ_i with respect to γ_j, denoted as $\partial(\gamma_i, \gamma_j)$, is the set of pixels in γ_i that are close to some pixel in γ_j. In our work "close" is defined as within 3 to 5 pixels of the neighboring regions and adjacency is defined in the 4-connected sense—a pixel p is adjacent to q if p and q are horizontal or vertical neighbors. Neighboring regions are merged if the following region merging criterion ε, defined as the sum of five terms, is negative:

$$\varepsilon \triangleq \kappa_g \varepsilon_g + \kappa_c \varepsilon_c + \kappa_w \varepsilon_w + \kappa_m \varepsilon_m + \kappa_o. \tag{11.1}$$

The first two terms, ε_g and ε_c, measure differences in the color distributions of the two regions (gradient and intensity-based measures, respectively), while the next two terms, ε_w and ε_m, measure the shape similarities to those of library brush strokes (the names stand for "weighted shape similarity" and "maximum shape similarity," respectively). Fig. 11.5 illustrates why the terms ε_g, ε_c, ε_w, and ε_m are necessary. The first four constants, κ_g, κ_c, κ_w, and κ_m, are all positive, while κ_o, a threshold offset, is negative. The values of these coefficients used for decomposing the Chinese painting shown in Fig. 11.4 are given in Table 11.1. Similar values are used for the other results.

Table 11.1. The coefficients used in Eq. (11.1) to decompose the painting shown in Fig. 11.4. The values used for the other experiments are similar

Coefficient	κ_g	κ_c	κ_w	κ_m	κ_o
Value	0.083	0.05	16	5	4.5

Dividing both sides of Eq. (11.1) by κ_o yields only 4 independent parameters. Although the ratio between κ_g and κ_c and the ratio between κ_w and κ_m have some effect on the decomposition result, the most significant factor is the ratio between $\kappa_g \kappa_c$ and $\kappa_w \kappa_m$. For paintings with strong edges in the stroke contours, better results are obtained using relatively high values of κ_w and κ_m. In our experiments we test the thresholds on a small representative portion of the painting before using them on the whole image.

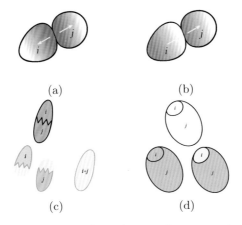

Fig. 11.5. Representative cases in the region merging process to illustrate the need for ε_g, ε_c, ε_w and ε_m. (a) ε_g: Regions i and j have the same color values in the boundary pixels, but they should not be merged because of the sharp difference between the gradients. (b) ε_c: Regions i and j have the same gradients along their common boundary, but they should not be merged due to the significant difference between the color values along the common boundary. (c) ε_w: Here the combined shape similarity is good enough to overcome the color difference. (d) ε_m: Here both the component strokes, i and j, and the combined stroke are all good fits with the strokes in the library. In this case ε_m cancels out ε_w, causing the merging decision to be made based on the boundary color and gradient distributions instead

11.3.2.1 Comparing boundary color distributions

To compare two boundary color distributions, we first extract two sets of gradients G_i and G_j, and two sets of color values C_i and C_j (ranging from 0 to 255 in each color channel) for the pixels in the boundary regions $\partial(\gamma_i, \gamma_j)$ and $\partial(\gamma_j, \gamma_i)$ respectively. Fig. 11.6 shows the boundary regions considered during the region merging process.

The color distribution criteria in Eq. (11.1) are defined as:

$$\varepsilon_g \triangleq \sum_{r,g,b} \left(\left|\overline{G_i} - \overline{G_j}\right| \arctan\left(\lambda_g \left(\frac{||G_i||}{\sigma^2(G_i)} + \frac{||G_j||}{\sigma^2(G_j)} \right) \right) \right), \qquad (11.2)$$

$$\varepsilon_c \triangleq \sum_{r,g,b} \left(\left|\overline{C_i} - \overline{C_j}\right| \arctan\left(\lambda_c \left(\frac{||C_i||}{\sigma^2(C_i)} + \frac{||C_j||}{\sigma^2(C_j)} \right) \right) \right), \qquad (11.3)$$

where λ_g and λ_c are constants and $\overline{X}$, $||X||$ and $\sigma^2(X)$ are the mean cardinality and variance of X respectively. In the above equations, by $\sum_{r,g,b}$ we mean the two features are computed for the r, g, and b channels separately and then added together. Note that $||G_i|| = ||C_i||$, since both of them refer to the number of pixels in the same boundary region. Similarly, $||G_j|| = ||C_j||$. In all our experiments, λ_g and λ_c were set to 0.05 and 0.75 respectively.

The gradient term ε_g measures the distance between the average local gradients along the two boundaries modulated by their combined certainties. Each measure of certainty increases with longer mutual boundaries and

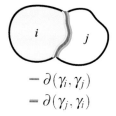

$$-\partial(\gamma_i, \gamma_j)$$
$$-\partial(\gamma_j, \gamma_i)$$

Fig. 11.6. Boundary region processing. Here, regions i and j are being considered for merging. $\partial(\gamma_i, \gamma_j)$ and $\partial(\gamma_j, \gamma_i)$ are the boundary regions used to partially decide if these regions should be merged. The red curve is one pixel thick, and consists of pixels common to both regions i and j. The yellow region is inside region i, adjacent to the red common boundary curve and 3 to 5 pixels thick. The green region is similarly defined for region j. $\partial(\gamma_i, \gamma_j)$ consists of yellow and red regions, while $\partial(\gamma_j, \gamma_i)$ consists of green and red regions. C_i is the set of colors in the yellow region and C_j, the set of colors in the green region. Gradients G_i and G_j are computed using pixels in $\partial(\gamma_i, \gamma_j)$ and $\partial(\gamma_j, \gamma_i)$ respectively. Note that here we use only the boundary regions, rather than the entire image region. The local computation strategy is necessary to handle strokes with significant texture variation, e.g. strokes created by dragging a semi-wet brush along a long trajectory

smaller variances. The positive coefficient λ_g and function arctan() are used to bracket the confidence value to $[0, \pi/2)$. The color term ε_c functions exactly the same way as ε_g, except that color intensities are compared instead of local gradients. Both ε_g and ε_c measure the homogeneity of the texture variation within each stroke region; we assume the texture variation within a stroke region to be homogeneous.

While there are alternatives to comparing boundary color distributions, our design decisions are governed by simplicity and symmetry of measurement. Estimation of ε_g and ε_c is a computational bottleneck because they are estimated for each adjacent region pair. The Kullback-Leibler divergence (or relative entropy), for example, may be used, but it is asymmetric with respect to the two probability distributions. The Chernoff distance, which is another information-theoretic distance measure, may also be used, but it requires computation of maxima (a non-trivial optimization problem).

11.3.2.2 Using the brush stroke library

The key to our decomposition approach is the use of a *brush stroke library*. The image of a painting can be segmented in a variety of ways, but the most natural approach would be to segment the image into hypothetical brush strokes that originally generated the painting. Each brush stroke depicts part of the scene; as such, the output of our segmentation allows the animation of the painting to look more natural.

We generated our brush library by digitizing single brush strokes drawn by an artist with ten years of experience in Chinese painting. This brush library is by no means exhaustive (future work is planned in this area); in our case the artist drew 62 different brush strokes that he thought were well representative of all the possible ones used in Chinese paintings. Each brush stroke was then binarized and its skeleton computed. Sample brush strokes from this library are shown in Fig. 11.7.

Fig. 11.7. Sample library brush shapes. Only 9 out of 62 shown here. The bottom row displays the modeled brush shapes in the library with their skeletons shown as red curves. The top row shows respective counterparts collected from real paintings

The brush stroke library acts as shape priors to guide the segmentation so as to avoid irregularly-shaped segments. The library also allows us to hypothesize overlaps between brush strokes, which facilitates their separation. Without the brush stroke library, we can extract strokes using *only* the color distribution in the original input image. The decomposition results would likely be irregularly-shaped segments; such segments would be unintuitive from the painter's perspective and thus difficult to animate. (Note that only regions that are relatively thick are processed using the brush library. Strokes that are thin are processed differently; see Sect. 11.3.4.)

Fig. 11.8 shows the effect of not using our stroke library, i.e. the stroke decomposition is performed purely based on color distribution without using any shape priors. Stroke decomposition results at different granularities are shown. (The different granularities refer to the different levels of coarseness controlled by segmentation parameter settings.) Regardless of the granularity, the decomposition results are not satisfactory. Ensuring proper brush stroke extraction without an explicit library is highly non-trivial. One could, for example, favor smoothness of the medial axis as well as the radius function along the axis. However, using such a heuristic would produce mostly symmetric, straight blobs, which would appear unnatural for Chinese paintings in general. In addition to producing false negatives, the smoothness preference may also result in strokes that practising artists would find inappropriate from an aesthetic point of view. Such strokes could very likely cause incorrect style or artist identification if they were to be analyzed.

11.3.2.3 Comparing shapes

We compare each region to the model strokes in our brush stroke library and find the model brush stroke with the highest shape similarity. Since the scale, orientation and shift of the observed brush stroke can be arbitrary, we find the best transform to optimize similarity to each library brush stroke.

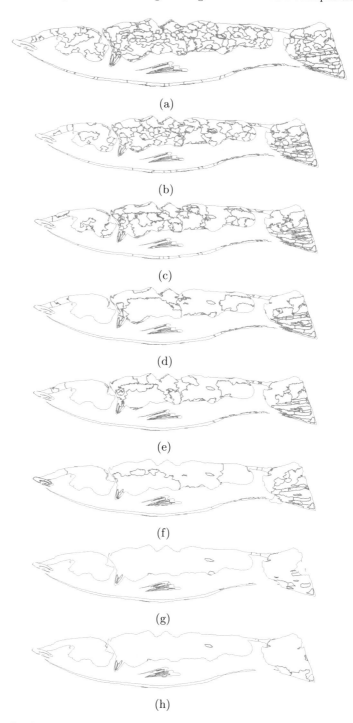

(a)

(b)

(c)

(d)

(e)

(f)

(g)

(h)

Fig. 11.8. Stroke decomposition without our stroke library. (a to h) show stroke decomposition results at different granularities (progressively coarser). Without the stroke library to guide the decomposition, stroke decomposition is uneven, resulting in irregular shapes

To compute the best transform, we first initialize the shift by aligning the centroids, the orientation by aligning the major axis directions, and the scale by comparing areas. The transform is then refined through gradient descent to maximize shape similarity. The appropriately transformed library brush stroke with the highest similarity with the observed brush stroke is then chosen.

There is extensive work on 2D shape matching; a good survey of techniques is given by Veltkamp [VH99]. We choose a simple (but effective) approach to shape similarity in order to keep the computation cost manageable. Specifically, we define a similarity measure $\varphi(\gamma_i)$, which describes how well a given region γ_i fits some stroke in the library:

$$\varphi(\gamma_i) = \max_k \frac{A(\gamma_i \cap T_{ki}\beta_k)}{A(\gamma_i \cup T_{ki}\beta_k)}$$

where $A(X)$ is the area of region X, β_k is the k-th stroke in the brush stroke library and T_{ki} is the optimal transform (shift, rotation, and scale) used to align β_k with γ_i. The functional $\varphi()$ ranges between 0 and 1—it is 1 when the two shapes are identical. Unlike many shape comparison approaches that compare contours, our shape-based criterion directly makes use of areas. Using areas is more reliable because there is high variability in the detail of the contours of brush strokes. (Pre-smoothing the contour may result in the loss of critical information.)

The shape-based criteria in Eq. (11.1) can be defined as:

$$\varepsilon_w \triangleq \frac{\varphi(\gamma_i)A(\gamma_i) + \varphi(\gamma_j)A(\gamma_j)}{A(\gamma_i \cup \gamma_j)} - \varphi(\gamma_i \cup \gamma_j), \tag{11.4}$$

$$\varepsilon_m \triangleq \max\{\varphi(\gamma_i), \varphi(\gamma_j)\} - \varphi(\gamma_i \cup \gamma_j). \tag{11.5}$$

Thus, ε_w compares the area-weighted sum of similarity measures associated with fitting two brush strokes against the area-weighted similarity measure for a single brush stroke for the combined regions. A large positive value of ε_w means that it is better to fit the two regions with two brush strokes instead of one. The second measure, ε_m, compares the similarities of the two strokes versus the combined stroke directly; a large value signifies that it is better not to merge the regions. Both ε_w and ε_m are used in objective function Eq. (11.1) because we need to balance two conflicting biases: the bias towards fitting a single brush stroke on the merged regions (ε_w) versus the bias towards preserving current regions that have a very good fit with the library (ε_m).

11.3.3 Stroke Refinement and Appearance Capture

Note that the extracted brush shapes are not the final shapes; the brush strokes in the library are used merely to guide the segmentation process. After the brush strokes have been identified, their shapes are refined using the final segmented regions in the image. The shape of each identified brush stroke is first scaled, shifted and rotated so as to maximize shape similarity with the corresponding stroke region. The modified shape is then dilated to assume the shape of the brush stroke as much as possible.

Once each shape has been refined, an optimization algorithm is used to produce a maximal-length skeleton within the region. This is accomplished by searching the positions of the two ends of the skeleton along the boundary. The search is done in the vicinity of the skeleton of the best-fit library brush stroke. A piecewise 3-degree Bézier curve is used to fit the skeleton.

The appearance of the brush stroke is then captured by directly sampling texture from the image. This is necessary in order to reproduce the appearance of the original painting. Sect. 11.4 describes how texture sampling is done.

11.3.4 Thin Brush Strokes

Because thin brush strokes are very difficult to model as part of a library, we treat them separately. Each region is categorized either as a regular brush stroke or as a thin brush stroke based on a simple aspect-ratio analysis of the regions. We label a stroke as being thin if the arc length of its skeleton is at least 10 times longer than its average stroke width. Adjacent thin strokes will also be merged if the difference between their average intensities is less than 10 levels and the gradients at their mutual boundaries differ by less than 10%.

Skeletons for thin brush strokes are extracted by using a thinning algorithm [ZQN95]. Interval piecewise Bézier splines [SF92, SXSC02] are then used to represent the thin strokes. A piecewise Bézier curve is used to fit the skeleton of the stroke, with local widths (corresponding to local brush thickness) and intensities recorded at the spline knots. We adapt Schneider's algorithm [Sch90] for this purpose. In addition to placing spline knots uniformly along the skeleton, we place additional spline knots at locations of high variation of local width or intensity. We resample the width and intensity until their local variations are within acceptable limits.

At this point let us discuss two important issues associated with our decomposition algorithm. First, what happens when the artist draws strokes that are not in the database? Our algorithm will try to force-fit the best brush stroke shape from the library. If the drawn stroke is only a little different from one of the library strokes and the drawn stroke is close to being a solid stroke (strong boundary edges with little contrast inside), it is likely that only one stroke will be extracted. However, if the drawn stroke is dramatically different from any stroke shape from the library, oversegmentation will likely happen (with possible overlap) because there is no single brush stroke that can fit it well. The second issue relates to the background of the painting. The background need not be white or some other constant color for our algorithm to work; it will work with any uniformly (finely) textured background. If the background is cluttered, it will be treated the same as the foreground objects and decomposed in exactly the same way. Our algorithm will work as long as there is enough contrast between strokes for separation.

11.4 Appearance Capture and Synthesis of Single Brush Strokes

11.4.1 Single-stroke Appearance Model

Fig. 11.9 shows an overview of how single brush strokes are refined and synthesized (if necessary).

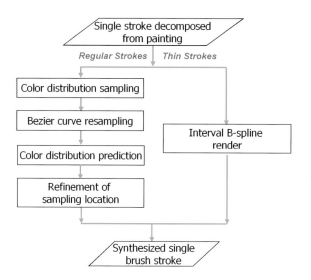

Fig. 11.9. Steps in analyzing and synthesizing a single brush stroke (The thin and regular strokes are handled differently.)

In the case of thin brush strokes, their skeletons are represented by interval B-splines, with local brush widths and intensities recorded at the spline knots. They can be directly rendered using this information.

For regular brush strokes (i.e. those that are not considered thin), we devised a single-stroke appearance model (Fig. 11.10). With the single-stroke model, each brush stroke undergoes a more complicated iterative process, which consists of four steps:

(1) **Color distribution sampling.** Given the shape of the brush stroke (i.e. skeleton and contour), normal lines are computed at regular sample points along its skeleton (Fig. 11.10(c)). The color distribution in RGB space of the brush stroke is sampled along each normal line, and is represented using a piecewise 3-degree Bézier curve. We use Schneider's algorithm [Sch90] to automatically segment the samples. We assume that the error in fitting the color distribution is Gaussian noise. The modeled Gaussian noise is then added to the fit color distribution to prevent the synthesized appearance from appearing too smooth.

(2) **Bézier curve resampling.** The number of Bézier segments may differ for a pair of adjacent normal lines. To simplify the next step of appearance

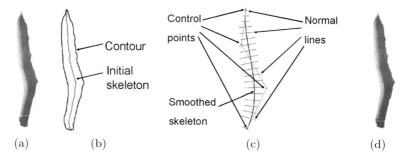

Fig. 11.10. Appearance capture of a single brush stroke. Given an input stroke (a), its contour and skeleton are initially extracted (b). The skeleton is then smoothed, and lines perpendicular to it are sampled from the input image (c). The stroke's appearance can then be generated (d)

prediction, we resample the number of segments of adjacent normal lines so that they contain the smallest common multiple of the number of samples in the originals. We refer to this process simply as Bézier curve resampling. Note that each sample line has two sets of representative Bézier segments, one to match the previous neighbor and the other to match the next neighbor. The exceptions are the first and last sample lines, which have only one set of Bézier segments.

(3) **Color distribution prediction.** Given the Bézier approximation of color and noise distributions, we can then synthesize the appearance of the brush stroke. Every pixel in the brush stroke is filled by linearly interpolating the nearest two normal lines. This can be easily done because the number of segments per normal line pair is the same (enforced by Step 11.4.1).

(4) **Refinement of sampling location.** The synthesized brush stroke is used to refine the locations of the sampling lines along the brush skeleton. We start off with a sufficiently high sampling density along the skeleton (sampling every pixel is the safest starting point). Sampling lines are chosen at random and tested to see if the degradation is significant when they are removed. If so, they stay; otherwise, they are permanently removed. This process (which is a form of analysis by synthesis) is repeated until either the error between the reconstructed and actual brush strokes is above a threshold, or the number of iterations exceeds a limit.

11.4.2 Why Direct Texture Mapping is Inadequate

A straightforward method to capture and reproduce the appearance of a brush stroke would be to triangulate it, followed by texture mapping. One possible tessellation strategy for dividing the brush stroke area into triangular strips is proposed by Hertzmann [Her99]. There are two main problems with this approach. First, the shape may be significantly distorted in the process of animation, causing non-uniform warping of texture. Although the texture deformation within one triangle is uniform, the discontinuity of deformed texture would become obvious across the edges of adjacent triangles. In contrast, our stroke appearance model ensures texture smoothness throughout the deformed stroke area because deformation is continuously distributed according to the skeleton of the stroke. Fig. 11.11 compares the results of significant shape distortion.

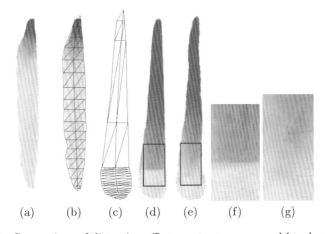

(a)   (b)   (c)   (d)   (e)   (f)   (g)

Fig. 11.11. Comparison of distortion effects on texture mapped brush stroke and our appearance model. Given the original stroke (a) and triangulation for texture mapping (b), significant deformation may result during animation (c). Compare the distorted strokes using texture mapping (d) and our appearance model (e). The close-up views of the two respective approaches, (f) and (g), demonstrate that the texture mapped version cannot handle this type of significant distortion as well as our appearance model

The second problem with direct texture mapping is that separate tessellation of the source and destination brush stroke shapes would introduce the non-trivial problem of establishing a one-to-one correspondence between the two tessellation results to map the texture. It is possible to handle this problem using a dynamic tessellation algorithm that generates consistent tessellation results, e.g. [ACOL00]. However, that would introduce significant additional complexity at the expense of speed. In addition, ensuring minimum distortion in the brush texture is not obvious. As a result it is also very hard to guarantee temporal coherence during animation if direct texture mapping is used. Our appearance model does not suffer from these problems.

Our appearance model also naturally supports Level-of-Detail (LOD) for strokes, and has the capability of predicting the appearance of areas that may be partially occluded. This predictive power is used for producing good initial appearances in the process of separating overlapping brush strokes (Sect. 11.5).

Although our appearance model outperforms texture mapping in terms of rendering quality, rendering through direct texture mapping is much faster, typically at interactive speeds. Also, when the brush shape deformation is not too significant, establishing the one-to-one correspondence between tessellation results for the initial and deformed brush shapes is not very challenging. Thus, we provide two rendering modes in generating an animation clip from a collection of brush strokes extracted from paintings. During the on-line authoring process, texture mapping is used for rendering. This is to enable the animator to manipulate the brush strokes and preview the results in real-time. Once the on-line authoring stage is accomplished, the actual animation clip is generated using our brush appearance model.

11.5 Separating Overlapping Brush Strokes

Brush strokes typically overlap in paintings (see, for example, Fig. 11.12(a)). In order to extract the brush strokes and animate them in a visually plausible way, we have to provide a mechanism to separate the recovered brush strokes at the overlap regions. Techniques for separation of transparent layers exist in the computer vision literature. For example, Farid and Adelson [FA99] showed how to separate reflections off a planar glass surface placed in front of a scene. Their method can restore the image of the scene behind the glass by removing the reflections. Unfortunately their algorithm does not handle the more general problem of image separation, i.e. under arbitrary motion and using only one image (as in our work). Another two-layer separation technique is that of Szeliski, et al. [SAA00]. However, they use multiple input images, assume planar motion for the two layers, and apply an additive model with no alpha.

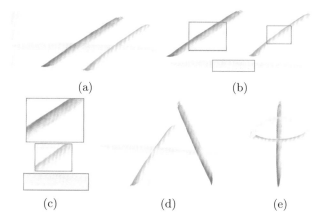

Fig. 11.12. Separation of overlapping brush strokes. Given the original image of three overlapping strokes (a), we obtain the separate strokes (b), with close-up views (c). These strokes can then be easily animated (d), (e)

Levin and Weiss [LW04] and Levin et al. [LZW04] also studied the problem of separating transparent layers from a single image. In the first approach gradients are precomputed, following which users are required to interactively label gradients as belonging to one of the layers. Statistics of images of natural scenes are then used to separate two linearly superimposed images. It is not clear if such an approach would work for typical Chinese paintings (which are not photoreal), even with the benefit of manual labeling. The second approach uses a similar framework, except that it minimizes the total number of edges and corners in the decomposed image layers. However, the minimal edge and corner assumptions are not valid for typical Chinese paintings due to the sharp edges of brush strokes. By comparison, our assumption of minimum variation on the texture of brush strokes along the stroke direction is more appropriate for our domain, and turns out to be effective for automatically separating overlapping brush strokes.

The overlap regions can be easily identified once we have performed the fitting process described in Sect. 11.3.3. Once the library brush strokes have been identified, their contours are refined using a similarity transform (scaling, shifting, and rotating) to maximize shape similarity with their corresponding stroke regions. The transformed brush strokes are further dilated enough to just cover the observed strokes in the image, after which the overlapping areas are identified.

We then apply an iterative algorithm to separate the colors at the overlap region. To initialize the separate color distributions, we use the same strategy described in Step 11.4.1 of Sect. 11.4 to interpolate the colors in the overlap regions using neighboring Bézier functions with known color distributions.

In real paintings, the color distribution in the overlap region is the result of mixing those from the separate brushes. We adapt the mixture model proposed by Porter and Duff [PD84] to model overlapping strokes as matted objects because the combination color in the overlapping brush region is generally the result of mixing and optical superimposition of different pigment layers. We did not use more sophisticated models such as the Kubelka-Munk model ([JW75], pages 420—438), because the problem of extracting all the unknowns from only one image is ill-posed. While the problem is similar to matting (e.g. [Chu01]), matting does not explicitly account for brush stroke texture and orientation. Currently we separate only pairs of brushes that overlap. Extending our method to handle multiple overlapping strokes is possible at higher computational cost.

Let $\psi_i(p)$ and $\psi_j(p)$ be the colors of two overlapping brush strokes at a given pixel location p, with brush stroke i over brush stroke j; let $\alpha_i(p)$ be the transparency of brush stroke i at p; and let $\psi_r(p)$ be the resulting color at that pixel. We model the appearance of these overlapping strokes using the ("unpremultiplied") compositing equation [PD84]:

$$\psi_r(p) = \alpha_i(p)\psi_i(p) + \big(1 - \alpha_i(p)\big)\psi_j(p). \tag{11.6}$$

In our case $\psi_r(p)$ is observed, and so our goal will be to solve for $\alpha_i(p)$, $\psi_i(p)$, and $\psi_j(p)$ at each pixel p for which the strokes overlap. This problem is, of course, underconstrained by this single equation. Thus we will solve for the values of these three variables that minimize a certain expression encoding some additional assumptions about the appearance of the strokes. In particular, we will assume that the colors ψ_i and ψ_j vary minimally along the lengths of their strokes, and that the transparency α_i varies minimally along both the length and breadth of the upper stroke.

Our objective function, which we will minimize using gradient descent subject to Eq. 11.6, is as follows:

$$\sum_{p \in \gamma_i \cap \gamma_j} (V_i(p) + V_j(p) + \lambda_t T_i(p)). \tag{11.7}$$

Here, V_i can be thought of as the "excess variation" of the color of stroke i along its length, while T_i is the variation of the transparency of stroke i along both its length and breadth.

To evaluate the excess variation, we will refer to the "average variation" $\overline{V_i}(p)$ of the color $\psi_i(p)$ in the parts of the stroke that do not overlap j in which that same color appears. We will call this "exposed" region $\gamma_{i \setminus j}(\psi_i(p))$. Let ℓ be the direction that is parallel to the length of the stroke at p. Then the average variation of the color ψ_i is given by

$$\overline{V_i}(p) = \frac{1}{A(\gamma_{i \setminus j}(\psi_i(p)))} \sum_{p \in \gamma_{i \setminus j}(\psi_i(p))} \|\partial \psi_i(p)/\partial \ell\|. \tag{11.8}$$

The excess variation $V_i(p)$ is then given by the amount to which the derivative of the color of stroke i at p along its length exceeds the average variation of that color in other parts of the stroke:

$$V_i(p) = \max \left\{ 0, \|\partial \psi_i(p)/\partial \ell\| - \overline{V_i}(p) \right\}. \tag{11.9}$$

Finally, the variation of the transparency is given by the sum of the derivatives of the transparency both along and across the stroke:

$$T_i(p) = \|\partial \alpha_i(p)/\partial \ell\| + \|\partial \alpha_i(p)/\partial b\|, \tag{11.10}$$

where b is the direction perpendicular to ℓ.

We generally set λ_t to a small number, around 0.05, since minimizing color variation appears to be more important than transparency variation in most cases. An example of brush separation is shown in Fig. 11.12. The original brush strokes are shown in (a), and the separated brush strokes are shown in (b).

Our compositing model is related to the Kubelka-Munk model [JW75], which assumes that additivity is valid for the absorption and scattering coefficients in the overlapping pigment layers. In other words, $K_r = c_i K_i + (1 - c_i)K_j$ and $S_r = c_i S_i + (1 - c_i)S_j$, where K_r, K_i, K_j are the absorption coefficients in the overlapping area, brush stroke i and brush stroke j, respectively. S_r, S_i, S_j are the respective scattering coefficients. $c_i, (1 - c_i)$ are the percentages of the amounts of pigment carried by the brush strokes i and j respectively. It is easy to see that our additive compositing equation is a highly simplified version of the Kubelka-Munk model.

The stroke decomposition and animation results show that the simple additive compositing model Eq. (11.6) is rather effective. Our compositing model is significantly less complex than the Kubelka-Munk model. In addition, it is not clear how the Kubelka-Munk model can be reliably used, as it requires the simultaneous recovery of multiple transparent layers from only one image.

A straightforward method for separating overlapping strokes would be to simply discard color information at the region of overlap and reconstruct via smooth interpolation from neighboring regions. However, when an artist paints a single stroke, the color distribution within that stroke is typically not uniform and not smooth. Reconstructing the missing overlap regions by just smoothly interpolating from neighboring regions will not only result in an overly smooth appearance, but also a visually incorrect one. By comparison, our technique accounts for the non-uniformity in color distribution.

11.6 Decomposition and Reconstruction Results

Fig. 11.13 shows step by step the process of our stroke decomposition approach on a flower painting. Here, for ease of illustration, we focus on only three extracted brush strokes. Another illustrative example is given in Fig. 11.14(a to i); here, both successful and failed stroke decomposition cases are shown. These cases are discussed in Sect. 11.8. Decomposition results for entire paintings are shown in Figs. 11.4 (a different flower painting) and 11.15 (fish painting). As can be seen in all these examples, the appearance of these paintings has been very well captured using our brush stroke library and appearance model. In the stroke decomposition result shown in Fig. 11.15(e), most parts of the fish body that animators would like to manipulate have been extracted as separate strokes. This decomposition is more convenient for animation than the results obtained without using our stroke library (Fig. 11.8). Without using the stroke library, regions are either over-segmented (Fig. 11.8(a to c)), under-segmented (Fig. 11.8(g to h)) or inconveniently segmented (recovered strokes straddling multiple actual strokes, Fig. 11.8(d to f)).

There are three reasons why stroke decomposition using only a simple shape smoothness assumption instead of our stroke library (Sect. 11.3.2.3) produces less desirable results. First, strokes with large variations in width and skeleton shape tend to be segmented incorrectly due to the violation of the smoothness assumption. Second, irregular contours of brush strokes (which occur rather often) would be similarly penalized, especially when overlapping occurs. Third, the smoothness assumption is intolerant of noisy or incomplete skeletons. Unfortunately, skeletons are noisy or incomplete in the initial stages of stroke decomposition, especially in the vicinity of overlaps. By comparison, our stroke-library-based approach is more robust because it incorporates more accurate domain-specific knowledge in the form of commonly used stroke shapes.

In the example of reconstructing strokes from a Chinese fish painting (Fig. 11.15), it may seem surprising to observe that the eye of the fish is captured in our brush stroke decomposition even though it has not been segmented

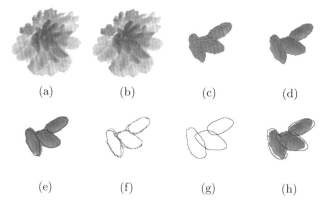

Fig. 11.13. The stroke decomposition process. We illustrate the decomposition process for input (a) by focusing on three brush strokes delineated in red (b). After over-segmentation (c), candidate stroke regions are extracted (d), followed by fitting the best library strokes (e). However, the best fit strokes typically do not completely cover the observed strokes (f), with blue contours representing the fit strokes and red contours representing the observed strokes. To correct the problem, we search (through gradient descent) the scaled rigid transform necessary for each fit stroke to minimally cover the observed stroke (g,h)

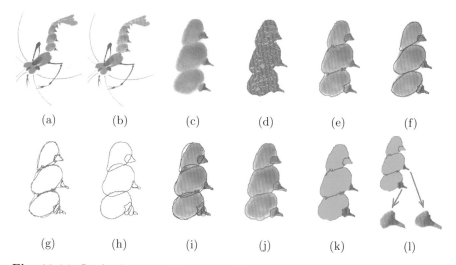

Fig. 11.14. Stroke decomposition example for shrimp painting. Given the input (a), we limit our analysis to three segments of the shrimp's body, delineated in red (b). From (c) to (f), respectively: close-up of original, after over-segmentation, after extracting candidate strokes and after fitting library strokes. As expected, the best-fit library strokes (in blue) do not completely cover the observed strokes (in red) (g). The refined best-fit library strokes that minimally cover the observed stroke region are shown in (h) and (i). These results are a little different from the manual decomposition results (j) done by the original painter. By superimposing both results (k), we see that the large brush strokes have been correctly extracted (in green); those that were incorrect were caused by oversegmentation (in purple). The enlarged views of the overly-segmented regions are shown in (l)

correctly. (It is difficult to segment correctly here because the size of the eye is very small.) The reason this "works" is that everything within the boundary of the refined brush stroke is considered its texture, and is thus sampled. Note that if overlapping brush strokes are detected, the algorithm described in Sect. 11.5 will automatically recover the appearances of the separated brush strokes. It is possible for a refined brush stroke shape to be bigger than it should be, and thus cover a little of the background or other brush strokes (as is in the case of the fish's eye in Fig. 11.15). While an imperfect segmentation will usually not affect the synthesized appearance of a still image, it will however introduce more sampling artifacts during animation.

We have also compared the results of our automatic stroke decomposition with those manually extracted by experts. Fig. 11.17 shows such an example. Typically, while our results are not identical to their manually extracted counterparts, the differences are minor in places where the brush strokes are obvious to the eye. Most of the differences are in locations of significant ambiguity, where even experts have trouble separating brush strokes.

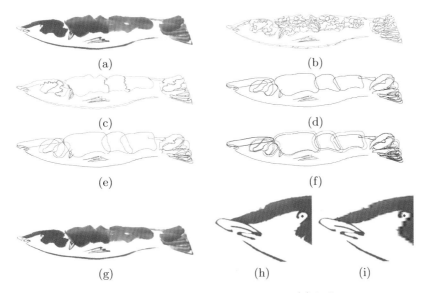

Fig. 11.15. Chinese painting of a fish. The input image (a) is first over-segmented (b). Candidate stroke regions are extracted (c) and fitted with library strokes (d). Note that the thin strokes are represented by their skeletons to distinguish them from regular brush strokes. The fitted regular library strokes are then refined through dilation (e). The dilation effect can be seen by superimposing the strokes (f). The painting can then be synthesized (g). Close-up views of the original (h) and synthesized (i) show the slight blurring effects. Selected keyframes of the animated fish painting are shown in Fig. 11.16

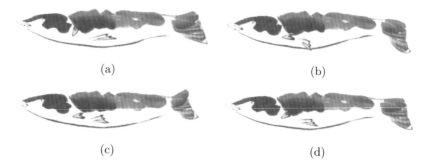

(a)   (b)

(c)   (d)

Fig. 11.16. Animated fish painting. Out of 150 frames in the animation clip, we show (a) the 1st frame, (b) the 20th frame, (c) the 60th frame, and (d) the 90th frame

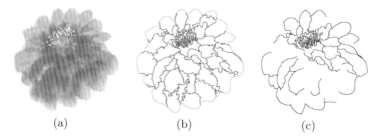

(a)   (b)   (c)

Fig. 11.17. A comparison between our decomposition result with manual stroke decomposition. (a) The flower portion of Fig. 11.1. (b) The decomposition result (candidate stroke regions). (c) The result of manual decomposition by an experienced Chinese painter who did not create the painting. The blue lines are the edges of strokes extracted with high confidence while lines in yellow are extracted with much less confidence (i.e. deemed ambiguous). Although (b) is different from (c) in a number of places, the major differences are mostly on the yellow lines, where multiple interpretations exist. Our recovered brush strokes agree well in areas where the brush strokes are distinguishable by the naked eye

11.7 Animating Paintings

Fig. 11.18 shows a screen shot of the user interface of our application program designed for animation. The animator can select and move any control point of either the skeleton or the contour of the stroke to be animated. The appearance of the modified stroke is automatically generated by rendering our single-stroke appearance model. The key-frames for the animation can thus be produced through very simple user manipulation.

The in-betweens are generated through interpolation. Note that our animation is done at the *brush-stroke level*. Our brush appearance and mixture models allow the animated painting to be visually acceptable.

Our animation system has the following important features that make it fast and easy to use:

(1) Addition and removal of brush strokes. Brush strokes from other paintings can be imported and used.

(2) Grouping of brush strokes for simultaneous manipulation or editing.

(3) Ability to edit shape and location of the common boundary between two adjacent strokes or to manually decompose a stroke into multiple separate strokes. The latter feature is useful if parts of the decomposition results are not considered fine enough.

(4) Preservation of stroke connectivity, so that changes to any brush stroke will be appropriately propagated.

(5) Shape interpolation using critical points (points with locally maximal curvature) on the stroke boundary to better preserve the local shape characteristics during animation.

(6) Timeline support for editing motion trajectories (e.g. changes in speed or phase). The motion trajectory for each brush stroke can be modified independently.

(7) The shapes of the brush contour and its skeleton are directly linked; if one of them is manipulated, the other is automatically updated.

(8) The user can operate directly on either the candidate strokes (Fig. 11.15(c)) or the refined strokes (Fig. 11.15(e)). Note that in Fig. 11.18, groups of candidate strokes are manipulated.

Snapshots of animations can be seen in Figs. 11.1 and 11.20.

It is possible for our stroke decomposition algorithm to make mistakes. It may over-segment (requiring more work to animate), under-segment (resulting in inadequate degrees of freedom for animation), or even produce segments straddling multiple actual strokes. Some of the features in our authoring tool are designed specifically to allow users to manually touch up the decomposition results or correct mistakes.

11.8 Discussion

There are other possible methods for extracting brush strokes. The simplest is to have the artist draw directly using an interface with the computer, e.g. a haptic interface [BSLM01]. Another method would be to record the painting process and infer the brush strokes. The idea would be to digitize the intermediate results of the painting after every stroke or group of strokes. This may be accomplished by using an overhead camera that sees the entire painting. To avoid the problem of occlusion, the artist could leave the field of view of the camera after each stroke or a small number of strokes. However, the painting process is no longer natural. The artist has to adapt to the change in the conditions for painting, be it using the haptic interface or (worse) with the stop-and-paint approach. Furthermore, existing paintings could not be handled.

Another straightforward (but more manually intensive) alternative is to design an authoring tool that allows users to merge small stroke segments into meaningful ones or have users roughly delineate the boundaries of strokes. This solution would provide a higher degree of control but comes at the cost

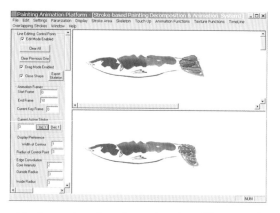

Fig. 11.18. Graphical user interface for animation. This interface uses as input the vectorized strokes generated by our decomposition algorithm. The blue dots are the control points of Bézier curves associated with the groups of brush strokes representing the fish's tail. There are four groups shown here. Note that each group is represented by a different line color, and each group's contour is that of the union of its constituent brush strokes. The shape of each group is manipulated by moving the control points. The top and bottom fish images are generated before and after manipulation-respectively

Fig. 11.19. The original lotus pond painting

of extensive manual effort. Automatic color separation such as ours would have to be incorporated in such a tool (common image editing tools such as Photoshop^{TM} do not have such a feature).

For the animation example shown in Figs. 11.19 and 11.20, it took a single animator 40 hours to use our authoring system to produce a 40-second clip. While there is no record of the exact cost of making the famous 18-minute 1988 video, "Shan Shui Qing" ("Love for Mountains and Rivers"), descriptions of the work involved (e.g. [Che94, CZ95]) suggest that it required dozens of people working for about a year.

What happens if we were to use only a subset of the brush stroke library for the decomposition process? Fig. 11.21 shows that the effect is over-segmentation, which worsens as the size of the library is decreased. This is not

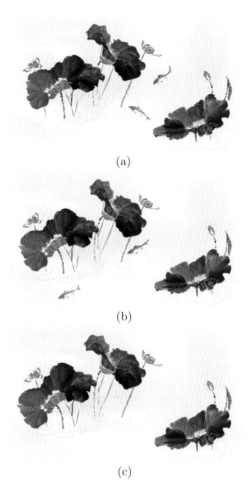

(a)

(b)

(c)

Fig. 11.20. Animated lotus pond painting. Out of the 580 frames in the animation clip, we show the 196th frame (a), the 254th frame (b), and the 448th frame (c). The 1st frame corresponds to the original painting, which is shown at Fig. 11.19

surprising, as the impoverished versions of the brush stroke library are unable to adequately account for the rich variety of stroke shapes in the painting.

Our algorithm can fail even for some Chinese paintings; more specifically, it is unable to decompose paintings drawn in a realistic style. Fig. 11.23 shows such a failure case. In such paintings both the shapes and the color of brush strokes are deposited strictly according to the actual appearance and geometry of real-world objects. This makes our brush appearance model no longer a good fit since there can be large color variations along the stroke skeletons. In addition, our stroke library would no longer be adequate because the shapes of brush strokes are drawn more arbitrarily to resemble the shapes of real-world objects. To make the painting as realistic as possible, many tiny strokes (which may significantly overlap each other) are often drawn.

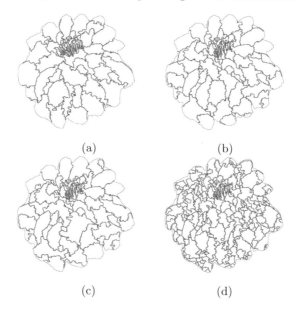

(a)   (b)

(c)   (d)

Fig. 11.21. The effect of different library sizes on decomposition. The example in Fig. 11.17 is used for comparison. (a) is the result using the full library (62 brush strokes), (b) is the result using 31 brush strokes, (c) with 16 brush strokes and (d) with 8 brush strokes. The brush stroke shapes in the libraries used for (b to d) are randomly chosen from the full library

This style of painting violates the mainstream principle of "economical use of brush strokes" for Chinese paintings.

Unfortunately, even a reasonable decomposition may not always be amenable to animation. This is especially true if the painting involves many small objects clustered closely together and if the animation requires complex interacting motions. A good example of such a case is shown in Fig. 11.24. While the decomposition of the grape painting looks reasonable, animating each grape and leaf relative to other objects would be challenging. For such complicated paintings, it is not clear what a good solution would be.

Our current implementation is unoptimized. For the flower example shown in Figs. 11.1 and 11.4 (with resolution $560 \times 1,080$), the times taken for each step on a Pentium III 1.2 GHz computer are: image segmentation (10 secs), region merging (5 hrs), regular stroke refinement (40 mins), regular stroke appearance capture (35 mins), thin stroke detection (10 mins) and interval spline fitting (1 min). We plan to optimize our code to speed up the performance. Note that these steps are done off-line and executed only once. During the actual on-line editing process, rendering of manipulated brush strokes is at interactive rates (30 FPS when simple texture-mapping is used for previewing).

Once the brush strokes have been identified, it is entirely possible to analyze the painting by analyzing the brush strokes themselves. By looking at the distribution of directions, stroke thickness, variation of thickness along each

Fig. 11.22. A failure example. One painting that our algorithm failed to decompose properly is *The Seine at La Grande* by Georges Seurat in 1888 (a). The stroke decomposition algorithm resulted in a very large number of small brush strokes. (b) is the close-up view of the area enclosed by the red box in (a). Its corresponding decomposition result is shown in (c), with the final refined brush strokes shown in (d) (Here we do not include the stroke skeletons in the stroke regions for ease of visualization). Obviously, animating paintings of this kind using our current algorithm would be very labor-intensive. Secondly, our brush appearance model is also no longer a good fit since there is large color variation along the brush strokes. This makes our stroke extraction less accurate

stroke, and the color distribution along each stroke and within the painting, the task of identifying the painting style and even the artist may be easier.

Decomposition results with arbitrarily shaped segments complicate the process of animation, and would very likely adversely affect the final visual output quality. Overly small segments increase the amount of effort involved in specifying their motion trajectories. (This effort can be reduced by grouping the small segments, but the grouping operation can be laborious and tedious as well.) On the other hand, overly large segments straddle multiple brush strokes (wholly or partially), which severely limits the degree of freedom in animating. In addition, in cases where the large segments straddle partial brush strokes, it is very difficult to ensure a correct appearance if the large segments are manipulated independently because the separated brush strokes are distorted differently.

Our current rendering implementation uses a simplistic approach to handle overlapping normal lines (which occur when the user puts a sharp kink

(a)   (b)

Fig. 11.23. A failure case for Chinese painting. Our decomposition algorithm usually fails for realistic Chinese paintings such as this one (a). The right side of the figure (b) shows a close-up of the painting, the decomposition result (candidate stroke regions), and the result of superimposing the decomposition result onto the original painting. Note the over-segmentation effect due to the original's arbitrarily-shaped brush strokes and significant color variation

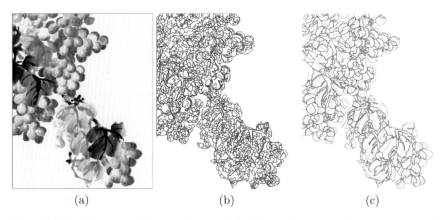

(a)   (b)   (c)

Fig. 11.24. A decomposition result unsuitable for animation. The input image of a grape painting (a), the initial segmented image regions (b) and the extracted candidate strokes with skeletons (c)

into the edited stroke, for example). The renderer merely averages the color distributions of the overlapping normal lines. It is not clear what the right solution to this situation is, but the technique used by Hsu and Lee [HL94] may be better. Another failure mode occurs when the brush stroke is too distorted, causing severe deformation of the local appearance. Fortunately these problems do not occur very often.

11.9 Conclusion and Future Work

11.9.1 Conclusion

We have shown a new technique for animating paintings from images. What is particularly interesting is that the animation is done at the *brush-stroke level*.

In order to decompose the image of a painting into hypothesized strokes, we proposed an approach that uses a library of brush stroke shapes to aid region segmentation. Our brush stroke model plays a critical role in allowing the painting's appearance to be captured and subsequently rendered with good fidelity. Finally, our overlap separation algorithm allows the full appearance of strokes to be extracted despite the presence of overlaps.

A key contribution of our work is the *automatic* recovery of separate, vectorized brush strokes . This is a tremendous time saver compared to manual segmentation, especially when the painting has hundreds of brush strokes. In addition, proper automatic color separation in the overlap regions is not trivial and is not a feature in common image editing tools such as Photoshop^{TM}. The animation is significantly easier once the segmentation is done.

Experiment results show that our method of decomposition is capable of producing high-quality reconstructions of paintings. The quality of the sample animations also serves to illustrate the effectiveness of our decomposition approach.

11.9.2 Future Work

As shown in Sect. 11.6, the reconstructed images look very similar to the original ones (e.g. Fig. 11.15). On closer examination however, we can see artifacts introduced by our brush stroke representation (Fig. 11.15 (h) and (i)). In all our examples we see that the reconstructed paintings appear fuzzier and the boundaries of the brush strokes are more irregular. This is due to the discrete sampling of the appearance along the brush skeleton (with intermediate areas merely interpolated). In addition, the sampling along the brush skeleton is done independently, i.e. there is no spatial coherence between samples. We plan to investigate sampling techniques that better handle spatial continuity along the brush stroke skeleton.

While many brush strokes appear to be correctly extracted, our algorithm did make mistakes, especially in areas where brush strokes overlap significantly and where the strokes are thick and short. One way of improving this is to extract the brush strokes globally, e.g. ensuring better continuity in the brush stroke direction. In addition, our overlap separation algorithm is currently applicable to overlaps between two brush strokes only. It is not clear how robust our current algorithm is to overlaps of an arbitrary number of brush strokes, but this is a topic we intend to investigate further.

Another limitation of our algorithm lies in the stroke separation and texture modeling steps being independent. As Fig. 11.14(k to l) shows, our algorithm resulted in over-segmentation. This is caused by significant texture changes within the failed regions. Our current stroke decomposition algorithm is designed under the assumption that texture variation within a stroke region is approximately homogeneous. Unfortunately, for paintings whose pigment/ink diffusion effect is significant, the uniform texture variation assumption no longer holds, leading to the failure cases in Fig. 11.14. To handle such a problem, we would have to incorporate texture modeling in the stroke decomposition process and replace the uniform texture variation assumption with the step of directly fitting a texture model. This would obviously increase the computational cost of the decomposition process.

Currently, our stroke model extracts transparency only at overlapping regions. The proper procedure would be to calculate transparency throughout the overlapping stroke region. Unfortunately, the separation of colors using *a single image* is ill-posed. We handle this by specifying relative transparency at the overlap regions with spatial regularization. One possible solution is to allow users to manually (locally or globally) specify the natural transparency of a stroke. In our current implementation, Eq. 11.6 assumes an additive color model, while ink tends to be subtractive. We would like to explore more sophisticated pigment mixing models in the future.

We currently use Chinese-style and watercolor paintings for our work. There are instances where our algorithm did not work well, e.g. Fig. 11.22, where there are extensive overlaps between many short brush strokes. Our brush appearance model is also no longer a good fit when there is large color variation along the brush strokes. Because the decomposition for such a painting would result in a large number of small brush strokes, the process of animating the painting would be very labor-intensive. We have plans to work on images of paintings with significantly different styles (e.g. Renaissance oil paintings). It is likely that we will need to expand our brush stroke library to handle the different brush stroke styles available in different types of paintings.

Our current decomposition algorithm does not handle very closely drawn brush strokes very well. In such cases it may create overly large refined strokes. It is possible to improve the decomposition process by looking at boundary concavities and hypothesizing those to be boundaries of at least two strokes. This is a difficult problem that we intend to investigate further.

References

[ACOL00] Marc Alexa, Daniel Cohen-Or, and David Levin. As-rigid-as-possible shape interpolation. In *SIGGRAPH '00: Proceedings of the 27th Annual Conference on Computer Graphics and Interactive Techniques*, New Orleans, LA, USA: ACM Press/Addison-Wesley Publishing Co., pages 157–164, 2000.

[BC02] William A. Barrett and Alan S. Cheney. Object-based image editing. In *SIGGRAPH '02: Proceedings of the 29th Annual Conference on Computer Graphics and Interactive Techniques*, San Antonio, TX, USA: ACM Press, pages 777–784, 2002.

[BH99] Dorothea Blostein and Lippold Haken. Using diagram generation software to improve diagram recognition: A case study of music notation. *IEEE Transactions on Pattern Analysis and Machine Intelligence*, 21(11):1121–1136, 1999.

[BSLM01] Bill Baxter, Vincent Scheib, Ming C. Lin, and Dinesh Manocha. DAB: Interactive haptic painting with 3D virtual brushes. In *SIGGRAPH '01: Proceedings of the 28th Annual Conference on Computer Graphics and Interactive Techniques*, Los Angeles, CA, USA: ACM Press, pages 461–468, 2001.

[Che94] Huangmei Chen, editor. *Encyclopaedia of China, Film Volume (in Chinese)*. Beijing, China: Encyclopaedia of China Press, 1994.

[Chu01] Yap S. Chua A Bayesian approach to digital matting. In *CVPR'2001: IEEE Computer Society Conference on Computer Vision and Pattern Recognition*, volume II, Kauai, Hawaii: IEEE Computer Society, pages 264–271, 2001.

[CM02] Dorin Comaniciu and Peter Meer. Mean shift: A robust approach toward feature space analysis. *IEEE Transactions on Pattern Analysis and Machine Intelligence*, 24(5):603–619, 2002.

[CZ95] Jihua Chen and Junxiang Zhang, editors. *Dictionary of Chinese Films (in Chinese)*. Shanghai, China: Shanghai Dictionary Press, 1995.

[Dan99] Eric Daniels. Deep canvas in Disney's Tarzan. In *SIGGRAPH '99: ACM SIGGRAPH 99 Conference Abstracts and Applications*, Los Angeles, CA, USA: ACM Press, page 200, 1999.

[DS02] Doug DeCarlo and Anthony Santella. Stylization and abstraction of photographs. In *SIGGRAPH '02: Proceedings of the 29th Annual Conference on Computer Graphics and Interactive Techniques*, San Antonio, TX, USA: ACM Press, pages 769–776, 2002.

[FA99] Hany Farid and Edward H. Adelson. Separating reflections from images by use of independent components analysis. *Journal of the Optical Society of America*, 16(9):2136–2145, 1999.

[FP02] David A. Forsyth and Jean Ponce. *Computer Vision: A Modern Approach*. Prentice Hall, 2002.

[FY74]   Jerome A. Feldman and Yoram Yakimovsky. Decision theory and artificial intelligence: I. a semantics-based region analyzer. *Artificial Intelligence*, 5(4):349–371, 1974.

[GCS02]   Bruce Gooch, Greg Coombe, and Peter Shirley. Artistic vision: painterly rendering using computer vision techniques. In *NPAR '02: Proceedings of the 2nd International Symposium on Non-photorealistic Animation and Rendering*, Annecy, France: ACM Press, pages 83–90, 2002.

[HAA97]   Youichi Horry, Ken-Ichi Anjyo, and Kiyoshi Arai. Tour into the picture: using a spidery mesh interface to make animation from a single image. In *SIGGRAPH '97: Proceedings of the 24th Annual Conference on Computer Graphics and Interactive Techniques*, Los Angeles, CA, USA: ACM Press/Addison-Wesley Publishing Co., pages 225–232, 1997.

[Her99]   Aaron Hertzmann. Introduction to 3D non-photorealistic rendering: silhouettes and outlines. In Ed. *Non-photorealistic Rendering. SIGGRAPH 99, Course Notes*, Los angeles, CA, USA: ACM Press, 1999.

[HL94]   Siu-Chi Hsu and Irene H. H. Lee. Drawing and animation using skeletal strokes. In *SIGGRAPH '94: Proceedings of the 21st Annual Conference on Computer Graphics and Interactive Techniques*, Orlando, FL, USA: ACM Press, pages 109–118, 1994.

[HLLS99] S.C. Hsu, I.H.H. Lee, C.W. Lou, and S.L. Siu. Software. In *Creature House (www.creaturehouse.com)*, 1999.

[Jai89]   Anil K. Jain. *Fundamentals of Digital Image Processing*. Prentice Hall, 1989.

[JP92]   S. H. Joseph and T. P. Pridmore. Knowledge-directed interpretation of mechanical engineering drawings. *IEEE Transactions on Pattern Analysis and Machine Intelligence*, 14(9):928–940, 1992.

[JW75]   Deane B. Judd and Gunther Wyszecki. *Color in Business, Science, and Industry*. John Wiley & Sons, Inc., 1975.

[KD99]   Sunil K. Kumar and Uday B. Desai. Joint segmentation and image interpretation. *Pattern Recognition*, 32(4):577–589, 1999.

[KMM+02] Robert D. Kalnins, Lee Markosian, Barbara J. Meier, Michael A. Kowalski, Joseph C. Lee, Philip L. Davidson, Matthew Webb, John F. Hughes, and Adam Finkelstein. WYSIWYG NPR: drawing strokes directly on 3D models. In *SIGGRAPH '02: Proceedings of the 29th Annual Conference on Computer Graphics and Interactive Techniques*, San Antonio, TX, USA: ACM Press, pages 755–762, 2002.

[LS01]   Lifeng Liu and Stan Sclaroff. Region segmentation via deformable model-guided split and merge. *In ICCV' 2001 Proceedings of the International Conference on Computer Vision*, Vancouver, Canada: IEEE Computer Society, volume 1, pages 98–104, 2001.

[LW94]   Peter Litwinowicz and Lance Williams. Animating images with drawings. In *SIGGRAPH '94: Proceedings of the 21st Annual*

Conference on Computer Graphics and Interactive Techniques, Orlando, FL, USA: ACM Press, pages 409–412, 1994.

[LW04] Anat Levin and Yair Weiss. User-assisted separation of reflections from a single image using a sparsity prior. In *ECCV'2004: European Conference on Computer Vision*, Prague, Czech Republic, pages 602–613, 2004.

[LZW04] Anat Levin, Assaf Zomet, and Yair Weiss. Separating reflections from a single image using local features. In *CVPR'2004: IEEE Computer Society Conference on Computer Vision and Pattern Recognition*, Seattle, WA, USA: IEEE Computer Society, pages 306–313, 2004.

[MMH88] Jan A. Mulder, Alan K. Mackworth, and Willian S. Havens. Knowledge structuring and constraint satisfaction: the mapsee approach. *IEEE Transactions on Pattern Analysis and Machine Intelligence*, 10(6):866–879, 1988.

[MSB03] Jose L. Marroquin, Edgar A. Santana, and Salvador Botello. Hidden Markov measure field models for image segmentation. *IEEE Transactions on Pattern Analysis and Machine Intelligence*, 25(11):1380–1387, 2003.

[Neu03] Anke Neumann. Graphical Gaussian shape models and their application to image segmentation. *IEEE Transactions on Pattern Analysis and Machine Intelligence*, 25(3):316–329, 2003.

[PD84] Thomas Porter and Tom Duff. Compositing digital images. In *SIGGRAPH '84: Proceedings of the 11th Annual Conference on Computer Graphics and Interactive Techniques*, Minneapolis, MN, USA: ACM Press, pages 253–259, 1984.

[SAA00] Richard Szeliski, Shai Avidan, and P. Anandan. Layer extraction from multiple images containing reflections and transparency. In *CVPR 2000: IEEE Computer Society Conference on Computer Vision and Pattern Recognition*, Hilton Head Island, SC, USA: IEEE Computer Society, volume I, pages 246–253, 2000.

[SABS94] Michael P. Salisbury, Sean E. Anderson, Ronen Barzel, and David H. Salesin. Interactive pen-and-ink illustration. In *SIGGRAPH '94: Proceedings of the 21st Annual Conference on Computer Graphics and Interactive Techniques*, Orlando, FL, USA: ACM Press, pages 101–108, 1994.

[Sch90] Philip J. Schneider. An algorithm for automatically fitting digitized curves. *Graphics Gems,* ed. A. S. Glassner, London, UK: Academic Press, pages 612–626, 1990.

[SF92] Thomas W. Sederberg and Rida T. Farouki. Approximation by interval Bézier curves. *IEEE Computer Graphics and Applications*, 12(5):87–95, 1992.

[SL97] Ray Smith and Elizabeth Lloyd. *Art School.* Dorling Kindersley Ltd., Inc., 1997.

[SL01] Stan Sclaroff and Lifeng Liu. Deformable shape detection and description via model-based region grouping. *IEEE Transac-*

tions on Pattern Analysis and Machine Intelligence, 23(5):475–489, 2001.

[Str86] Steve Strassmann. Hairy brushes. In *SIGGRAPH '86: Proceedings of the 13th Annual Conference on Computer Graphics and Interactive Techniques*, Dallas, TX, USA: ACM Press, pages 225–232, 1986.

[SXSC02] Sara L. Su, Ying-Qing Xu, Heung-Yeung Shum, and Falai Chen. Simulating artistic brushstrokes using interval splines. In *Proceedings of the 5th IASTED International Conference on Computer Graphics and Imaging*, Kauai, Hawaii, USA, pages 85–90, 2002.

[TB77] Jay M. Tenenbaum, and Harry G. Barrow. Experiments in interpretation-guided segmentation. In *Artificial Intelligence*, 8(3):241–274, 1977.

[VH99] R. C. Veltkamp and M. Hagedoorn. State of the art in shape matching. In *Technical Report UU-CS-1999-27*, Netherlands: Utrecht University, 1999.

[WJ93] Jin Wang and Jack Jean. Segmentation of merged characters by neural networks and shortest-path. In *SAC '93: Proceedings of the 1993 ACM/SIGAPP Symposium on Applied Computing: States of the Art and Practice*, Indianapolis, IN, USA: ACM Press, pages 762–769, 1993.

[WS88] Ching-Huei Wang and Sargur N. Srihari. A framework for object recognition in a visually complex environment and its application to locating address blocks on mail pieces. *International Journal of Computer Vision*, 2(2):125–151, 1988.

[WS03] Song Wang and Jeffrey M. Siskind. Image segmentation with ratio cut. *IEEE Transactions on Pattern Analysis and Machine Intelligence*, 25(6):675–690, 2003.

[XTLP04] Songhua Xu, Min Tang, Francis C. M. Lau, and Yunhe Pan. Virtual hairy brush for painterly rendering. *Graphical Models*, 66(5):263–302, 2004.

[ZBC02] Richard Zanibbi, Dorothea Blostein, and James R. Cordy. Recognizing mathematical expressions using tree transformation. *IEEE Transactions on Pattern Analysis and Machine Intelligence*, 24(11):1455–1467, 2002.

[ZQN95] R. W. Zhou, C. Quek, and G. S. Ng. A novel single-pass thinning algorithm and an effective set of performance criteria. *Pattern Recognition Letters*, 16(12):1267–1275, 1995.

Part VI

Perspectives

Final Fantasies for Digital Painting and Calligraphy

No Dream Too Big, No Dreamer Too Small.

Kate Bredimus, Richmond.com

12.1 Perspectives on Digital Paintbrush Research

It is not unreasonable to suggest that an ideal digital paintbrush system should not only perform as expressively as, or mimic, any arbitrary paint-brush in the real world, but should also be able to achieve certain effects that are not possible with any physical paintbrush. We examine both the realistic and the surreal goals in this section.

12.1.1 An Ideal Digital Paintbrush System

First and foremost, an easily agreeable goal for the design and development of a digital paintbrush system is for the resulting e-brush to be functionally equivalent to a physical paintbrush, thus rendering the latter completely re-placeable by an e-brush. That is, the ideal system should support the creation of serious artwork in an entirely digital fashion, the quality of which could rival that of paintings done by physical brushes. The following elaborates on the functionalities of such an e-brush.

12.1.1.1 Types of paintings

A wide variety of different kinds of paintings should be simulated including, but not limited to, woodwork painting, watercolor painting, acrylics painting, oil painting, egg tempera painting, mixed-media painting, encaustic painting, pastel painting, fabric painting, etc. Since the types of paper and pigments are usually dictated by the kind or style of paintings, this also means the ideal digital paintbrush should be able to emulate the features of all sorts of papers and pigment species existing in the real world.

It is worth noting at this juncture the very recent introduction by Brooks of "mixed-media painting" in the field of painterly rendering [Bro07]. He successfully demonstrated by some hybrid deployment of multiple traditional painting styles, e.g. paint daubs, watercolor, colored pencil, photocopy, that some impressive and effective painting effects could be achieved. An ideal digital painting environment should surely be able to support the flexible mix-and-match of various painting styles without imposing any burden on the end user.

12.1.1.2 Paintings effects

For each painting method, an ideal digital paintbrush should support the generation of all the effects that are in the repertoire, for example from very wet ink to the very dry, from intensive pressing of the brush against the paper surface to mere touching and sliding of the brush over the paper surface. Especially in the practice of Oriental painting, the way a painter fluently and skillfully manoeuvers his brush is a key to mastery, which is a major learning component of any standard Oriental painting training and education program. An ideal e-brush should therefore be sensitive enough to observe and track the painter's manoeuvering of the brush and then accurate enough in simulating the corresponding effects from the manoeuver.

12.1.1.3 Real-time response

Regardless of the type of paintings the user is doing and the specific painting effects going on, the system should operate and interact with the user in real time. We can expect it takes no less than a reasonable amount of computing power to realize that goal, but meanwhile are mindful that this is not the place where super-computing support should be demanded. If an e-brush is by any means to be popular and easily accessible, an ordinary PC platform is what should be expected. In the age of pervasive computing however, even this might be too luxurious. To be able to substitute for the real physical brush which is handy and portable anywhere (call that pervasive painting), an ideal digital paintbrush should also be able to function on even very power limited computing platforms, say PDAs or cell phones. In view of the current advances in small-device computing, it might take a while to actually reach this status.

12.1.1.4 The issue of resolution

An ideal digital paintbrush should support digital painting at arbitrary levels of resolution when so desired without excessively straining the system resources. Currently, as far as we could observe, all the digital paintbrush simulations only support the creation of painting effects at a certain pre-chosen resolution. For vector-based painting, like those done using Adobe

Illustrator, this is not an issue. However, there are many painting effects which are feasible in vector mode. The practice today is that the user has to first choose or commit to a certain resolution before he/she starts painting and enjoys these effects. Once the painting is done, trying to change or improve the resolution is either not allowed or non-trivial. Many on-going research efforts are actively trying to solve this problem

[CB97, BS98, EF99, Cha01, RC02, FJP02, BK02, Cap04, NY05, CM05, WTS05, SC05, BF06, TTT06, JCC07, BACM⁺07, NLT07], but still there are a lot of challenges ahead. Interestingly, the situation resembles the resolution issue of digital cameras versus conventional analogue (optical) cameras. An ideal digital camera will ultimately be expected to produce digital photographs at any resolution imaginable, making it completely indistinguishable from an optical camera. Before that happens, digital cameras will still be the underdog in the resolution race.

12.1.1.5 Realistic brush dynamics

Brush dynamics are crucial to the faithful simulated reproduction of real brush behavior, and are keys to the successful production of many realistic as well as unrealistic painting effects. Unfortunately, a typical head bundle of a paintbrush comprises hundreds if not thousands of hair strands. Computing the motion of so many objects in real time is non-trivial. In addition, the motion of condensed glue, which is commonly used to model pigment materials, presents another great difficulty in computational dynamics. On top of these, there are these apparently conflicting real-time and accuracy requirements the simulation has to meet. All this calls for the most careful and optimal algorithm design and software implementation. But things could be even more complicated than this. Once the brush head is dipped into the ink bottle and loaded with some pigment glue or pounder, the synergism of pigment materials and the hair volume at the brush tip is a complex body of motions, making the overall situation even more challenging. Despite the formidable technical obstacles, we believe it is necessary and worthwhile in the long run to tackle these computational challenges anyway, due to two reasons: 1) A high accuracy in the simulation is important for producing a facsimile of many artistic features, such as the splitting of the brush tip in delicate dry brush effects, or the random piling up of dense pigment materials during oil painting, or impasto in particular; 2) The user ought to feel the brush being manoeuvered, which critically depends on the faithful and accurate simulation of brush dynamics. If the virtual paintbrush deviates in any way in its behavior from that of a physical paintbrush, a likely immediate consequence would be an inaccurate calculation of the resultant footprint of the brush head on the paper. If there is to be a compromise, either the artist has to re-learn the use of the (virtual) brush, or the computer system has to labor to fine-tune its behavior to meet the user expectation and habit. The latter may be called human-centric software design, which is easier said than done. In the case of the digital paintbrush simulation as is done today, the designer tends to succumb to the technical implementation difficulties and consequently overlooks the real needs of the end users. We advocate making a digital paintbrush system capable of resolving brush dynamics as realistically as possible, so that the user can concentrate on the artwork creation process without being bothered or distracted by having to learn or adapt to a new or different tool.

12.1.1.6 Haptic feedback

Feedback is one of the most helpful aids for a person seeking to behave properly and profitably when trying to achieve certain goals in real life. The brush-based painting experience in reality or in the virtual world is no exception, where haptic feedback can help the artist develop an adept control over the movement of the brush. Therefore, as important as achieving accuracy in brush dynamics simulation is the need for the ideal paintbrush system to provide a realistic haptic feedback. This calls for a special input device that is haptic, and corresponding to more complex brush dynamics simulation methods, algorithms and implementations.

12.1.1.7 Sensitivity to external conditions

There are many external conditions which could affect the visual impression given by a painting. Consider for instance these two conditions: viewing and aging of the painting. By viewing conditions, we refer to the situation where a painting may have a different appearance when given different lighting conditions, as is the case for virtually any physical object in the world. To allow the user to experience delicate and realistic visual experiences with the painting, it is essential for the system to implement a correct or close approximation to the real situation in the physical world. In terms of aging, any physical painting will undergo an aging process, due possibly to the aging of the pigment materials as well as the canvas. Although it is arguable whether the support of aging is desirable for paintbrush systems in general, this is a very interesting process or effect to simulate, which might lead to some interesting research results, if not a practical tool.

12.1.1.8 Authenticity of digital paintings

A real painting is unique by definition (under a magnifying glass). The chance that a second painting looks exactly the same as this one is practically zero. This however becomes an issue for digital paintings, which must be carefully addressed and resolved if any digital painting system is to be adopted by serious artists to do serious work. With some advanced computer science techniques, we believe it is possible to render automatic protection to an original digital painting to guarantee its authenticity. On the other hand, if there are valid reasons for legally copying a part, or the entirety, of a painting, which is such a unique function in the digital world, some mechanism should be there to preserve the authorship or ownership information. This prevents plagiarism, and provides an assurance for the integrity of intellectual property rights on the Internet, which is very much a requirement for web browsing, downloading, and more generally any digital library services. The feasibility of legally copying an art piece leads to the very interesting area of "collaborative art creation" where cut-and-paste will be seen as a part of the process.

12.1.1.9 Choices of display

Instead of limiting display to the commonplace computer screen or projection screen, an ideal digital paintbrush system could be equipped with a specialized display so that both the painter and the audience could examine and appreciate the painting in a most favorable setting as if in a real world exhibition center where the optimal design of the environment and lighting makes a huge difference. Indeed, many environmental factors could affect the overall painting viewing experience, as revealed by many psychological studies. For the best and most realistic approximation to the visual experience in real exhibition halls, a natural display medium and setup are desired. It is no secret that most of todays monitors are unable to display accurately certain real-life colors, which a real physical painting would certainly contain. We not want to see an art idea or creation being unable to reveal its full glory because of the limitation of the display hardware.

12.1.2 A Surreal Digital Paintbrush System

Just now we looked the various issues and requirements of a realistic paintbrush simulation system. If one ever enjoys playing with electronic music or producing film feature effects using software studios, the desire for a surreal digital paintbrush system would loom large. This actually served as our drive when we started our digital paintbrush research many years ago. Having achieved the functionalities of the physical paintbrush in the electronic system, many opportunities to enhance the simulated brush and its repertoire of functions became apparent. Taking advantage of these opportunities then led to a digital mimic which was superior to its original counterpart in reality. We feel this is a common bottleneck for many serious digital simulation projects: an artificially duplicated tool or process would at best be as good as its real world counterpart. So despite faithful reproduction, such simulated computer models or tools stand no chance of beating the original ones in reality on account of output quality. Thus, before launching a nontrivial digital simulation effort, some surreal functionalities should be made outwardly desirable. In the following, we discuss some of these functionalities as they pertain to an ideal digital paintbrush system.

12.1.2.1 Revisable painting

When anyone is asked to suggest the leading feature of a digital word processing software over traditional pen and paper, ease of editing would likely be the answer. Similarly, the traditional brush and canvas in painting or calligraphy creation lack that wonderful advantage of easy editing. We are not at all excited by the unprecedented convenience offered by the copy, paste, redo and undo functionalities in a painting system. But how this convenience would profoundly change the paradigm of painting as practiced or upheld by professional artists brings the real excitement. with editing in the artist's toolbox, we have a new painting paradigm in which re-do and touchup become a part of the techniques. Indeed, in many critical epochs during the evolution of human civilization, the invention of a new tool would profoundly change and refine peoples way of working, which was never intended by the inventor of the tool. "We shape our tools first and then they shape us." The Internet is such an example: the way it is shaping every person on earth and every functioning unit of the society has probably amazed its inventors. The modern computer is another example. It is now every writer's habit to improve, correct or polish his composition through many rounds of revision. Yet the same kind of conduct is very foreign to painters as it is still largely a technical impossibility to delete and redraw parts of a painting. This is very much the case in Oriental painting where "no redrawing and correction" has been for thousands of years a standard methodological advice and golden rule. In comparison, revision is possible to a limited extent in oil painting, although not an easy thing to do. We cannot argue that more revision made to a piece of artwork will surely lead to greater artistic success and a higher aesthetic value. But we do envisage an important opportunity to redefine the traditional painting process—a new set of painting skills specially geared towards "painting revision" may be invented by talented digital artists. Emerging from all this may be a new breed of painters whose paintings, after rounds of correction and revision, would become "optimized".

12.1.2.2 Surreal pigment and paper

Equally important to the simulation of paintbrush behavior is the simulation of the behavior of the virtual pigments and the paper/canvas. As discussed in Chapter 6, there are certain pigment materials in the physical world that are very rare and expensive to acquire, and only well-to-do painting professionals could afford them. In the realm of digital painting there is no such budget constraint and the sky is the limit as far as how much variety there is in the "materials". Developing new digital pigment and paper materials that cater to special user needs could be at no additional financial cost. If we temporarily forget about the limits of computer display hardware, which we believe will be overcome given more time, digital painters can enjoy a much wider space for their creativity. The possibilities are unlimited. For example, some pigment materials may emit very strong light, similar to sunshine; some pigment could appear differently when viewed from different angles, leading to some interesting creations not all that feasible in real paintings. Some pigment may even have odor, adding an olfactory sensation to the viewing experience. How wonderful it would be, for instance, when observing a countryside landscape painting, if the viewer could smell the grass. All in all, virtual pigments could be made a stimulus of different sensations, in addition to their usual visual effects. Similarly, virtual paper or canvas may also possess physically impossible or impractical properties to enrich the possibilities and stretch the limits of virtual painting.

12.1.2.3 Multi-resolutional painting

In computer science, there has been much effect to address the levels-of-details issue [Cla76]. The key finding is that multi-resolutional strategy and treatment can aid the viewer's perception and benefit the computer systems performance. For digital painting, we see that this promises some improvement opportunities. It is often heard that some paintings do not appear meaningful or attractive when viewed closely, but would shine and unleash their full glory when observed at a certain distance. This phenomenon can be taken into account by a museum curator when he prepares and sets up an exhibition. What is behind this phenomenon is the existence of an optimal resolution at which a painting would project its best image. Technically it will not be difficult to detect the distance of the viewer from the painting. At this distance, and with the actual screen size and maybe even the viewer's vision condition as parameters, the system can automatically adjust the image to its optimal resolution with respect to those parameters.

12.1.2.4 Cooperative painting

With the Internet constantly improving in speed and bandwidth, multiple people could collaborate in one common painting process. We envision a potentially new style of painting and its practice. Collaboration is common or the norm in some art forms, such as music performance, where the overall audio effect comes from the collective labor of multiple performing musicians. The aggregation of their individual artistries results in a wonderful rendition of a music piece that is never possible with a single musician. Painting on the other hand is mostly individual. The possibility of collaboration is automatically ruled out by the limited physical space that is involved in a painting process. This is true even of very large paintings. Now with a digital canvas and the infinite space provided by the Internet, a computer-supported Internet based cooperative painting environment can be made available to geographically scattered human artists so that they can collaborate on the creation of a single painting. It is interesting to imagine when multiple artists are painting on a common, single canvas simultaneously, how they may mutually inspire and influence each other. Through such a collaborative creation process, the final resultant artwork represents the "product" of multiple creative motives and ideas of the contributing artists, which because of the mutual inspiration will likely be much greater than the mere sum of those ideas. In music performance, collaboration brings us the most beautiful sounds of the greatest symphonies ever heard on earth. Maybe it is time for other art forms, including painting, do the same.

12.1.2.5 3D painting

When painters perform impasto, often a kind of 3D structure can be observed. This is like those cream flowers on a birthday cake. This is an example of how a little bit of 3D structure of a much simpler complexity than a sculpture added to painting could be artistically and practically interesting. Here 3D painting means applying any brush like tool to create a 3D structure. People in 3D graphics have done much exploration of 3D practically, e.g. [Wil90, HH90], but the field practically is still in its infant stage. Much work has yet to be done for improving user friendliness and ways to create visually interesting 3D components and effects as well as overall impressions.

12.1.2.6 Automatic rectification of imperfections

The computer can play a smart and faithful assistant who is never tired of correcting the many small mistakes and imperfections that we tend to make all the time in our creation. Although simulating human level intelligence is still largely an unrealized goal at present, for many practical applications some small corrections here and there by the computer already mean a lot. When it comes to painting, "small" intelligence could go a long way in benefiting art creation. Take for example senior citizens or individuals with a disability who have difficulties controlling their body movements; expecting them to command the brush fluently to create decent painting is too demanding. In this situation, machine intelligence can help implement an online rectification process to correct wrong movements or turn imperfect ones into perfect ones on the fly.

12.1.2.7 Temporal painting

As opposed to animation, painting is still and static. In the virtual world this does not have to be so. Paintings in digital form can change with time, which is definitely feasible technically. This can add a brand new dimension to painting as an art form, giving all of a sudden a breath of life to paintings. Some standard animation packages are already equipped with such an animated painting capability, e.g. Maya. Currently there is already some real-life deployment of temporal painting, which is often achieved through specialized image processing or animation packages. One of the most notable examples is a digital greeting card that features a painting. When a fountain or a creek or a butterfly is needed in the painting, this special element would be presented in motion. But the temporal painting function we envisage is more than simple animation of a painted butterfly. The function should be offered as part of the digital painting program, and sufficiently versatile to support a range of possible ideas. For instance, the artist may paint some scene with a morning view and then he could adjust the colors or some of the strokes to vary the scene to match its sunset view. Given these two "frames", the system can generate a progression of the scene over a full day. Technically, to realize this feature requires a good integration of a digital painting system and an animation package.

12.1.2.8 Smart duplication

In both Western and Oriental paintings we often see scenarios that have been painted to be like the real thing. Producing these scenes is usually very labor intensive and time consuming. To achieve a faithful and consistent reproduction of the real scene, it often takes a large amount of repetitive painting work, which is largely mechanical and very tedious. We think there is much space here for the computer to offer some help. For the images in question to be painted, the system could offer a high-level primitive for inserting those repeatedly painted patterns at the artist's discretion. Compared with the brush stamp painting function in Photoshop where a high-level pattern (brush stamp) must be defined in advance, the painting pattern in the smart duplication feature we conceive is dynamic, adaptive and user-specific. Another important difference is that pattern multiplication in smart duplication does not have to be based on the same exact pattern for every copy. The duplication can be location aware, for instance, which means automatically adjusting the image pattern by taking into account the surrounding elements in the painting and the overall painting layout. This in fact mimics the mental and creative process of the human painter who would adjust the repetitive patterns to satisfy a more global view of the scene being created.

12.1.2.9 Brushless painting

We are accustomed to writing with a pen and painting with a brush. But are these still the most desirable metaphors when the actual functionalities of the pen and brush can be fully replaced by a set of invisible computer algorithms? Long before the emergence of the digital replacement of the pen and brush, people probed the idea of alternative painting devices, such as finger painting in Oriental painting. This dawns on us that in the digital system at least we should support finger painting as an alternative to the conventional brush based painting. Indeed, the finger's orientation and pressure can be captured through either sensory hardware or a vision-based software approach. From a human-computer interaction's point of view, the use of fingers belongs to research on gestural interfaces. Here the gestures posed by the fingers are interpreted and carefully mapped onto certain brush motions on which the virtual painting simulation relies. Stretching our imagination more, one may also use five or ten fingers to control the movement of, and pigment distribution at, the virtual brush head; this way painting becomes like playing the piano. Going further, one could use the whole body to do painting, and painting then becomes a form of dancing. The idea may sound rather weird— why should we move our whole body in order to paint just one small stroke? The argument is that to many, professional and amateur painters alike, the joy of painting does not necessarily come only at the end when seeing the result, but also throughout the process. This is analogous to amateur fishing, in which people may enjoy the process more than they enjoy the catch. The combined form of painting and dancing could turn into a new kind of art performance, and performance calls for practising, but offers wider room than pure painting to display one's artistic talents and also higher entertainment values.

12.1.2.10 Verbal touchup

Recently, research and development on audio interfaces has become a heated area, involving experts from many disciplines both in and out of the field of computer science. There are at least two areas where the technology can be applied to enrich the digital painting experiences. First is the *verbal painting touchup* feature, for either individual strokes or a collection of strokes. This is very useful for painting beginners or naive amateur painters who would like to enjoy the fun of painting with the least amount of time and energy commitment. They usually know intuitively what effects they want to have in the painting but due to their skill level, these people just cannot command the brush to achieve the desired effects. This coincides with the case mentioned earlier about certain people who cannot control the brush because of physical ineptness or disability. Under such circumstances they could rely on the computer to make the correction or to complete the stroke. It is up to the digital painting system, after processing the verbal command, to try to automatically set a corresponding computational goal to optimize the shapes and appearance of the painted strokes. That way, no more extensive training and practice needs to be invested, and no endless repainting of a stroke over and over again is necessary any more. Similar operations can also be introduced to touch up a collection of strokes in a digital painting, e.g. to tell the system to make the colors a bit more blueish, which can save a lot manual work and time.

12.1.2.11 Painting by verbal commands or gestures

Extending the above idea of verbal painting touchup a bit, we have a more powerful feature: *verbal painting creation*. For a handicapped individual who does not have an arm, to create a painting on their own is literally impossible. Occasionally, in newspapers and magazines, we hear impressive reports on handicapped people creating excellent paintings using their mouth, head or foot (see the real-life stories provided on the website of "Handicapped Artist Painting Productions and You" at http://asclepius.com/happy/). Now via machine intelligence and powerful digital media technologies, it is possible to allow artistically talented yet physically handicapped people to realize their dream to paint through oral and gesture commands. One implementation strategy may be to start with a template of frequently used stroke samples. Navigating the sample stroke library can also be under verbal or gestural control. The rest is very much the same as in the case of verbal painting touchup, as discussed above.

12.1.2.12 Painting by thinking

What if the handicapped person cannot even talk? In fact they are not alone, as perfectly normal individuals could also run into the situation in which they simply could not think of a verbal or gestural expression for an idea. We notice that it is not very hard for an ordinary person to develop and retain a clear mental picture of a certain object. This is supported by our dreams. We "see" things in our dreams which are fairly recognizable, thus proving that our brain could develop clear imagery over the reality. But not all mental images can be easily expressed verbally or by gesture. This is where wearable devices could come in—devices that could track the brain activities. Although this might sound fanciful the possibility is there, given the advances in brain and neural research. Controlled experiments can be designed and carried out to establish a correlation between certain mental images and brain wave patterns. Once the relationship is reliably set up, the computer system might be able to draw images on the screen according to best-effort reconstruction of the detected brain wave patterns. Realizing a system with such a capability is not only meaningful for computer art research, but probably also important for demonstrating the idea of a brain-computer interface, a field which has recently become very popular spanning cognitive sciences, neuroscience, psychology and computer science [MK00, MKMM01, JT02, dRM03, MB04, BK04, SE06, LG06, dRM06, Ort07, KBCM07, NT07].

12.1.2.13 Robotic painting

In an ideal digital painting process, the computer captures not just the final painting but also the process. One possible use of this recorded painting information is to make robots that can paint. Since detailed information on the position, orientation, pressure and speed of the penholder of the paintbrush during a painting session has all been accurately recorded, we can certainly work on the robotic control to reproduce the entire painting process. To the robot, this is teaching by example. The example is the human painter. Note that although many researchers from time to time have suggested the idea of robotic painting, to teach a robot to paint by example is far more difficult than anyone can imagine. This is because even a tiny difference in manoeuvering the paintbrush could lead to a significant deviation in the final painted results. Such a precision demand in capturing this is largely beyond the capability of current sensory hardware or computer vision algorithms. Even if such hardware is indeed available, setting it up might result in too much of an intrusion or distraction for the artist.

The excitement over robotic painting in the robotics field aside, robotic painting does have many practical applications. An example is mammoth-size painted-on advertisements that can be seen in places like airports, streets, plazas, sight-seeing spots and hillsides. Such advertisements are best done by crawling robots that have been taught to paint because of human safety as well for as for other reasons. Furthermore, the robot can achieve better precision in the painting than the human painter because of the sheer size of the painting. Also, the robotic painting process can be conducted at any time, regardless of the weather conditions. With robotic painting becoming a possibility, in the future talented artists only need to sit in their cozy work studio and do their painting task on whatever scale they feel most comfortable with. It is the robot's responsibility to scale up to the desired size and to perform the actual outdoor painting. Since robots can do large-scale painting very efficiently, this can also lead to some opportunities in tourism. For example, people could rent a temporary space in which to paint a picture or message.

One can also do remote painting with the assistance of painting robots. The artist does his painting with a computer, say in a scenic area in Hawaii; meanwhile, the painting commands are sent to a diligently working robot in the desert of the Sahara whose only mission in life is to always reproduce exactly what the artist does. If painting robot had existed way back in history, Michelangelo would not have had to struggle so hard to paint his ideas on the Sistine Chapel ceiling, which is one of the most documented art history stories. Similarly, in China those distinguished artists of Dunhuang would not have had to go through so much torture in order to complete the frescos in the famous cave of Dunhuang.

12.1.2.14 Animal painting

Can an animal paint? To approach this problem seriously we need to answer these three related questions: 1) Can an animal appreciate painting? 2) Can an animal create paintings? 3) Is animal painting the same as human painting, i.e. whether those visual signals making most sense to animals are the same as those for humans?

For the first question, we can interpret it more generically as "Can an animal respond to paintings discriminatively?" i.e. would an animal react differently to paintings and non-paintings? The latter can be understood to be arbitrary, randomly collected or generated visual signals. Although it might be difficult to draw a line between painting and non-painting, it is not difficult to identify some commonly agreed upon examples of painting and pure noise by the visual sensation they raise. So at least we could use these extreme examples to test whether animals would react to these different visual stimuli differently.

For the second question, there have been cases reported in real life of monkeys having been trained to do a few things with the paintbrush and some paints. Other than for the sake of entertaining the audience, the monkeys failed to generate a painting in any serious sense. Animals do not seem to have been bestowed with the motory skills to manipulate the paintbrush with their body parts. But does one really have to hold and actually control the paintbrush in order to qualify as a painter? Or rather we should judge him by his mental capacity—whether he can think like a painter? Even if animals can paint with the brain, they cannot show it in actions. For these animals there is a gap between being able to paint in the head and being capable to paint physically through arm and finger control. With information technology it might be possible to bridge this gap. One possibility would be for the animal to wear some MRI (Magnetic Resonance Imaging) sensory equipment. The equipment would capture and record the brain activities of the animal in real-time. A mapping is then artificially established for the different brain wave patterns to correspond to different movements of the arm for controlling the paintbrush. That way, animals are liberated from their physical inability to command a paintbrush and they may then start to paint at will.

For the third question the answer is difficult as the authors all came from a purely computer science background. But the issue should be most interesting to psychologists and cognitive scientists. We human beings believe that although we are not as strong as a lion, as forceful as a bear, as flexible as a squirrel, as prompt as a gibbon, and we cannot sing like a bird swim like a dolphin, we are the most intelligent of all creatures in terms of brain functions. Note however the difference between general intelligence and specific intelligence. From time to time we hear reports about some mentally disabled individual displaying remarkable talent in music performance or painting or other art areas. This suggests that intelligence specific to art might not have a positive correlation with the general intelligence one may possess. If we consider bird singing and the like as a kind of art talent, then there are reasons to suspect that animals might have more talents of certain types than humans. The answer to whether this can be true or not may come from the hard work of both cognitive scientists and computer scientists in the future. If indeed we can invent a digital device to help animals to paint, we can then study and conclude whether animals also have art talents, and whether one species may possess a type of talent in a specific art area more than humans do.

12.1.2.15 A study of brain activities

Painting can be thought of as a mapping process, from a real-world imagery to a visual representation which is largely subjective. This is especially true for impressionism which emphasizes expressing the emotional sensation aroused by a scene rather than the scene's image. With an ideal digital painting system, we can record even the most minute control commands applied to the paintbrush by an artist. Then there should be a way to study the potential relationship between the brain activities and the actual painted strokes as well as the relationship between an object as it appears in reality and its painterly depiction. The brain activities can be traced and recorded through some magnetic resonance imaging equipment. This procedure and the analysis results can help uncover the mystery surrounding our thought process in mentally forming a painting, which could add to our understanding of the functioning of the human brain and human intelligence.

12.1.2.16 Using painting for psychotherapy

Ip et al. [IHT02] recently developed an innovative interactive environment called "body brush", which can capture the human body motion for generating artistically interesting patterns on a large visual display. They applied such a system for psychotherapy, e.g. for helping students with learning difficulties [IK06]. Their novel treatment approach receives encouraging results. Inspired by this work and many existent successful cases in applying music for psychotherapy, we see a possibility to construct an intelligent painting system with which people can create very rich and interesting patterns using a minimum amount of effort. The patterns shall also correspond well with the user input so that the users feel their intent being respected and reflected in the visual output. Seeing the intriguing and highly aesthetic patterns being painted by or generated under their guidance with ease, it may help them develop a positive mental condition.

12.2 Perspectives on Intelligent Calligraphy Research

12.2.1 An Ideal Intelligent Calligraphy System

12.2.1.1 Faithful imitation of handwriting

Among all the functions people would expect of an ideal intelligent calligraphy system, probably the most desired and practical feature would be for the system to be able to imitate the style of a famous calligraphist, or more generally any arbitrary style. In our system, although this was precisely one of our initial goals, as discussed in Chapter 10, we still have a long way to go before the system has the ability to be on a par with real human experts. One difficult issue is that a calligraphist may write the same character in different ways. To simplify our task, we assume this variation is largely due to the influence of adjacent characters, and exclude the possibility of mood or other personal factors. Properly catching such a contextual variation needs some careful tactic during the learning phase. The aim is for the system to be able to reproduce such variation during automatic calligraphy generation. These variations are important for the generated artwork so as to stay away from monotones in style. This is what is unique about calligraphic art as opposed to printed or computer fonts. In a font system, the same character will always look the same which gives the overall document a consistency in style. But for a computer calligraphy generation system, being able to reproduce the variations in the writing style is strongly desired, which can add substantially to the overall aesthetic value of the generated artwork.

12.2.1.2 Style awareness

When judging a calligraphic character, the intelligent calligraphy system we built would not distinguish between styles; in fact the current system is not so much aware of writing styles. Right now, as long as the computer-generated calligraphic characters appear visually pleasing, our algorithm would assign a high score to them. However, there are situations where a particular writing style or class of styles is more desirable. For example, a love letter and a rhyme to extol a great warrior would call for a different styles of writing. We believe therefore that enhancing the calligraphic character beauty evaluation algorithm to be style aware can benefit many applications. On the other hand, we realize that evaluating calligraphic writing is a highly subjective task. Beauty is in the eyes of the beholder. A beautiful piece of calligraphy in the eyes of one person may be judged to be absolutely disdainful by another person. So instead of a grading algorithm that would work for the general audience, designing a numeric grading method which recognizes a certain style or class of styles as embraced or appreciated by a particular group of viewers would be much more feasible and practical. Also, such style specific grading ability can help improve the accuracy of the handwriting style mimicking algorithm, by incorporating a feedback component.

12.2.1.3 Automation in the facsimile and learning phases

An ideal intelligent calligraphy system is expected to be fully automatic. Although the majority of the algorithmic steps of our intelligent calligraphy system have been made automatic, the pattern recognition component in the facsimile and learning phase needs further enhancement. The challenging technical problems include: 1) The segmentation and recognition of individual calligraphic characters in a piece of cursive calligraphic artwork where the characters tend to be intimately connected; and 2) the segmentation and parameterization of individual strokes in a cursive calligraphic character which represents a heavy distortion from its standard counterpart. Successfully solving both of these problems would mean a kind of breakthrough in artificial intelligence research because both problems require neithes simple intelligence nor domain expertise. We believe these problems will eventually be solvable. The way to go is probably to allow the computer to learn more: the larger the learning example set, the more capable the overall system would become.

12.2.1.4 Anonymous learning capability

An ideal intelligent calligraphy system should be able to perform anonymous learning. This can be done automatically so that the system is equipped to surf the Internet to look for calligraphic images to serve as learning examples. The captions associated with the found images can help the system to obtain the style and other meta-information such as the authors of the calligraphic artwork. If there are multiple characters in the image, automatic character segmentation will be performed before passing the characters to the recognition and machine learning stage. This way, the world wide web becomes the system's infinite source of knowledge and best tutor. Given sufficient learning time, we expect the intelligent calligraphy system to evolve into an expert that could rival if not surpass real human calligraphists, since no human being can afford as much learning time and memory.

12.2.1.5 Handwriting evolution

Evolution is one of the most powerful laws of nature. We feel that the capability to self-improve or evolve for the better is the most wonderful thing to add to an intelligent calligraphy system. The idea can be quite simple: we have the intelligent calligraphy generation system automatically create new calligraphy in the first place; meanwhile, an evaluation score is assigned to the generated calligraphy on the fly; based on these scores, the intelligent calligraphy system adapts its aesthetic constraints for calligraphy generation to either embrace or avoid a certain calligraphy style. This process is in line with the typical learning scenario for reinforcement learning.

We see at least three possible ways to realize such reinforcement learning: 1) A human could suggest the numeric score to the system, which is the easiest way and yet most user unfriendly. 2) Evaluation by facial expression, where the system applies real-time detection of human facial gestures as the feedback signal; a happy face suggests endorsement and a sad face rejection. There exist many facial expression recognition algorithms which can be made use of here, e.g. [BY97, CQB+02, DCPA02, PHL+05, KIW06, WFC+06, CCCC07]. 3) Natural language understanding. With this method the user not only can comment on the overall visual quality of an automatically generated character, but also can point out more concretely which strokes in the character are problematic and why, or even any structural problem of stroke combination. This method presents some non-trivial technical challenges for implementation: how to interpret the verbal comments from the user, and how to translate these comments into concrete numerical goals for the optimization of the generated calligraphy.

12.2.1.6 A lightweight design

Since our intelligent calligraphy system can beautify human handwriting, it has good market value if the system can be embedded in a range of devices, including PDAs and cell phones. This asks for much optimization work in the algorithm design and its implementation, including optimizing the mathematical model for the analogous reasoning process. Also, much work needs to be done on reducing the system's memory consumption. Once the system's overheads can be significantly reduced, we can then make the system pervasively available, as a web application or an applet on portable devices. Since any educated individual would deal with characters almost all the time, an intelligent calligraphy and handwriting enhancement system will be an indispensable tool.

12.2.2 Intelligent Calligraphy System for Font Applications

There is a close relationship between our research on intelligent calligraphy generation and font systems. This relationship can be clearly seen during the calligraphy generation process when the system relies on commercially available font systems to extract feature vectors for carrying out the constraint-based analogous reasoning process. In the reverse direction, we feel there are plenty of opportunities for our intelligent calligraphy system to do the font systems a favor.

12.2.2.1 Personalized font systems

At present only a few famous calligraphic writing styles have been made into commercially available font systems. It means absolute prestige to be chosen as the contributing calligraphists. Occasionally some rich and famous people would create their own personal fonts. The barrier to widespread production of individual font systems is the highly expensive process for producing individual character encodings for the Chinese character set. Even the smallest set, of the most frequently used Chinese characters, contains as many as 6,000 or so characters. Any such character set would easily take three to five man years to create using the traditional method, and engaging professional people. The high cost is due to the fact that at the beginning a calligraphist must write out each character meticulously at least once; this is followed by an equally burdensome process to manually digitize every character. A powerful intelligent calligraphy system may render all this tedium unnecessary. Anyone who is interested in creating his own personal font needs only to write a few dozen representative characters. Then, based on intelligence arising from these samples, the system will try to figure out the writings of all the remaining characters in the set. Additionally, the newly generated characters would automatically be in a parametric representation as that is the default representation of our system's reasoning mechanism. This does away with a major step in the character symbol encoding process, which otherwise would have to be done at the back end through a rather tedious and error-prone manual process.

12.2.2.2 Font system support with minimum memory consumption

Since the ideal intelligent calligraphy system aims at minimum memory consumption and CPU overhead, we can assume an optimized implementation of the system can be run as a background process. With this active process on the alert, the need for keeping font files online, which translates to a large memory requirement, can be much reduced. Basically, we identify and compute a few most representative fonts as the generation "kernel" and then rely upon the system to generate any runtime requested font on the fly. This may not make practical sense for desktop computers but, for portable devices whose memory is at a premium, this would offer an attractive alternative for system designers. This means that even for a highly constrained device, it is possible to support the display of a multitude of font styles. When personalized fonts become the fashion, the number of different fonts per device (the desktop computer included) may increase significantly, which may then necessitate the idea of on-demand dynamic font generation.

The idea can be extended to calligraphic images: Instead of storing the images as pixel arrays we can, via the set of kernel fonts as well as the synthesizing power of the intelligent calligraphy system, represent all the calligraphic images parametrically, i.e. as synthesized results of these kernel fonts through the analogous reasoning mechanism of the intelligent calligraphy system. This leads to much bandwidth and storage saving when dealing with a large quantity of calligraphic artwork images, and adds convenience to the high-level calligraphy processing and retrieving services.

12.2.2.3 Personalized publishing and rich font support

We examine the two dominant types of publishing: web publishing and paper-based publishing.

Consider web publishing. One of desirable features is comprehensive font support in every web browser. This means web browsers will be able to display webpages in any user selected font(s). For many companies as well as personal websites, projecting a unique look could be very important, and fonts are definitely one of the crucial design elements.

Intelligent font support has a place in paper-based publishing too. A new functionality for "automatic calligraphic design and layout" can be introduced whereby a book can be published in the author's own handwriting and with an optimal text layout. This can alleviate the burden on the author to manually and painstakingly write out all the characters in the final manuscript. A "handwritten" autobiography will likely be more attractive to more readers. Likewise, a handwritten letter has a much stronger personal touch than a conventional printed one. Since the ideal intelligent calligraphy system can capture the spatial relationship between characters, the same can be applied to the design and layout of texts. For publishing using regular fonts, this might not be that useful. But if handwriting characters are used instead, how to layout the texts is indeed a new problem. Historically, printers opened up their hardware facilities for many people to realize their dreams to do personal printing or self-publishing. We envisage the same—the introduction of intelligent support for personal handwriting and automatic layout can make it possible for people to do fancy and personalized publishing on their own.

12.2.2.4 Automatic graphical layout design

Taking the previous discussion on automatic text layout further, we think of automatic graphical layout. In China and may Eastern cultures, painting and calligraphy go hand in hand. Indeed, all the famous painters excel in calligraphy and very rarely would we see a painting without a calligraphic caption. Many paintings are decorated by beautiful calligraphy of poetic verses or background information about the painting. It takes skills to optimally place these characters in a painting. The coming together of the two art forms—painting and calligraphy—presents a new research problem in layout design for achieving the best artistic effect. It is interesting to compare this with the work of TeX by Knuth, where the problem is to insert images optimally in a corpus of texts. Whereas in our case the problem is to embed characters in a painting. Unlike laying out blocks of texts which are approximately rectangular in shape, painting and calligraphy pieces do not adhere to any particular shape, which makes the problem more difficult. We can think of context-sensitive shape grammar as a potentially useful tool for solving the problem.

We can apply the same kind of problem-solving strategy for painting-calligraphy layout to graphical layout design in general. An example of an application of this is automatic poster design. In some professions, people at various levels need to frequently make posters and brochures. Beside having to cook up catchy slogans and phrases and striking graphics to be included in the poster, blending the graphical and text elements sensibly so that the message is clearly conveyed can be a huge challenge. Why not learn by example? The Internet is replete with successful cases of layout. Some kind of mining technique can unearth the keys to success and arrive at the guiding rules for creating impressive posters.

12.2.3 Intelligent Calligraphy Study for Other Applications

12.2.3.1 Evolution of handwriting styles

A person's handwriting may change from time to time, and these changes are not random. It is interesting to be able to model the pattern of such changes. There are many possible factors underlying these changes, including aging, change of physical condition, change of life style, etc. It is not a trivial task to trace the changes in the handwriting to these factors. But at least for some of the important figures in history, we have abundant data to establish a theory behind the changes in their handwriting. From a cognitive science point of view, this modeling work might offer a new window for a better understanding of how the human brain works and evolves. We also can see that a few important applications may come out of such a study:

(1) Such modeling may lead to some medical applications. This is inspired by the fact that gait analysis has become quite popular in many medical diagnosis and rehabilitation applications [Whi96, LG05, DL05, CD05]. Modern medical and psychology research has revealed how much insight we can gain about one's health condition by examining one's recent dreams. Like dreams, handwriting is a type of expression of the inner person, which is both more accessible and easier to parse due to its relatively low dimensionality. If a traced handwriting pattern matches the sample patterns of a certain group of patients, it raises a medical alert. Most people know less about what is happening to their own body than many other things in the world. Looking at the myriads of medical cases, we would be amazed at how many early warnings about a person's health condition had unfortunately been ignored or overlooked. Whether handwriting can indeed link to a person's health condition is worth probing.

(2) We may also be interested in the potential relationship between person's handwriting and their gender, career, personality, temper, physical condition, etc. It is a belief of many calligraphy experts in Asian that a person's handwriting can tell a lot about the person. The statement remains empirical. Using data mining algorithms, we can certainly find support for or against the argument. If the assertion is indeed valid, then on the one

hand we can infer some very valuable facts about a person based on his handwriting. Such discovered information could serve as a reference for human resources departments on the suitability of a certain person, and his potential. Police departments might also rely on the information for their detective work. On the other hand, it could mean that by changing a person's handwriting we try to change the actual person.

(3) More accurate identification of human handwriting. Right now, the design of identification algorithms ignores the issue of handwriting style. As discussed before, a piece which was created by a young calligraphist may not look the same if the piece is re-done in his elderly years. Taking into account the variation in the handwriting style can reduce false positives and false negatives during identification time.

12.2.3.2 Decoding ancient character symbols

Many civilizations of the past no longer exist today, but they left behind manuscripts and documents that are gems for archeologists and historians. But archeological research to rediscover these cultures continues to progress sluggishly. One of the hindrances is the difficulty in translating their character symbols. Take Chinese *oracle bone script* for example; over one million characters have so far been discovered, but only around 1,500 characters have been successfully deciphered and translated into Chinese characters. Such ancient character decoding work has traditionally been carried out in a purely manual fashion where the experts analyze, compare and make a guess at the ancient character symbols based entirely on their memory of known mappings between modern and ancient characters. Although, in general, human intelligence is more superior than machine intelligence, pattern matching against a large quantity of memorized facts is certainly an area where machine intelligence surpasses the intelligence of the human brain. We think combining pattern matching, digital morphology analysis, searching and data mining techniques, etc. to attack this problem might lead to some breakthrough in archeological research. An approach that is worth considering is to treat the character symbol evolving process as a general handwriting style evolving process. Thus the learning examples for the algorithm are the pair of character shapes in ancient and modern typefaces. After feeding all the currently known characters to the algorithm, the algorithm would discover a new mapping relationship between shapes of the same character in ancient and modern typefaces. This problem scenario can be seen as a classical case of analogous reasoning. A more refined treatment is to set up the matching between the shape of the unknown ancient character and the shape of the most ancient character which is still legible. Since the actual character writing evolving process is a gradual process, the shorter the time gap between the unknown and known character systems, the greater is the likelihood of discovering the ancient symbolic system.

12.3 An Ideal Painting Animation System

An ideal painting animation system should be able to animate its graphical elements in some automatic fashion, hence alleviating some of the onuses on the human animators. Such an autonomy could be provided by either a data-driven approach or a dynamics or kinematics-based simulation approach. For the data-driven approach, we can rely on motion-capture data or videos of a similar object that is in motion. When working with the motion-capture data, a 3D graphical model of the target object is needed for conversion of the motions in the 3D object space to the 2D screen space. When working with captured video, the challenge is how to identify and map similar motions in the video onto the 2D object in the painting, which may also need a morphing process. In this approach, properly handling occlusions is one of the big technical challenges. For the simulation-based approaches, some suitable dynamics or kinematics model of the target object needs to be established first and then tacked onto the object. Then in the same way as virtual objects are animated in a realistic simulation scenario, the painting elements will be animated similarly.

We feel one of the keys to success for an ideal painting animation system lies in the human computer interface. The computer is to serve and satisfy the human animator. Thus communication between the human artists and the computer animation system is absolutely critical. The more friendly and natural the interface is, the more productive will be the animation system when deployed in reality. Gestural interface is potentially a very good candidate. People can convey the motions of the animated object by hand gestures. The rationale is that human hands are probably the most natural, convenient and fluent control one could use to express a certain motion. Gestural interfacing occurs a lot in real life. For instance, in animation or film studios, when studying a script, people often use hand gestures to demonstrate the motion of a small object. When it comes to animating human characters, people would use their whole body instead of just hands to act out the animation, which is where motion capture technology is most useful. There is another kind of interface which has received a lot of attention lately: sketching based interface. Essentially, one would sketch out (with a pen) the animation trajectory and rough contour of the character. The painting animation system would then try to match the painting object onto the trajectory and contour expected of the object. Compared with data sampling-based methods, such a method takes advantage of the convenience and fluency of pen-based drawing. In fact, sketching-based authoring is widely practised in film production centers and animation studios, although at present it is still done predominantly by hand and without the support of the computer.

References

[BACM+07] Dacil Barreto, Luis D. Alvarez-Corral, Rafael Molina, Aggelos K. Katsaggelos, and G. M. Callico. Region-based super-resolution for compression. *Multidimensional System and Signal Processing*, 18(2-3):59–81, 2007.

[BF06] Isabelle Begin and Frank P. Ferrie. Comparison of super-resolution algorithms using image quality measures. In *CRV '06: Proceedings of 3rd Canadian Conference on Computer and Robot Vision*, Quebec, Canada: IEEE Computer Society, page 72, 2006.

[BK02] Simon Baker and Takeo Kanade. Limits on super-resolution and how to break them. *IEEE Transactions on Pattern Analysis and Machine Intelligence*, 24(9):1167–1183, 2002.

[BK04] Steffi Beckhaus and Ernst Kruijff. Unconventional human computer interfaces. In *SIGGRAPH '04: ACM SIGGRAPH 2004 Course Notes*, Los Angeles, CA, USA: ACM Press, page 18, 2004.

[Bro07] Stephen Brooks. Mixed media painting and portraiture. *IEEE Transactions on Visualization and Computer Graphics*, 13(5):1041–1054, 2007.

[BS98] Sean Borman and Robert L. Stevenson. Super-resolution from image sequences—a review. In *MWSCAS '98: Proceedings of the 1998 Midwest Symposium on Systems and Circuits*, Notre Dame, IN, USA: IEEE Computer Society, page 374, 1998.

[BY97] Michael J. Black and Yaser Yacoob. Recognizing facial expressions in image sequences using local parameterized models of image motion. *Int. J. Comput. Vision*, 25(1):23–48, 1997.

[Cap04] David Capel. *Image Mosaicing and Super-Resolution (Cphc/Bcs Distinguished Dissertations)*. Springer-Verlag, 2004.

[CB97] Ming-Chao Chiang and Terrance E. Boult. Local blur estimation and super-resolution. In *CVPR '97: Proceedings of the 1997 Conference on Computer Vision and Pattern Recognition*, San Juan, Puerto Rico, USA: IEEE Computer Society, page 821, 1997.

[CCCC07] Shyi-Chyi Cheng, Ming-Yao Chen, Hong-Yi Chang, and Tzu-Chuan Chou. Semantic-based facial expression recognition using analytical hierarchy process. *International Journal of Expert Systems with Applications*, 33(1):86–95, 2007.

[CD05] Sarah A. Curran and Howard J. Dananberg. Future of gait analysis: a podiatric medical perspective. *Journal of the American Podiatric Medical Association*, 95(2):130–142, 2005.

[Cha01] Subhasis Chaudhuri. *Super-Resolution Imaging*. Norwell, MA, USA: Kluwer Academic Publishers, 2001.

[Cla76] James H. Clark. Hierarchical geometric models for visible surface algorithms. *Commun. ACM*, 19(10):547–554, 1976.

[CM05]   Subhasis Chaudhuri and Joshi Manjunath. *Motion-Free Super-Resolution.* Springer-Verlag New York, Inc., 2005.

[CQB+02] S. Campanella, P. Quinet, R. Bruyer, M. Crommelinck, and J. M. Guerit. Categorical perception of happiness and fear facial expressions: An ERP study. *J. Cognitive Neuroscience*, 14(2):210–227, 2002.

[DCPA02] Matthew N. Dailey, Garrison W. Cottrell, Curtis Padgett, and Ralph Adolphs. Empath: a neural network that categorizes facial expressions. *J. Cognitive Neuroscience*, 14(8):1158–1173, 2002.

[DL05]   Elodie Desseree and Louis Legrand. First results of a complete marker-free methodology for human gait analysis. In *Proceedings of the IEEE 27th Annual Conference on Engineering in Medicine and Biology*, Shanghai, China: IEEE Computer Society, pages 7455–7458, 2005.

[dRM03]   Jose del R. Millan. Adaptive brain interfaces. *Communications of ACM*, 46(3):74–80, 2003.

[dRM06]   Jose del R. Millan. Brain-computer interaction. In *UIST '06: Proceedings of the 19th Annual ACM Symposium on User Interface Software and Technology*, Montreux, Switzerland: ACM Press, pages 277–278, 2006.

[EF99]   Michael Elad and Arie Feuer. Super-resolution reconstruction of image sequences. *IEEE Transactions on Pattern Analysis and Machine Intelligence*, 21(9):817–834, 1999.

[FJP02]   William T. Freeman, Thouis R. Jones, and Egon C Pasztor. Example-based super-resolution. *IEEE Computer Graphics and Applications*, 22(2):56–65, 2002.

[HH90]   Pat Hanrahan and Paul Haeberli. Direct wysiwyg painting and texturing on 3D shapes. In *SIGGRAPH '90: Proceedings of the 17th Annual Conference on Computer Graphics and Interactive Techniques*, Dallas, TX, USA: ACM Press, pages 215–223, 1990.

[IHT02]   Horace H. S. Ip, Young Hay, and Alex C. C. Tang. Body-brush: a body-driven interface for visual aesthetics. In *MULTIMEDIA '02: Proceedings of the 10th ACM International Conference on Multimedia*, Juan-les-pins, France: ACM Press, pages 664–665, 2002.

[IK06]   Horace H. S. Ip and Belton Kwong. Smart ambience games for children with learning difficulties. In *Proceedings of Edutainment 2006 International Conference on E-learning and Games*, Hangzhou, China: ACM Press, pages 484–493, 2006.

[JCC07]   C. V. Jiji, Subhasis Chaudhuri, and Priyam Chatterjee. Single frame image super-resolution: should we process locally or globally? *Multidimensional Syst. Signal Process.*, 18(2-3):123–152, 2007.

[JT02]   Catholijn M. Jonker and Jan Treur. Modelling multiple mind-matter interaction. *Int. J. Hum.-Comput. Stud.*, 57(3):165–214, 2002.

[KBCM07] Roman Krepki, Benjamin Blankertz, Gabriel Curio, and Klaus-Robert Muller. The Berlin Brain-Computer Interface (BBCI) — towards a new communication channel for online control in gaming applications. *Multimedia Tools Appl.*, 33(1):73–90, 2007.

[KIW06] Masood M. Khan, Michael Ingleby, and Robert D. Ward. Automated facial expression classification and affect interpretation using infrared measurement of facial skin temperature variations. *ACM Transactions on Autonomous and Adaptive Systems*, 1(1):91–113, 2006.

[LG05] Sudeep Sarkar, P. Jonathon Phillips, Zongyi Liu, Isidro Robledo Vega, Patrick Grother, Kevin W. Bowyer. The HumanID Gait Challenge Problem: Data Sets, Performance, and Analysis. *IEEE Transactions on Pattern Analysis and Machine Intelligence*, 27(2):162–177, 2005.

[LG06] Yuanqing Li and Cuntai Guan. An extended em algorithm for joint feature extraction and classification in brain-computer interfaces. *Neural Comput.*, 18(11):2730–2761, 2006.

[MB04] Eduardo Miranda and Andrew Brouse. Toward direct brain-computer musical interfaces. In *NIME '05: Proceedings of the 2005 Conference on New Interfaces for Musical Expression*, Singapore: National University of Singapore, pages 216–219, 2004.

[MK00] Melody M. Moore and Philip R. Kennedy. Human factors issues in the neural signals direct brain-computer interfaces. In *Assets '00: Proceedings of the Fourth International ACM Conference on Assistive Technologies*, Arlington, VA, USA: ACM Press, pages 114–120, 2000.

[MKMM01] Melody Moore, Philip Kennedy, Elizabeth Mynatt, and Jennifer Mankoff. Nudge and shove: frequency thresholding for navigation in direct brain-computer interfaces. In *CHI '01: Extended Abstracts on Human Factors in Computing Systems*, Seattle, WA, USA: ACM Press, pages 361–362, 2001.

[NLT07] Michael Ng, Edmund Lam, and Chong-Sze Tong. Superresolution imaging: theory, algorithms and applications. *Multidimensional Syst. Signal Process.*, 18(2-3):57–58, 2007.

[NT07] Anton Nijholt and Desney Tan. Playing with your brain: brain-computer interfaces and games. In *ACE '07: Proceedings of the International Conference on Advances in Computer Entertainment Technology*, Salzburg, Austria: ACM Press, pages 305–306, 2007.

[NY05] Michael K. Ng and Andy C. Yau. Super-resolution image restoration from blurred low-resolution images. *J. Math. Imaging Vis.*, 23(3):367–378, 2005.

[Ort07] Sixto Ortiz Jr. Brain-computer interfaces: where human and machine meet. *Computer*, 40(1):17–21, 2007.

[PHL+05] Frederic Pighin, Jamie Hecker, Dani Lischinski, Richard Szeliski, and David H. Salesin. Synthesizing realistic facial expressions from photographs. In *SIGGRAPH '05: ACM SIG-*

GRAPH 2005 Courses, Los Angeles, CA, USA: ACM Press, page 9, 2005.

[RC02] Deepu Rajan and Subhasis Chaudhuri. An mrf-based approach to generation of super-resolution images from blurred observations. *J. Math. Imaging Vis.*, 16(1):5–15, 2002.

[SC05] Eli Shechtman and Yaron Caspi. Space-time super-resolution. *IEEE Transactions on Pattern Analysis and Machine Intelligence*, 27(4):531–545, 2005.

[SE06] Le Song and Julien Epps. Classifying eeg for brain-computer interfaces: learning optimal filters for dynamical system features. In *ICML '06: Proceedings of the 23rd International Conference on Machine Learning*, Pittsburgh, PA, USA: ACM Press, pages 857–864, 2006.

[TTT06] Yu-Wing Tai, Wai-Shun Tong, and Chi-Keung Tang. Perceptually-inspired and edge-directed color image super-resolution. In *CVPR '06: Proceedings of the 2006 IEEE Computer Society Conference on Computer Vision and Pattern Recognition*, New York, NY, USA: IEEE Computer Society, pages 1948–1955, 2006.

[WFC⁺06] Christian Wallraven, Jan Fischer, Douglas W. Cunningham, Dirk Bartz, and Heinrich H. Bulthoff. The evaluation of stylized facial expressions. In *APGV '06: Proceedings of the 3rd Symposium on Applied Perception in Graphics and Visualization*, Boston, MA, USA: ACM Press, pages 85–92, 2006.

[Whi96] M. W. Whittle. Clinical gait analysis: a review. *Human Movement Science*, 15: 369–387, 1996.

[Wil90] Lance Williams. 3D paint. In *SI3D '90: Proceedings of the 1990 Symposium on Interactive 3D Graphics*, Snowbird, UT, USA: ACM Press, pages 225–233, 1990.

[WTS05] Qiang Wang, Xiaoou Tang, and Harry Shum. Patch based blind image super resolution. In *ICCV '05: Proceedings of the Tenth IEEE International Conference on Computer Vision*, Beijing, China: IEEE Computer Society, volume 1, pages 709–716, 2005.

Index